PRACTICAL PRESTRESSED CONCRETE

Practical Prestressed Concrete

H. KENT PRESTON, P.E.

Engineer, Construction Materials
John A. Roebling's Sons Division
The Colorado Fuel and Iron Corporation
Fellow, American Society of Civil Engineers
Professional Member, Prestressed Concrete Institute

McGRAW-HILL BOOK COMPANY, INC.

New York   Toronto   London

1960

PRACTICAL PRESTRESSED CONCRETE

50825

PREFACE

Since its introduction into the United States in 1950 the many advantages of prestressed concrete have caused its use to spread more rapidly than that of any other building material. This book is designed to furnish the structural engineer with all the information required for the design of safe, economical prestressed concrete structures.

Basic principles, design procedures, and numerical examples are presented in terms of simple arithmetic and the formulas for stress and moment which are familiar to all structural engineers. The design examples are based on Tentative Recommendations for Prestressed Concrete, which is a completely detailed recommended practice for design that was prepared by an ACI-ASCE committee of prestressed concrete experts.

Construction methods and equipment are discussed and illustrated in a manner that will enable the engineer to design members which can be fabricated economically and also help the fabricator to understand the factors which require his special attention. High-strength tendons are described and their properties analyzed to ensure proper use in design and during construction of these materials, which are relatively new to the construction industry. The practical suggestions based on experience in the United States will be helpful to both the designer and the fabricator. The typical structures illustrated include some of the prestressed concrete sections which have already been standardized by the fabricators in the industry or by committees established for this purpose.

The author wishes to express appreciation to his father Howard K. Preston, Professor Emeritus of the University of Delaware, for his painstaking review and constructive criticism of the first draft of this book. To his wife go the author's special thanks for her patient and accurate typing and retyping of the manuscript including "all those confusing equations and tables" while concurrently caring for a home, children, and a husband.

At the time this book was set in type, John A. Roebling's Sons Corporation was a wholly owned subsidiary of The Colorado Fuel and Iron Corporation. As shown on the title page, it is now John A. Roebling's Sons Division of The Colorado Fuel and Iron Corporation, and all credits to Roebling should be so interpreted.

H. Kent Preston

CONTENTS

NOTATIONS

The majority of notations listed here follow Proposed Definitions and Notations for Prestressed Concrete* by Joint ACI-ASCE Committee 323 on Prestressed Concrete. Only symbols needed in this book have been listed, and some of the author's own have been added for items not covered in the report.

Notations not given here will be found in Sec. 104 of Tentative Recommendations in Art. 8-2.

Cross-sectional constants:

A_c = area of entire concrete section (steel area not deducted)
c.g.c. = center of gravity of entire concrete section
c.g.s. = center of gravity of steel area
y_b = distance from bottom fiber to c.g.c.
y_t = distance from top fiber to c.g.c.
e = eccentricity of c.g.s. with respect to c.g.c.
I_c = moment of inertia of entire concrete section about c.g.c.
Z_b = section modulus of bottom fiber referred to c.g.c.
Z_t = section modulus of top fiber referred to c.g.c.

Loads, moments, and forces:

w_G = dead weight per unit length of prestressed member itself
w_S = additional dead load per unit length
w_D = total dead load per unit length = $w_G + w_S$
w_T = uniform load per unit length due to parabolic path of tendons
w_L = live load per unit length
P_L = concentrated live load
M_G = bending moment due to w_G
M_S = bending moment due to w_S
M_D = bending moment due to w_D
M_L = bending moment due to w_L and/or P_L
M_e = bending moment due to eccentricity of prestress force
M_u = bending moment under ultimate load condition
V_L = live-load shear
V_u = ultimate load shear
F = effective prestress force after deduction of all losses

*J. Am. Concrete Inst., October, 1952.

F_I = initial prestress force

F_o = prestress force after release of tendons from external anchors (applicable to pretensioned members)

F_A = arbitrarily assumed final tension

Concrete stresses:

$f^b{}_F, f^t{}_F$ = stress in bottom (top) fiber due to F

$f^b{}_{F_I}, f^t{}_{F_I}$ = stress in bottom (top) fiber due to F_I

$f^b{}_{F_o}, f^t{}_{F_o}$ = stress in bottom (top) fiber due to F_o

$f^b{}_G, f^t{}_G$ = stress in bottom (top) fiber due to w_G

$f^b{}_S, f^t{}_S$ = stress in bottom (top) fiber due to w_S

$f^b{}_D, f^t{}_D$ = stress in bottom (top) fiber due to w_D

$f^b{}_L, f^t{}_L$ = stress in bottom (top) fiber due to w_L and/or P_L

$f^b{}_T, f^t{}_T$ = stress in bottom (top) fiber due to w_T

f_{tp} = permissible tensile stress

f^t, f^s, f^{ts} = see Fig. 9-3 and explanation in adjacent text. Applicable to composite sections with different strengths of concrete

$f^b{}_{FA}, f^t{}_{FA}$ = stress in bottom (top) fiber due to F_A

Deflection or camber:

$\triangle_{F_I}$ = deflection due to F_I

$\triangle_{F_o}$ = deflection due to F_o

$\triangle_F$ = deflection due to F

$\triangle_G$ = deflection due to w_G

$\triangle_S$ = deflection due to w_S

$\triangle_D$ = deflection due to w_D

$\triangle_L$ = deflection due to w_L and/or P_L

Summation of stress, camber, etc.:

The summation of two or more stresses can be written in two ways thus:

$f^b{}_F + f^b{}_G + f^b{}_L$ can also be written $f^b{}_{F+G+L}$.

$\triangle_F + \triangle_G + \triangle_L$ can also be written $\triangle_{F+G+L}$.

Steel stresses:

f_{F_I} = stress in tendons due to F_I

f_{F_o} = stress in tendons due to F_o

f_F = stress in tendons due to F

PRACTICAL PRESTRESSED CONCRETE

CHAPTER 1

BASIC PRINCIPLES

1-1. Characteristics of Concrete. In many localities concrete is the cheapest material available for carrying compressive loads. On the other hand its tensile strength is only 10 to 15 per cent of its compressive strength, and this value is often reduced to zero by shrinkage cracks which occur during curing.

About A.D. 1900 engineers began to use concrete for flexural members by putting steel bars on the tension side of the member to carry the entire tensile load. This gave a member with a low-cost material to carry compressive stresses plus steel with a minimum amount of fabrication to carry tensile stresses. One of the chief disadvantages of reinforced concrete is the fact that all the concrete on the tensile side of the neutral axis is a useless dead weight except that it serves as a connection between the compressive concrete and the steel.

Prestressed concrete goes two steps beyond reinforced concrete. First, all the concrete on the tensile side of the neutral axis is put under an initial compressive stress of such a magnitude that all design loads which are to be applied to the structure in the future can reduce this stress but will not put the concrete in tension. Second, the prestress is applied in such a manner that it creates a moment of opposite sign to those which will be produced by applied dead and live loads. In the ideal design this negative moment carries all the dead load and creates the maximum allowable compressive stress in the concrete on the tensile side of the member. As far as the stresses in the prestressed member itself are concerned, it is then a weightless structure with all its moment carrying capacity available for live load—an especially important feature on long spans.

1-2. Plain Concrete. Figure 1-1 shows a plain, unreinforced, unprestressed concrete beam. It is a solid rectangular beam 9 in. high by 6 in. wide on a 15-ft 0-in. span. Live load is 184 lb per ft. The following calculations cover section properties, bending moments, unit stresses, and summation of stresses.

Area $= A_c = 9 \times 6 = 54$ sq in.
Dead weight $= w_G = 54 \times {}^{150}\!/_{144} = 56$ lb per ft

Section modulus of top fiber $= Z_t$
Section modulus of bottom fiber $= Z_b$
$Z_t = Z_b = 6\,(9^2)/6 = 81$
Dead-weight bending moment $= M_G$
$M_G = 56\,(15^2) \times {}^{12}\!/_8 = 18,900$ in.-lb
Stress in top fiber due to dead weight $= f'_G$
Stress in bottom fiber due to dead weight $= f^b_G$
$f'_G = 18,900 \div 81 = +233$
$f^b_G = 18,900 \div 81 = -233$
(In prestressed concrete calculations a compressive stress in the concrete is indicated by a plus sign and a tensile stress by a minus sign.)

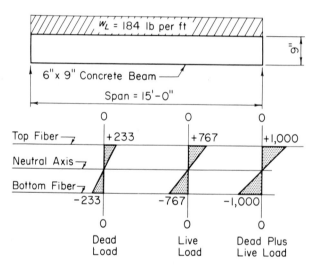

Diagrams of Stresses at ℄ Span

Fig. 1-1. Plain concrete beam.

Live-load bending moment $= M_L$
$M_L = 184\,(15^2) \times {}^{12}\!/_8 = 62,100$ in.-lb
Stress in top fiber due to live load $= f'_L$
Stress in bottom fiber due to live load $= f^b_L$
$f'_L = 62,100 \div 81 = +767$ psi
$f^b_L = 62,100 \div 81 = -767$ psi

Summation of stresses:
In top fiber: $f'_G + f'_L = +233 + 767 = +1,000$ psi
In bottom fiber: $f^b_G + f^b_L = -233 - 767 = -1,000$ psi

Obviously this beam would fail in tension before all the load was applied.

1-3. Centroidal Prestressing. Figure 1-2 shows the same beam as Fig. 1-1 except that it is prestressed by a force of 54,000 lb acting on the c.g.c. (center of gravity of the concrete section). This force creates a uniform compressive stress of $+1,000$ psi over the entire cross section of the beam. The stresses due to dead and live load are the same as in Fig. 1-1. The

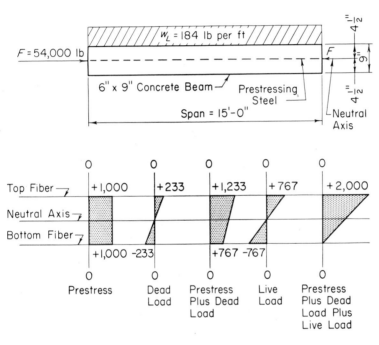

Diagrams of Stresses at ₵ Span

FIG. 1-2. Concrete beam with prestressing force on its center of gravity.

following calculations cover stress due to prestressing force and summation of stresses.

$f^t{}_F$ = stress in top fiber due to final prestressing force
$f^b{}_F$ = stress in bottom fiber due to final prestressing force
$f^t{}_F = f^b{}_F = F/A_c = 54,000 \div 54 = +1,000$ psi

Summation of stresses:
In top fiber: $f^t{}_F + f^t{}_G + f^t{}_L = +1,000 + 233 + 767 = +2,000$ psi
In bottom fiber: $f^b{}_F + f^b{}_G + f^b{}_L = +1,000 - 233 - 767 = 0$

Under the same dead and live loads as the beam in Fig. 1-1, this beam has a net compressive stress of 2,000 psi in the top fiber and zero stress in the bottom fiber. A beam made of good concrete could safely carry these stresses.

1-4. Eccentric Prestressing. Figure 1-3 shows the same beam as Fig 1-1 with the same prestressing force as the beam in Fig. 1-2 except that in Fig. 1-3 the prestressing force is applied 1½ in. below the c.g.c. The distance from the c.g.s. (center of gravity of the steel creating the pre-

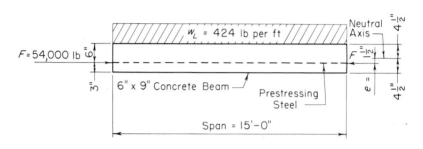

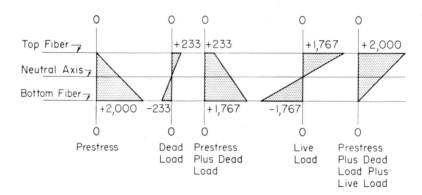

Diagrams of Stresses at ₵ Span

FIG. 1-3. Concrete beam with eccentric prestressing force.

stressing force) to the c.g.c. is called *e*, or eccentricity. Thus in Fig. 1-3, $e = 1\frac{1}{2}$ in. The stresses due to dead load are the same as in Fig. 1-1. The following calculations cover stress due to prestressing force and summation of stresses.

In this example the stress in the concrete due to the prestressing force *F* is not uniform because the prestressing force is not applied on the c.g.c. Stresses in the concrete due to *F* can be found by the familiar method of replacing the eccentric force by an equal force on the c.g.c. and a couple. The force on the c.g.c. creates a uniform compressive stress over the entire section equal to the force divided by the area of the section, or F/A_c. The couple creates a bending moment equal to the force times the eccentricity, or Fe. Stress in the concrete due to the couple is equal to the moment divided by the section modulus of the concrete member, or Fe/Z. Thus the stress in the top or bottom fiber of the concrete member due to the eccentric prestressing force can be expressed by the equation

$$f_F = \frac{F}{A_c} \pm \frac{Fe}{Z} \qquad (1\text{-}1)$$

The sign of Fe/Z is plus (indicating compressive stress) when the prestressing steel is on the same side of the c.g.c. as the fiber for which the stress is being computed and minus when on the opposite side.

Equation (1-1) can be used to find the stresses due to the prestressing force at any point in a *simple span* member. This is true no matter what path the prestressing steel follows and regardless of its elevation at the ends of the member. The value of e used in the equation is that measured at the point on the beam where the stresses are being computed. Equation (1-1) *does not apply* to beams continuous over one or more supports.

Use Eq. (1-1) to compute stresses in top and bottom fibers due to prestressing force.

$$f^t_F = \frac{F}{A_c} - \frac{Fe}{Z_t} \qquad (1\text{-}1a)$$

$$f^t_F = \frac{54,000}{54} - \frac{54,000 \times 1.5}{81}$$

$$f^t_F = 1,000 - 1,000 = 0$$

$$f^b_F = \frac{F}{A_c} + \frac{Fe}{Z_b} \qquad (1\text{-}1b)$$

$$f^b_F = \frac{54,000}{54} + \frac{54,000 \times 1.5}{81}$$

$$f^b_F = 1,000 + 1,000 = +2,000 \text{ psi}$$

In Fig. 1-2 the centroidal prestressing force of 54,000 lb created a compressive stress of 1,000 psi in the bottom fiber and the beam was able to support a total load of $56 + 184 = 240$ lb per ft. Having a compressive stress of 2,000 psi, the beam in Fig. 1-3 should be able to support a total load of $2 \times 240 = 480$ lb per ft or a live load of $480 - 56 = 424$ lb per ft. Check stresses using $w_L = 424$ lb per ft.

$$M_L = 424\,(15^2) \times 1\frac{7}{8} = 143,100 \text{ in.-lb}$$
$$f^t{}_L = 143,000 \div 81 = +1,767 \text{ psi}$$
$$f^b{}_L = 143,000 \div 81 = -1,767 \text{ psi}$$

Summation of stresses:

In top fiber: $f^t{}_F + f^t{}_G + f^t{}_L = 0 + 233 + 1,767 = +2,000$ psi

In bottom fiber: $f^b{}_F + f^b{}_G + f^b{}_L = +2,000 - 233 - 1,767 = 0$

The beam in Fig. 1-3 has the same cross section and total prestressing force as the beam in Fig. 1-2, yet it is carrying more than twice as much live load with the same net unit stress. This greater efficiency was achieved by locating the prestressing force in the area of the beam which is subject to tension under applied loads.

1-5. Buckling of Prestressed Concrete Members. In Figs. 1-2 and 1-3 the 54,000-lb prestressing force is shown as a load applied at each end of the concrete member. When a compression load is applied to a structural member, the effect of buckling must be considered in addition to the direct stresses. Buckling due to the prestressing load is not a consideration in prestressed concrete members where the tensioning element is closely encased by the concrete. The tendency to buckle under a compression load does exist, but if the member tries to buckle, it must deflect the tensioning elements as it moves. Since the tension in the tendons acts to keep them in a straight line, they resist the buckling of the concrete and a stable structure results. The same principle applies to members with curved tendons like those shown in Fig. 1-4.

Compression loads other than the prestressing force cause buckling which must be resisted by the stiffness of the structural member just as in any other building material. The tension in the tendons is sufficient only to balance the buckling due to the prestressing force.

1-6. Deflected Prestressing Steel. Since the prestressing steel in Fig. 1-3 is at the same elevation for the full length of the beam, the stresses due to *F* are the same at all points along the beam. Since there is no bending moment at the supports due to applied loads, the net stresses at the supports are those due to *F*. The *e* used in Fig. 1-3 was chosen to give maximum prestress in the bottom fiber without creating tension in the top fiber. If the *e* were increased, $f^t{}_F$ would become a tensile stress. At the center of the span a certain amount of tensile stress in the top fiber from *F* is permissible because it is offset by the dead-load moment which is always acting in a prestressed beam. Tensile stress in the top fiber at the end of the span is not desirable because there is no dead-load moment to relieve it. The benefits of greater eccentricity in the region where dead-load moments exist can be obtained by deflecting the prestressing steel as shown in Fig. 1-4.

In the calculations for Fig. 1-3 we found that $f^t{}_F = 0$ when $e = 1\frac{1}{2}$ in.

At the center of the span the eccentricity can be increased until the prestressing force causes a tensile stress in the top fiber equal to the compressive stress from the dead-load bending moment. From previous calculations $f'_G = +233$ psi. The additional e required to create an equivalent tensile stress can be found from the equation

$$f^t_G = \frac{Fe}{Z_t}$$

Substituting numerical values,

$$233 = \frac{54,000e}{81}$$

from which

$$e = 0.35 \text{ in.}$$

On this basis we can establish the eccentricity at the center of span as $e = 1.50 + 0.35 = 1.85$ in. With this eccentricity the beam should support a live load of $424 + 56 = 480$ lb per ft without tensile stress. The following calculations are for the beam in Fig. 1-4.

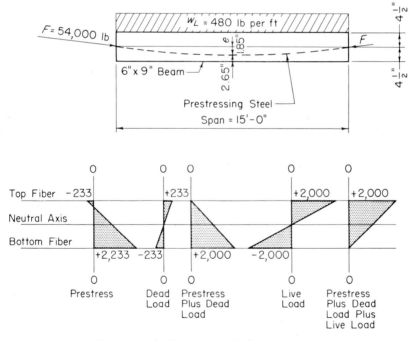

Diagrams of Stresses at ₵ Span

FIG. 1-4. Concrete beam prestressed with deflected tendons.

Substituting in Eqs. (1-1*a*) and (1-1*b*)

$$f'_F = \frac{54,000}{54} - \frac{54,000 \times 1.85}{81}$$

$$f'_F = 1,000 - 1,233 = -233 \text{ psi}$$

$$f^b_F = \frac{54,000}{54} + \frac{54,000 \times 1.85}{81}$$

$$f^b_F = 1,000 + 1,233 = +2,233 \text{ psi}$$

$$M_L = 480(15^2) \times 1\tfrac{7}{8} = 162,000 \text{ in.-lb}$$

$$f'_L = 162,000 \div 81 = +2,000 \text{ psi}$$

$$f^b_L = 162,000 \div 81 = -2,000 \text{ psi}$$

Summation of stresses at center of span under dead load only:
  In top fiber: $f'_F + f'_G = -233 + 233 = 0$
  In bottom fiber: $f^b_F + f^b_G = +2,233 - 233 = +2,000$ psi

Summation of stresses at center of span under all loads:
  In top fiber: $f'_F + f'_G + f'_L = -233 + 233 + 2,000 = +2,000$ psi
  In bottom fiber: $f^b_F + f^b_G + f^b_L = +2,233 - 233 - 2,000 = 0$

To simplify calculations the steel tendons have been located on the c.g.c. over the supports creating a uniform compressive stress. They can just as readily be located above or below the c.g.c. to suit the details of a particular structure as long as they do not create stresses in excess of those allowed by the specification.

A comparison of the loads carried by the beams in Figs. 1-3 and 1-4 shows that curving the prestressing steel can increase the load-carrying capacity of a beam by an amount equal to its own dead weight. This advantage of curved prestressing steel over straight steel becomes more significant as the span and the dead weight increase.

When a steel tendon is curved as in Fig. 1-4, its tension varies slightly as its slope changes. In order to satisfy the conditions of equilibrium, the horizontal component of the tension in the tendon must be constant for its full length. At the center of the span where the tendon is horizontal, its horizontal component is equal to its total tension. The tendon has its maximum slope and therefore its maximum tension at the ends of the beam. In most prestressed concrete members, however, the slope of the tendon is so small that total tension and horizontal component are taken as equal to the horizontal component. For unusually deep members this relationship should be checked.

CHAPTER 2

PROPERTIES PECULIAR TO PRESTRESSED CONCRETE

2-1. Prestressing Methods. There are two kinds of tensioning elements for prestressed concrete: pretensioned and post-tensioned. The pre-stressing tendons in a given member will be all one kind or the other or a combination of the two, depending upon conditions.

The term pretensioned means that the tendons are tensioned to their full load before the concrete is placed. They are held under tension by anchors beyond the ends of the prestressed concrete member. After the concrete has been placed and allowed to cure to sufficient strength, the load in the tendons is transferred from the external anchors into the newly poured member, thus prestressing it. In the United States the standard tendons for pretensioned work are seven-wire uncoated stress-relieved prestressed concrete strands as listed in Table A-1. The pre-tensioned method is described fully in Chap. 6.

The term post-tensioned means that the tendons are tensioned after the concrete has been placed and allowed to cure. Frequently the ten-don is placed inside a flexible metal hose, the entire assembly is placed in the form, and concrete is poured around it. After the concrete has cured, the tendon is tensioned and held under load by anchor fittings at its ends. Bond between the tendon and the concrete member is achieved by pumping the metal hose full of grout. Several types of post-tensioned tendons are available as listed in Tables A-2 to A-4 and in Chap. 7.

2-2. Prestressing Force. Examples in Figs. 1-2 to 1-4 used a prestress-ing force F equal to 54,000 lb. In the list of notations F is defined as "effective prestress force after deduction of all losses." In other words, F is the force that can be counted upon to remain active throughout the life of the structure. In the notations F_I is defined as "initial prestress force," which means the load to which the tendons are tensioned when the prestressed concrete member is being fabricated. F_I is always larger than F because several factors contribute to a reduction of tension in the tendons.

2-3. Shrinkage. Shrinkage of concrete is a process known to every-one familiar with reinforced concrete. As concrete cures, its total vol-

9

ume decreases slightly and it tends to shrink in all three dimensions. We are particularly concerned with the fact that it tends to shorten.

When the tension in pretensioned strands is transferred from external anchorages to the concrete members, the compressive force created in the concrete closes all the existing shrinkage cracks and both the concrete member and the strands shorten an amount equal to the sum of the widths of the shrinkage cracks. Although the rate of shrinkage is greatest when the member is first cast, it continues for some time after the prestressing operation. Since the continuing shrinkage cannot cause cracks in the concrete which is now in compression, it causes additional shortening. In the final analysis the pretensioned strands shorten an amount equal to the total shrinkage. This shortening causes a reduction of the tensile stress in the strands.

When a tendon is post-tensioned, it closes the existing shrinkage cracks during the tensioning operation. Since the initial tension F_i in this tendon is measured at the end of the tensioning operation after the existing cracks are closed, there will be no stress loss in the tendon due to the shrinkage which precedes the tensioning operation. In a post-tensioned tendon the only stress loss due to shrinkage is due to the shrinkage which takes place after the tensioning operation.

2-4. Elastic Compression. Elastic compression of the concrete member takes place as the prestressing force is applied. As in any elastic material its magnitude is a function of the modulus of elasticity of the concrete and the intensity of the compressive stress.

Since the pretensioned strand is under initial tension when the concrete member under zero stress is bonded to it, the strand shortens an amount equal to the elastic compression when the prestressing force is transferred from the anchorages to the concrete member.

If a post-tensioned member is stressed with only one tendon, all the elastic compression has taken place when the initial tension is measured at the end of the tensioning operation. In this case there will be no stress loss due to elastic shortening. When two or more tendons are post-tensioned in sequence, the first one tensioned will undergo the elastic shortening resulting from the tensioning of the remaining tendons. This is usually eliminated by computing the shortening which will result from tensioning the remaining tendons and overstretching the first tendons by this length.

2-5. Creep. Creep of concrete, often referred to as plastic flow, is inelastic shortening which takes place over a period of time. It is caused by a constant compressive stress, and its magnitude is a function of the intensity of that stress. Both pretensioned and post-tensioned tendons shorten an amount equal to the entire creep. It is of interest to note that the shortening due to creep is approximately twice that due to elastic compression.

2-6. Relaxation. Relaxation of prestressing tendons is the fourth cause of stress loss. Since these tendons are used at an initial tension of 65 to 70 per cent of their ultimate strength, they, too, undergo a creep or plastic flow due to the constant high stress. Conditions, however, are somewhat different from those in the concrete. If a weight were hung on a tendon to create a stress equal to 70 per cent of its ultimate strength, the tendon would slowly elongate or creep just as the concrete slowly shortens. In an actual structure the tendon is not held at a constant load; it is not even held at a constant length. As the concrete member shortens from the factors described above, the tendon shortens too. There is a certain amount of plastic flow within the tendon which, since it cannot cause a gradual increase in length, shows up as a gradual drop in stress. This reduction in stress is called "relaxation." The magnitude of this relaxation is small and, in the United States, seldom exceeds 4 per cent of the initial tension. This value is correct only when the high-quality materials called for in the specifications are used.

In summary, F, the prestressing force remaining in the steel tendons after all losses, is less than F_i, the initial force in the tendons, by the following:

For pretensioned tendons:
   100 per cent of shrinkage, 100 per cent of elastic shortening, 100 per cent of creep of concrete, and 100 per cent of relaxation of steel

For post-tensioned tendons:
   Approximately 50 per cent of shrinkage, 100 per cent of creep of concrete, and 100 per cent of relaxation of steel

The stress losses just discussed make it necessary to use high-strength steel at high unit stresses for the tendons. Reference to the specifications in Chap. 8 shows that they allow for a stress loss of approximately 35,000 psi in a pretensioned tendon. An ordinary steel bar tensioned to its yield point, 33,000 psi, would lose its entire prestress by the time all stress losses had taken place. However, the initial tension in seven-wire strands is in the neighborhood of 175,000 psi. A stress loss of 35,000 psi reduces this to a final stress of 140,000 psi, which is sufficient to create the required prestressing force at a reasonable cost.

CHAPTER 3

DESIGN PROCEDURE

In many ways it may seem that this chapter should follow the one on specifications. It was finally decided, however, that a basic knowledge of design procedure is needed to help the reader to understand the chapters on materials and methods of fabrication.

The object of this chapter is to present a step-by-step analysis of the design of a simple prestressed concrete beam. Definitions of the notations used are tabulated in Notations.

Design of a prestressed concrete beam for an actual structure involves two steps: choice of the shape and dimensions of the concrete member and analysis of the member under the specified loading conditions to check unit stresses and determine the amount and details of the prestressing steel. Facility in the choice of a proper section will come with experience. In addition to having sufficient section modulus to carry the applied loads, the concrete cross section must be properly proportioned to provide room for the tensioning elements. Once the section has been chosen, the following method of analysis can be applied.

During the calculations it may become apparent that the concrete section chosen is not adequate or that it is larger than necessary. If it is not adequate, a new section must be designed and the calculations repeated. In some cases it will prove economical to use an oversize member even at low stresses because it can be fabricated in existing forms. When this is not the case, an effort should be made to select a section in which the working stresses are reasonably near those permitted by the specification.

STEPS IN DESIGN PROCEDURE

Step 1. Compute the properties of the concrete cross section.

If the cross section is not uniform for the full length of the beam it is usually best to analyze the section at the point of maximum moment and then check at any other points which might be critical because of the change in section. Properties to be computed are:

A_c = area of entire concrete section (steel area not deducted)
y_t = distance from top fiber to c.g.c. (center of gravity of entire concrete section)
y_b = distance from bottom fiber to c.g.c.
I_c = moment of inertia of entire concrete section about c.g.c.
Z_t = section modulus of top fiber referred to c.g.c.
Z_b = section modulus of bottom fiber referred to c.g.c.
w_G = dead load of member per unit length

Step 2. Compute stresses in member due to its own dead weight.

M_G = bending moment due to w_G
$f^t{}_G$ = stress in top fiber due to M_G
  = $M_G \div Z_t$
$f^b{}_G$ = stress in bottom fiber due to M_G
  = $M_G \div Z_b$

Step 3. Compute stresses in member due to applied loads.

In most cases these will be made up of additional dead load such as roof deck or highway wearing surface and live load. (For the case where the prestressed member becomes a composite section with poured-in-place concrete see Chap. 9.)

w_S = additional dead load
M_S = bending moment due to w_S
$f^t{}_S$ = stress in top fiber due to M_S
  = $M_S \div Z_t$
$f^b{}_S$ = stress in bottom fiber due to M_S
  = $M_S \div Z_b$
w_L = distributed live load per unit length
P_L = concentrated live load
M_L = bending moment due to w_L and/or P_L
$f^t{}_L$ = stress in top fiber due to M_L
  = $M_L \div Z_t$
$f^b{}_L$ = stress in bottom fiber due to M_L
  = $M_L \div Z_b$

Step 4. Determine the magnitude and location of the prestressing force at the point of maximum moment.

The prestressing force must meet two conditions:

1. It must provide sufficient compressive stress to offset the tensile stresses which will be caused by the bending moments.

2. It must not create stresses either tensile or compressive which are in excess of those permitted by the specification.

As illustrated in Chap. 1 the stress in the concrete due to the prestressing force is a function of the magnitude of the force and also of its eccentricity e with regard to the c.g.c.

Since we are considering a simple span beam, the moments due to the applied loads create compressive stresses in the top fiber and tensile stresses in the bottom fiber.

In order to meet the first condition the prestressing force must create sufficient compressive stress in the bottom fiber to offset the tensile stresses from the bending moments. In other words f^b_F, stress in the bottom fiber due to the prestressing force F, must be equal in magnitude and of opposite sign to $f^b_G + f^b_S + f^b_L$. From Eq. (1-1) we can write

$$f^b_F = \frac{F}{A_c} + \frac{Fe}{Z_b}$$

Setting this value of f^b_F equal in magnitude to and of opposite sign to the sum of the bending moment stresses, we get

$$\frac{F}{A_c} + \frac{Fe}{Z_b} = -f^b_G - f^b_S - f^b_L$$

Use of this equation will give zero stress in the bottom fiber under full design load. For some structures the specifications permit a small tensile stress f_{tp} under design load conditions. In this case the magnitude of the compressive stress to be created by the prestressing force can be reduced by f_{tp} as shown in Eq. (3-1).

$$\frac{F}{A_c} + \frac{Fe}{Z_b} = -f^b_G - f^b_S - f^b_L + f_{tp} \qquad (3\text{-}1)$$

When no tensile stress is permitted, f_{tp} equals zero.

In order to meet the second condition the prestressing force must not create excessive stresses in the top fiber. For most designs the prestressing force, because of its eccentricity, causes a tensile stress in the top fiber. Since the dead load is always acting and the compressive stress it causes helps to offset the tensile stress, the net stress in the top fiber is the stress caused by the prestressing force plus the stress caused by the dead-load bending moment. To keep the tensile stress in the top fiber within allowable limits we can write the following equation:

$$\frac{F}{A_c} - \frac{Fe}{Z_t} + f^t_G = f_{tp}$$

In this equation $F/A_c - Fe/Z_t$ represents the stress due to the prestressing force, f^t_G is the stress due to dead-load bending moment, and f_{tp} is the allowable tensile stress. This equation can be written

$$\frac{F}{A_c} - \frac{Fe}{Z_t} = -f'_G + f_{tp} \tag{3-2}$$

In an actual design we would have numerical values from the calculations in Steps 1 to 3 for all factors in Eqs. (3-1) and (3-2) except F and e. The solution of the two equations for the unknown quantities is quite simple. Multiply Eq. (3-2) by Z_t/Z_b to get

$$\frac{Z_t}{Z_b} \frac{F}{A_c} - \frac{Fe}{Z_b} = \frac{Z_t}{Z_b} (f'_G + f_{tp}) \tag{3-3}$$

Add Eq. (3-1) to Eq. (3-3). The terms $-Fe/Z_b$ and Fe/Z_b cancel each other, giving

$$\left(1 + \frac{Z_t}{Z_b}\right) \frac{F}{A_c} = \frac{Z_t}{Z_b} (f'_G + f_{tp}) - f^b_G - f^b_S - f^b_L + f_{tp} \tag{3-4}$$

In a specific design all the symbols in Eq. (3-4) except F will have actual numerical values, so it can readily be solved for F.

The value of e can be found by substituting the value of F in Eq. (3-1) or (3-2). If e is so large that the tendons would be below the bottom of the beam, see Step 5.

Step 5. Select the tensioning elements to be used and work out the details of their location in the member.

Frequently e will be so large that it refers to a point below the bottom of the member or so close to the bottom that the tendons cannot be satisfactorily located. There are two remedies for this situation.

If the member being considered is symmetrical (one in which the section modulus of the top equals the section modulus of the bottom) and has stresses near the maximum allowed, a new section should be chosen. The new section should have more concrete in the top than in the bottom, thus raising the c.g.c. above the middle of its height, but the section modulus of the bottom should not be less than in the previous section.

For unsymmetrical sections in which the section modulus of the top is greater than that of the bottom or for symmetrical sections operating at low stresses, the value of e can be arbitrarily reduced until the tendons are far enough above the bottom of the member to permit satisfactory details. Changing the value of e will also change F. The new F should be found by substituting all known values including e in Eq. (3-1) and solving for F.

Decreasing e and increasing F will create a compressive stress in the top fiber. This can be computed by solving

$$f^t_F = \frac{F}{A_c} - \frac{Fe}{Z_t} \tag{3-5}$$

Check the maximum stress in the top fiber by adding

$$f^t_F + f^t_G + f^t_S + f^t_L$$

Step 6. Establish the concrete strength f'_{ci} at the time of prestressing and check stresses under the initial prestress condition.

The specifications permit higher unit stress in relation to f'_{ci} under this condition than with relation to f'_c under the final condition, so it is not always a governing factor but it must be checked.

Step 7. Establish the path of the tendons and check critical points along the member under initial and final conditions.

All the preceding calculations have been concerned with the point of maximum moment. In some members other points may also be critical. These can usually be located by inspection of the moment diagrams, member properties, and location of prestressing steel.

There are two combinations of conditions which should be checked for maximum stress.

1. Final prestress plus full design load

2. Initial prestress plus dead load only (It is seldom necessary to check prestress alone without the benefit of dead load. As the prestressing force is applied, it creates a negative moment and the member develops a camber which raises the center portion off the form. Since the member is resting on each end, its dead-weight bending moment is effective.)

Step 8. Check ultimate strength to make sure it meets the requirements in the specification. Check percentage of prestressing steel.

There is no constant ratio between the design strength and the ultimate strength of a prestressed concrete member as there is in structural steel. Two prestressed concrete members of different cross section can have exactly the same load-carrying capacity based on allowable design stresses yet have entirely different ultimate strengths.

Use the method outlined in Sec. 209.2 of the ACI-ASCE Recommendations in Art. 8-2.

If too much prestressing steel is used, failure of the member will occur by crushing of the concrete. This is not desirable because there is no warning of impending failure and the failure is of the explosive type. Check the amount of prestressing steel by the method shown in Sec. 209.2.3 of the ACI-ASCE Recommendations in Art. 8-2.

Step 9. Design of shear steel.

Although an analysis of shear and diagonal tension by Mohr's Circle method is sometimes used, experience indicates that the most satisfactory results are obtained by using an emperical formula based on test data. The web reinforcement should be designed in accordance with Sec. 210 of the ACI-ASCE Recommendations in Art. 8-2.

Step 10. Compute camber.

Use the standard formulas for deflection of elastic members such as would be applied to a structural steel member. Compute camber at time of prestressing and also for long-time loading.

For E_c see ACI-ASCE Recommendations Sec. 203.2 at time of prestressing and Sec. 203.3 for long-time camber in Art. 8-2. For normal designs satisfactory accuracy is obtained by using the I of the concrete cross section. Effect of holes for tendons and prestressing steel can be ignored.

CHAPTER 4

NUMERICAL EXAMPLE OF DESIGN PROCEDURE

4-1. Conditions of Design. The purpose of this chapter is to explain the mathematics involved in the design of a typical prestressed concrete member. Each step will be numbered and will follow the procedure established for that step in Chap. 3.

Since this is a mathematical example and we have not studied specifications yet, we shall simply state material strengths, stress losses, loading conditions, etc., as they are needed in the analysis.

Definitions of the symbols used in the analysis will be found in Notations.

4-2. Design of a Bridge Girder. General conditions:

Span = 80 ft 0 in.

Live load = AASHO-H20-S16

Girders spaced 3 ft 6 in. center to center. Assume that they are connected to provide normal transverse distribution of load.

Wearing surface = 2 in. of asphalt at 20 psf

Initial tension in tendons = 175,000 psi

Stress loss = 35,000 psi

$f'_c = +5,000$ psi

$f'_{ci} = +4,000$ psi

Try the girder cross section shown in Fig. 4-1.

Step 1. Compute properties of the concrete cross section in Fig. 4-1.

Find the moment of inertia I_T about the top surface by taking moments about line T-T.

Section	Area, A		y	Ay	Ay^2	I_o
I = 42 × 6	= 252		3	756	2,268	756
II = 2 × 3 × 3 × ½ =	9		7	63	441	4
III = 6 × 30	= 180		21	3,780	79,380	13,500
IV = 2 × 5 × 5 × ½ =	25		34.3	858	29,455	35
V = 16 × 6	= 96		39	3,744	146,016	288
Total	562			9,201	257,560	14,583
					14,583	
				$I_T =$	272,143	

18

$$y_t = 9,201 \div 562 = 16.37 \text{ in.}$$
$$y_b = 42.00 - 16.37 = 25.63 \text{ in.}$$
$$I_c = 272,143 - 562(16.37^2) = 121,540$$
$$Z_t = 121,540 \div 16.37 = 7,424$$
$$Z_b = 121,540 \div 25.63 = 4,742$$

Assume that the section is made of regular-weight concrete at 150 lb per cu ft. Then

$$w_G = {}^{150}\!/_{144} \times 562 = 585 \text{ lb per ft}$$

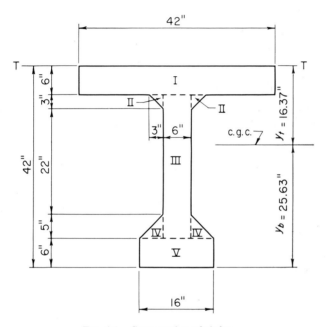

FIG. 4-1. Cross section of girder.

Step 2. Compute stresses in the girder at the center of span due to its own dead weight.

$$M_G = \frac{585(80^2) \times 12}{8} = 5,616,000 \text{ in.-lb}$$

$$f^t{}_G = 5,616,000 \div 7,424 = +757 \text{ psi (compression)}$$
$$f^b{}_G = 5,616,000 \div 4,742 = -1,184 \text{ psi (tension)}$$

Step 3. Compute stresses in girder at center of span due to applied loads.

The only dead load besides the girder itself is the wearing surface at 20 psf over the entire 3½-ft width of the girder.

$$w_S = 20 \times 3.5 = 70 \text{ lb per lin ft}$$

$$M_S = \frac{70(80^2) \times 12}{8} = 672{,}000 \text{ in.-lb}$$

$$f^t_S = 672{,}000 \div 7{,}424 = +91 \text{ psi}$$

$$f^b_S = 672{,}000 \div 4{,}742 = -142 \text{ psi}$$

From AASHO tables the live-load bending moment per lane is 1,164,900 ft-lb. From AASHO Specification:

Impact $= 50/(80 + 125) = 24.4\%$
Wheel load per stringer $= 3.5 \div 5 = 0.70$
Wheel load $=$ one-half lane load

from which the net live-load moment per stringer is

$$M_L = 1{,}164{,}900 \times 1.244 \times .70 \times \tfrac{1}{2} \times 12 = 6{,}086{,}000 \text{ in.-lb}$$

$$f^t_L = 6{,}086{,}000 \div 7{,}424 = +820 \text{ psi}$$

$$f^b_L = 6{,}086{,}000 \div 4{,}742 = -1{,}283 \text{ psi}$$

Step 4. Determine the magnitude and location of the prestressing force at center of span.

This computation is based on final conditions, that is, after all stress losses have taken place.

For simplicity in this first example we shall assume the following limits on final stresses in the concrete:

Maximum compressive stress $= 0.40f'_c = 0.40 \times 5{,}000 = 2{,}000 \text{ psi}$
Maximum tensile stress $=$ zero $= f_{tp}$

Equation (3-1) from Step 4 in Chap. 3 is

$$\frac{F}{A_c} + \frac{Fe}{Z_b} = -f^b_G - f^b_S - f^b_L + f_{tp} \tag{3-1}$$

Substitute in Eq. (3-1) all the known values from calculations in Steps 1, 2, and 3 to get

$$\frac{F}{562} + \frac{Fe}{4{,}742} = 1{,}184 + 142 + 1{,}283 + 0$$

which reduces to

$$\frac{F}{562} + \frac{Fe}{4{,}742} = +2{,}609 \tag{4-1}$$

From this we see that the compressive stress created by prestressing will be 2,609 psi, but the specification limits us to a maximum stress in the concrete of 2,000 psi. At the center of the span the maximum stress will be the algebraic sum of the prestressing stress and the dead-load stress, or

$$2,609 - 1,184 = +1,425 \text{ psi}$$

which is within allowable limits. In Step 7 we shall find that the tendons must be curved up to keep the net stress within the required limits near the ends of the span where the dead-load stresses are small.

Equation (3-2) from Step 4 in Chap. 3 is

$$\frac{F}{A_c} - \frac{Fe}{Z_t} = -f'_G + f_{tp} \tag{3-2}$$

Substituting known values we get

$$\frac{F}{562} - \frac{Fe}{7,424} = -757 + 0 \tag{4-2}$$

Multiplying (4-2) by $Z_t/Z_b = 7,424/4,742 = 1.56$, we get

$$\frac{1.56F}{562} - \frac{Fe}{4,742} = -1,180 \tag{4-3}$$

Adding (4-1) to (4-3),

$$\frac{2.56F}{562} = 1,429 \tag{4-4}$$

from which

$$F = 313,000 \text{ lb}$$

Substituting this value of F in (4-1),

$$\frac{313,000}{562} + \frac{313,000e}{4,742} = 2,609$$
$$558 + 66.1e = 2,609$$
$$e = 31.00 \text{ in.}$$

Since y_b is only 25.63 in., this value of e would put the tendons below the bottom of the girder.

Step 5. Select the tensioning elements to be used and work out the details of their location in the member.

Step 5 in Chap. 3 tells us to choose a reasonable value for e when the solution of the equations gives an e too large to suit the dimensions of the girder. Try $e = 17.25$ in. Then the c.g.s. (center of gravity of the tendons) will be $25.63 - 17.25 = 8.38$ in. above the bottom of the girder, which should provide room for the tendons needed.

To find F substitute in Eq. (4-1)

$$\frac{F}{562} + \frac{17.25F}{4,742} = 2,609$$

Multiply by 562.

$$F + 2.04F = 1,466,000$$
$$F = 482,000 \text{ lb}$$

Since we have not yet studied the chapters on Materials and Specifications, we do not have enough information to choose the tendons and work out a pattern. We shall assume that we have selected a group of tendons which have $F = 483,840$ lb and a c.g.s. that is 7.62 in. above the bottom of the girder. Then

$$e = 25.63 - 7.62 = 18.01 \text{ in.}$$

From Chap. 3, Step 5,

$$f^t_F = \frac{F}{A_c} - \frac{Fe}{Z_t} \tag{3-5}$$

Substituting known values,

$$f^t_F = \frac{483,840}{562} - \frac{483,840 \times 18.01}{7,424}$$
$$f^t_F = 861 - 1,174 = -313 \text{ psi}$$

Net stress in the top fiber under prestress plus dead load only is

$$f^t_F + f^t_G = -313 + 757 = +444 \text{ psi}$$

Net stress in the top fiber under all applied loads is

$$f^t_F + f^t_G + f^t_S + f^t_L = -313 + 757 + 91 + 820 = +1,355$$

From this we see that the stress in the top fiber at the center of span will vary from $+444$ psi under prestress plus dead load to $+1,355$ psi under prestress plus all applied loads. These stresses are within the specified limits of zero to $+2,000$ psi.

The stress in the bottom fiber due to prestress is

$$f^b_F = \frac{F}{A_c} + \frac{Fe}{Z_b} = \frac{483,840}{562} + \frac{483,840 \times 18.01}{4,742} = +2,699$$

Net stress in the bottom fiber under prestress plus dead load only is

$$f^b_F + f^b_G = +2,699 - 1,184 = +1,515 \text{ psi}$$

Net stress in the bottom fiber under all applied loads is

$$f^b_F + f^b_G + f^b_S + f^b_L = +2{,}699 - 1{,}184 - 142 - 1{,}283 = +90 \text{ psi}$$

From this we see that the stress in the bottom fiber at the center of span will vary from $+1{,}515$ psi under prestress plus dead load to $+90$ psi under all applied loads. These stresses are within the specified limits of zero to $+2{,}000$ psi.

Since both the top and bottom fiber stresses at the center of span are within the specified limits for all design bending moment conditions, the concrete cross section and tendons selected are satisfactory and it is probable that conditions at other points along the span can be met satisfactorily.

At this point we should review the results of our calculations and consider the economy of the member chosen. Under the extreme conditions of design load, the maximum stress in the top fiber is $+1{,}355$ psi and in the bottom fiber it is $+1{,}515$ psi, yet the specification permits $+2{,}000$ psi. Study Fig. 4-1 to see how we can save some concrete. The simplest method would be to leave the depth unchanged, making the top slab thinner and the bottom flange narrower. This would reduce the section modulus, increase the stresses to near the maximum allowed, and have little or no effect on the number of tendons, since the general shape and depth of the girder are not changed. The saving would be represented by the concrete saved and the smaller dead weight to be carried by the piers.

In this particular case we cannot follow the simplest method because of the details of the structure. The 6-in. top slab is needed to carry the concentrated loads of truck wheels, and the area of the bottom flange is needed for the placement of the tendons. The only remaining course is to reduce the depth of the girder. This is seldom economical because the only concrete saved is a small amount equal to the thickness of the web times the reduction in depth, and this is offset by the fact that a reduction in depth requires an increase in the prestressing force. Under the existing circumstances the only reason for changing the section chosen would be one external to the structure. For instance, it might pay to reduce the depth because clearance is a problem and a reduction in depth of girder would reduce the amount of fill in the approaches to the bridge.

For the purposes of this example we shall continue with the section shown in Fig. 4-1.

Step 6. Establish the concrete strength f'_{ci} at the time of prestressing and check stresses under the initial prestress condition.

At the beginning of this example it was stated that $f'_{ci} = +4{,}000$ psi.

For a bridge the specification would set concrete stresses under initial tension at

Maximum compressive stress $= 0.60f'_{ci} = 0.60 \times 4{,}000 = 2{,}400$ psi

Maximum tensile stress $= 3\sqrt{f'_{ci}} = 3\sqrt{4{,}000} = -190$ psi

The initial tension in the tendons was set at 175,000 psi, and stress losses at 35,000 psi. From this the final tension will be $175{,}000 - 35{,}000 = 140{,}000$ psi. The initial prestressing force F_I can now be found in terms of the final prestressing force F.

$$F_I = F\frac{175{,}000}{140{,}000} = 1.25F \qquad (4\text{-}5)$$

$$= 1.25 \times 483{,}840 = 604{,}800 \text{ lb}$$

The stress in the top fiber due to the initial prestressing force F_I can be found by using Eq. (3-5) and substituting F_I for F.

$$f^t{}_{F_I} = \frac{F_I}{A_c} - \frac{F_I e}{Z_t}$$

Substituting,

$$f^t{}_{F_I} = \frac{604{,}800}{562} - \frac{604{,}800 \times 18.01}{7{,}424}$$

$$= 1{,}076 - 1{,}467 = -391$$

Note that $F_I = 1.25F$ and $f^t{}_{F_I} = 1.25f^t{}_F$. The ratio between the stress due to F and the stress in the same location due to F_I is the same as the ratio between F and F_I. This relationship can be applied to simplify the calculation of the stresses due to F_I when the stresses due to F are known. Thus in this example

$$f^t{}_{F_I} = 1.25f^t{}_F = 1.25\,(-313) = -391 \text{ psi}$$

In the same manner

$$f^b{}_{F_I} = 1.25f^b{}_F = 1.25\,(+2{,}699) = +3{,}375 \text{ psi}$$

Under initial prestress plus dead load

$$f^t{}_{F_I} + f^t{}_G = -391 + 757 = +366 \text{ psi}$$
$$f^b{}_{F_I} + f^b{}_G = +3{,}375 - 1{,}184 = +2{,}191 \text{ psi}$$

Under initial prestress plus all applied loads

$$f^t{}_{F_I} + f^t{}_G + f^t{}_S + f^t{}_L = -391 + 757 + 91 + 820 = +1{,}277 \text{ psi}$$
$$f^b{}_{F_I} + f^b{}_G + f^b{}_S + f^b{}_L = +3{,}375 - 1{,}184 - 142 - 1{,}283 = +766 \text{ psi}$$

From this we see that all the stresses under the condition of initial prestress are within the allowable stresses for that condition.

In a post-tensioned member, the tension in the tendons at the completion of the prestressing operation is F_I. There have been no stress losses.

In a pretensioned member the tension in the tendons after their load has been transferred from the anchorages to the concrete members is F_o. F_o is less than F_I by the amount of certain stress losses which take place as the load in the tendons is transferred. A complete discussion of this factor will be given in Chap. 9 at which time the reader will be better prepared to understand it.

Step 7. Establish the path of the tendons and check any critical points along the member under initial and final conditions.

The foregoing calculations show that the chosen prestressing force and its eccentricity will offset the tensile stresses at the point of maximum moment without creating excessive stresses under any condition. It is obvious, therefore, that this same force can be used to offset the tensile stresses at points of lesser moment. The problem is to locate the prestressing force at an elevation at each point along the girder such that the tensile forces are overcome without creating excessive stresses.

Since this is a simple span girder, there is no bending moment at the ends and the only stresses are those due to the prestressing force. If the prestressing force is left at the same eccentricity as at the center of the span, these stresses will be

$$f^t_{F_I} = -391 \text{ psi} \quad f^b_{F_I} = +3,375 \text{ psi}$$
$$f^t_F = -313 \text{ psi} \quad f^b_F = +2,699 \text{ psi}$$

All these stresses are greater than the allowable, but all can be brought within the allowable by decreasing the eccentricity e, i.e., raising the center of gravity of the prestressing force. How much should e be decreased? At least enough to bring the stresses within those allowed by the specification.

Compute e for this condition. A small reduction in e will change the top fiber stress from tension to compression, so stress in the top fiber is not a governing condition. Under final prestress e must be such that f^b_F does not exceed 2,000 psi. Then $f^b_{F_I}$ will be $2,000 \times 1.25 = 2,500$ psi. Since the allowable stress under initial prestress is only 2,400 psi, $f^b_{F_I}$ is the governing condition.

$$f^b_{F_I} = \frac{F_I}{A_c} + \frac{F_I e}{Z_b}$$

$$f^b_{F_I} = 2,400 = \frac{604,800}{562} + \frac{604,800e}{4,742}$$

$$2,400 = 1,075 + 127.5e$$

$$e = (2,400 - 1,075) \div 127.5 = 10.40 \text{ in.}$$

Check the other three conditions:

$$f^t{}_{F_I} = \frac{F_I}{A_c} - \frac{F_I e}{Z_t}$$

$$= \frac{604,800}{562} - \frac{604,800 \times 10.40}{7,424}$$

$$= 1,075 - 845 = +230 \text{ psi}$$

As shown previously for this example $f^b{}_{F_I} = 1.25 f^b{}_F$; therefore we can write $f^b{}_F = f^b{}_{F_I} \div 1.25$. Then

$$f^b{}_F = 2,400 \div 1.25 = +1,920 \text{ psi}$$
$$f^t{}_F = +230 \div 1.25 = +184 \text{ psi}$$

Since all these stresses are within allowable limits, we could set $e = 10.40$ in. at the ends of the girders. Then the c.g.s. would be $25.63 - 10.40 = 15.23$ in. above the bottom of the girder. As the girder is 42 in. deep, there is plenty of room to move the c.g.s. higher. Should it be raised and if so how much? Several factors enter into this decision.

1. The most important factor is the shape of the bending moment curve. The eccentricity of the tendons at any point along the girder must be large enough so that $f^b{}_F$ is equal to or greater than the tensile stress caused by the sum of the moments at that point. At the same time, at any point, $f^b{}_F + f^b{}_G$ must not be greater than the maximum allowable compressive stress.

2. In Step 10 we shall compute the camber, and the path of the tendons will have considerable effect on the result we get. Under prestress plus dead load the typical prestressed concrete girder will have an upward camber because the bottom fibers are shortened by a high compressive stress while the top fibers have only a small stress.

The magnitude of the camber is a function of the difference in stress between the top and bottom fibers. As the stress difference increases, the camber increases. The stress difference in each differential length of the girder contributes to the total camber, which is the sum of all these differential contributions. At the center of the span when the moment is large, the difference between the top and bottom fiber stresses must be large. As the bending moment decreases toward the supports, the difference in stress can remain the same or can decrease in proportion to the drop in moment. If the tendons are raised the minimum amount, to an e of 10.40 in., the camber will be maximum. This camber can be decreased by raising the tendons.

By varying the elevation of the tendons the designer can adjust the magnitude of the camber as long as the requirements of other controlling factors are met.

3. In Step 9 we shall design web reinforcement as a function of the shear carried by the concrete section.

Since the tendons are on a slope, they have both a horizontal and a vertical component. The horizontal component creates the prestress in the girder, and the vertical component reduces the shear carried by the concrete section. That is, the tendons carry an amount of shear equal to their vertical component, thus reducing the shear the concrete must carry. As the tendons are raised at the ends, the shear they carry is increased.

The shear carried by the tendons is considered in the design of the web reinforcement, but changing the elevation of the tendons within the allowable limits seldom makes a significant change in the web reinforcement.

4. In Step 5 we chose what appeared to be the most economical tendons for this girder. We must now consider the characteristics of these tendons to make sure that they can be placed economically in the path chosen for them. In many instances the path is selected to suit the characteristics of the tendons being used.

For this example we shall assume that the details of the tendons limit the c.g.s. to 15.50 in. above the bottom of the girder. Then $e = 25.63 - 15.50 = 10.13$ in. With this e the stresses at the end are

$$f^{b}{}_{F_I} = \frac{604{,}800}{562} + \frac{604{,}800 \times 10.13}{4{,}742}$$

$$= 1{,}076 + 1{,}291 = +2{,}367 \text{ psi}$$

$$f^{t}{}_{F_I} = \frac{604{,}800}{562} - \frac{604{,}800 \times 10.13}{7{,}424}$$

$$= 1{,}076 - 825 = +251 \text{ psi}$$

$$f^{b}{}_{F} = 2{,}367 \div 1.25 = +1{,}894 \text{ psi}$$

$$f^{t}{}_{F} = 251 \div 1.25 = +200 \text{ psi}$$

All these stresses are within the allowable.

Now that the position of the tendons has been established at the center of the span and at the ends of the girder, we must establish the path the tendons will follow between the two points. This can be done by plotting the curve of the tensile stress in the bottom fiber due to all applied loads and then establishing the path of the tendons so that the compressive stress they create is always greater than the tensile stress.

The moments due to the weight of the girder and the wearing surface are computed by conventional formulas. The moments due to live loads at points other than the center of span are computed by the simplified method outlined in Appendix D. In computing live-load moment remember that Step 4 showed that this particular girder must be

X*, ft	M_{G+S}†	M_L	M_{G+S+L}	f^t_{G+S+L}	f^b_{G+S+L}
8	189,000	195,000	384,000	+620	−972
16	336,000	339,000	675,000	+1,090	−1,710
24	440,000	438,000	878,000	+1,420	−2,220
32	504,000	492,000	996,000	+1,610	−2,520
40	524,000	507,000	1,031,000	+1,668	−2,609

* X is the distance from support to point being considered.
† Moments are in foot-pounds.

designed to carry 0.35 lane load and an impact factor of 24.4 per cent.

As shown in Fig. 4-2 we can now plot the stresses f^b_{G+S+L} for the full length of the girder and the stresses f^b_F at the center of span and at the end of the girder. We shall assume that the tendons being used are the

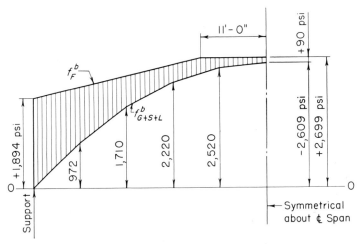

FIG. 4-2. Diagram of stresses in bottom fiber under final prestress plus all applied loads.

type which follow straight lines rather than curved paths, that they remain at one elevation through the center portion of the girder's length and then change direction to move in straight lines to the already selected points at the ends of the girder. The problem is to choose the point at which the path of the tendons changes direction. In Fig. 4-2 this point has been located 11 ft 0 in. from the center of the span. It could just as correctly have been located nearer to the center of the span as long as the curve of the compressive stress due to prestress remained above the curve of the tensile stress due to applied loads. Figure 4-3 shows the path chosen for the c.g.s. Since the tendons are at a constant elevation

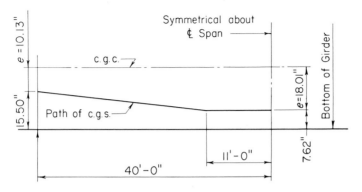

Fig. 4-3. Path of tendons.

from the center of span to the point 11 ft 0 in. away, the stress due to the tendons is constant in that portion of the girder. Since the tendons change elevation in a straight line from the 11-ft 0-in. point to the end of the girder, the stress due to the tendons in that portion of the girder also changes in a straight line.

Figure 4-2 is now completed. The stresses caused by the tendons are compressive and those caused by the applied loads are tensile, so the net stress, represented by the shaded area of Fig. 4-2, is the difference between the two.

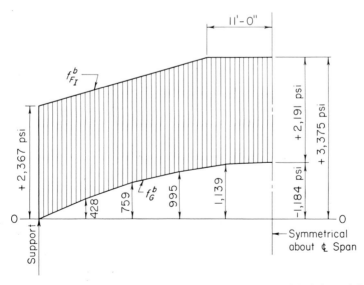

Fig. 4-4. Diagram of stress in bottom fiber under initial prestress plus girder weight only.

The second part of Step 7 is to "check any critical points along the member under initial and final conditions."

Figure 4-2 provides a complete check on bottom fiber stresses under final prestress plus all applied loads. The other critical condition for bottom fiber stresses is initial prestress plus girder weight only. This is covered in Fig. 4-4. The net stress is shown by the shaded area.

Checking stresses already computed for the top fiber shows that no combination of loadings is critical. For reference as an example in cases where top fiber stress is critical Fig. 4-5 has been plotted for the condition of final prestress plus all applied loads. The net stress is shown by the shaded area.

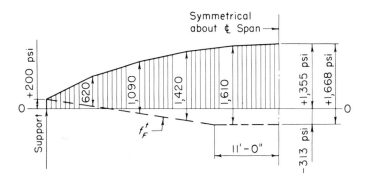

Fig. 4-5. Diagram of stress in top fiber under final prestress plus all applied loads.

Step 8. Check ultimate strength to make sure it meets the requirements of the specification. Check percentage of prestressing steel.

Refer to Sec. 209.2 of the Practice in Art. 8-2.

First we must establish the location of the neutral axis under the ultimate condition. This is done by the formula in Sec. 209.2.1(b)

$$1.4 \frac{dpf_{su}}{f'_c}$$
$$d = 18.01 + 16.37 = 34.38 \text{ in.}$$

The tendons selected give $A_s = 3.482$ and

$$f'_s = 248{,}000 \text{ psi}$$
$$f'_c = 5{,}000 \text{ psi}$$
$$p = \frac{A_s}{bd} = \frac{3.482}{42 \times 34.38} = 0.00241$$

From Sec. 209.2.2

$$f_{su} = f'_s \left(1 - \frac{0.5 p f'_s}{f'_c}\right)$$

$$= 248{,}000 \left(1 - \frac{0.5 \times 0.00241 \times 248{,}000}{5{,}000}\right) = 233{,}000$$

Substituting these values we get

$$1.4 \frac{34.38 \times 0.00241 \times 233{,}000}{5{,}000} = 5.40 \text{ in.}$$

Since the flange thickness is greater than 5.40 in., the formula for rectangular sections in Sec. 209.2.1(a) applies. This is

$$M_u = A_s f_{su} d \left(1 - \frac{k_2}{k_1 k_3} \frac{p f_{su}}{f'_c}\right)$$

Given in Sec. 208.2.1(a)

$$\frac{k_2}{k_1 k_3} = 0.60$$

Substituting,

$$M_u = 3.482 \times 233{,}000 \times 34.38 \left(1 - \frac{0.6 \times 0.00241 \times 233{,}000}{5{,}000}\right)$$

$$= 26{,}020{,}000 \div 12 = 2{,}170{,}000 \text{ ft-lb}$$

This is the ultimate moment the girder can carry.

The specification will require that the minimum ultimate moment capacity of the girder be at least

1.5 dead-load moment + 2.5 live-load moment

From Step 2

$$M_G = 5{,}616{,}000 \div 12 = 468{,}000 \text{ ft-lb}$$

From Step 3

$$M_S = 672{,}000 \div 12 = 56{,}000 \text{ ft-lb}$$

and $\quad\quad M_L = 6{,}086{,}000 \div 12 = 507{,}167$

Therefore the required ultimate moment is

$$1.5 \,(468{,}000 + 56{,}000) + 2.5 \,(507{,}167) = 786{,}000 + 1{,}267{,}918$$
$$= 2{,}053{,}918$$

Since this is less than M_u, the girder meets the ultimate strength requirement.

Check the percentage of prestressing steel in accordance with Sec. 209.2.3 of the Practice in Art. 8-2.

$$\frac{pf_{su}}{f'_c} \quad \frac{0.00241 \times 233,000}{5,000} = 0.1123$$

Since this is less than 0.30, the girder is not over-reinforced.

Step 9. Design of shear steel.

Refer to Sec. 210 of the Practice in Art. 8-2.

From Sec. 210.2.1 web reinforcement is not needed when

$$\frac{pf'_s}{f'_c} \lessgtr 0.3 \frac{f_{se}}{f'_s} \frac{b'}{b}$$

Substituting numerical values from calculations in preceding steps,

$$\frac{0.00241 \times 248,000}{5,000} \lessgtr 0.3 \frac{140,000}{248,000} \frac{6}{42}$$

$$0.1195 \lessgtr 0.024$$

Therefore web reinforcement is definitely needed.

Since this is a simply supported member carrying moving loads, the second paragraph of Sec. 210.2.5 is applicable. From this the maximum shear to be designed for is that which occurs at the quarter point of the span.

The total dead weight is 585 lb per ft of girder plus 70 lb per ft of wearing surface = 655 lb per ft. This gives a shear at the quarter point of $655 \times 20 = 13,100$ lb.

The live-load shear per lane at the quarter point is 45,600 lb as computed in Fig. 4-6. At the quarter point the shear and moment are distributed across the full width of the lane so that each girder carries only 35 per cent of a lane load. As the truck approaches the end of the bridge, the amount of transverse distribution decreases. Since one line of wheels can be directly over one girder, the total shear per girder with no distribution approaches one-half of the lane-load shear. Until more complete data on transverse distribution of shear are available, the safe procedure is to design for one-half lane-load shear per girder. Then the live-load shear per girder is $0.50 \times 45,600 = 22,800$ lb.

Ultimate shear factors are the same as ultimate moment factors, so

$$V_u = (1.5 \times 13,100) + (2.5 \times 22,800)$$
$$= 19,650 + 57,000 = 76,650 \text{ lb}$$

Compute the shear carried by the tendons under final prestress. From Fig. 4-3 the tangent of the tendons is $(15.50 - 7.62)/(29.0 \times 12) = 0.0226$, $F = 483,840$. Then the shear carried by the tendons is $483,840 \times 0.0226 = 10,935$ lb.

Therefore the effective V_u is $76,650 - 10,935 = 65,715$ lb.
Apply the formula given in Sec. 210.2.2:

$$A_V = \frac{(V_u - V_c)s}{2f'_y jd}$$

For this example $V_c = 180b'jd$.
Since the tendons slope, d at the quarter point is less than at mid-span. Refer to Fig. 4-3. The tendons slope $15.50 - 7.62 = 7.88$ in. in 29 ft. Since the quarter point is 20 ft from the end, the drop of the tendons to this point is

$$\frac{20}{29} \, 7.88 = 5.44 \text{ in.}$$
$$10.13 = e \text{ at end from Fig. 4-3}$$
$$16.37 = \text{top fiber to c.g.c. from Fig. 4-1}$$
$$\overline{d = 31.94 \text{ in.}}$$

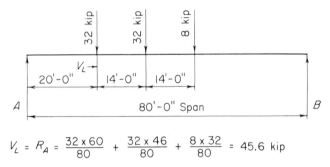

$$V_L = R_A = \frac{32 \times 60}{80} + \frac{32 \times 46}{80} + \frac{8 \times 32}{80} = 45.6 \text{ kip}$$

FIG. 4-6. Truck loading which produces maximum shear at quarter point.

Then $p = \dfrac{3.482}{42 \times 31.94} = 0.00260$

$$f_{su} = 248,000 \left(1 - \frac{0.5 \times 0.00260 \times 248,000}{5,000}\right) = 232,000$$

j can be computed from the following portion of formula (a) in Sec. 209.2.1(a):

$$\left(1 - \frac{k_2}{k_1 k_3} \frac{pf_{su}}{f'_c}\right)$$

Substituting numerical values,

$$j = \left(1 - 0.6 \frac{0.00260 \times 232,000}{5,000}\right) = 0.928$$

Then $V_c = 180 \times 6 \times 0.928 \times 31.94 = 32{,}000$ lb

From Sec. 210.2.4 the maximum spacing of stirrups is three-fourths of the depth of the member.

Use $s = \frac{3}{4} \times 42 = 31.5$ in.

Use intermediate-grade reinforcing bars for stirrups with $f'_y = 40{,}000$ psi.

Substituting known values,

$$A_V = \frac{(65{,}715 - 32{,}000)\,31.5}{2 \times 40{,}000 \times 0.928 \times 31.94} = 0.448 \text{ sq in.}$$

From Sec. 210.2.3 the minimum amount of web reinforcement is

$$A_V = 0.0025b's$$

Substituting numerical values,

$$A_V = 0.0025 \times 6 \times 31.5 = 0.4725$$

Therefore this requirement governs, and the same stirrups can be used the full length of the girder.

$$\text{Two } \tfrac{1}{2}\text{-in.-diameter bars} = 2 \times 0.1963 = 0.3926$$

$$31.5 \times \frac{0.3926}{0.4725} = 26.17$$

Use two $\frac{1}{2}$-in.-diameter bars at 26-in. centers for the full length of the girder.

Step 10. Compute camber.

Although we use precise engineering formulas in computing the camber of prestressed concrete members, the results are accurate only within the accuracy with which we can determine the modulus of elasticity of the concrete. Section 203.2 of Art. 8-2 gives a formula, $E_c = 1{,}800{,}000 + 500f'_c$, and states that actual values can vary as much as 25 per cent.

Compute instantaneous camber under prestress plus dead weight of girder only. At this time $f'_{ci} = 4{,}000$ psi. Then

$$E_c = 1{,}800{,}000 + (500 \times 4{,}000) = 3{,}800{,}000$$

Under this condition the camber will be the algebraic sum of the deflection due to dead load plus the deflection due to the prestress. Deflection due to dead load is computed by the standard formula

$$\Delta_G = \frac{5wl^4}{384EI}$$

$$= \frac{5 \times 585\,(80^4)\,12^3}{384 \times 3{,}800{,}000 \times 121{,}540} = -1.17 \text{ in.}$$

The minus sign indicates a downward deflection, which is a negative camber.

As discussed in Chap. 1 in the development of Eq. (1-1), an eccentric prestressing force can be replaced by a force on the c.g.c. and a couple. We do the same thing in computing camber. The force on the c.g.c. can be ignored because it creates a uniform compressive stress over the entire cross section so that the entire section shortens the same amount and there is no change in camber. The couple produces a bending moment which does cause camber. The bending moment is equal to the prestressing force multiplied by its eccentricity with respect to the c.g.c. The initial prestressing force is 604,800 lb. From Fig. 4-3 we can compute the bending moment due to the eccentricity of the prestressing force. At the ends of the girder

$$M_e = 604{,}800 \times 10.13 = 6{,}126{,}624 \text{ in.-lb}$$

At the center of span

$$M_e = 604{,}800 \times 18.01 = 10{,}892{,}448 \text{ in.-lb}$$

The moment diagram for this condition is plotted in Fig. 4-7.

Deflection at the center of span due to the moments shown in Fig. 4-7 can be computed by the moment-area method. When applied to this particular problem, the moment-area method says that the deflection at the center of span is equal to the moment of the area of the M/EI diagram about the support. The moment diagram in Fig. 4-7 has been divided into three simple sections, so the moment of the M/EI diagram for each can be easily figured and the total deflection Δ_{F_I} can be obtained by adding the three results.

$$\Delta_I = \frac{6{,}126{,}624\,(40 \times 12)\,(20 \times 12)}{EI} = \frac{705{,}787\,(10^6)}{EI}$$

$$\Delta_{II} = \frac{4{,}765{,}824\,(29 \times 12)\,\tfrac{1}{2}\,(\tfrac{2}{3} \times 29 \times 12)}{EI} = \frac{192{,}387\,(10^6)}{EI}$$

$$\Delta_{III} = \frac{4{,}765{,}824\,(11 \times 12)\,(34.5 \times 12)}{EI} = \frac{260{,}443\,(10^6)}{EI}$$

$$\Delta_{F_I} = \Delta_I + \Delta_{II} + \Delta_{III} = \frac{1{,}158{,}617\,(10^6)}{EI}$$

$$\Delta_{F_I} = 1{,}158{,}617\,(10^6) \div [3.8\,(10^6) \times 121{,}540] = +2.51 \text{ in.}$$

Net camber = $+2.51 - 1.17 = +1.34$ or an upward camber of 1.34 in.

Accurate computation of final camber in a member is even more difficult because of the variables involved. Section 203.3 of the Practice indicates that the long-time increase in deflection under sustained loads can be 100 to 300 per cent of the instantaneous deflection. Even the erection schedule can influence the final camber. If a bridge girder is erected and the wearing surface is applied as soon as the concrete in the girder reaches the required strength, the increase in camber will be a function of the camber under dead load plus wearing surface. If the girder alone is allowed to stand for some time before it is erected, a part of the increase in camber will be a function of the camber under dead load only and the final camber will be greater than if the wearing surface load had been applied sooner.

Choice of the percentage of increase in deflection must be based on experience in the locality of the structure and with the materials being used. We shall assume a 150 per cent increase.

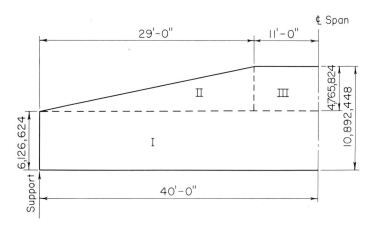

Fig. 4-7. Bending moment due to initial prestress.

We shall also assume that the member is erected and the wearing surface placed shortly after the tensioning operation. This means that the major part of camber growth will take place with the wearing surface in place and will be a function of $\Delta_{F_I} + \Delta_G + \Delta_s$.

$$w_s = 70 \qquad w_G = 585$$

Thus

$$\Delta_s = \Delta_G \frac{w_s}{w_G} = -1.17 \frac{70}{585} = -0.14 \text{ in.}$$

$$\Delta_{F_I} + \Delta_G + \Delta_s = +2.51 - 1.17 - 0.14 = +1.20 \text{ in.}$$

Total final camber is

$$1.20 + 150\% (1.20) = 3.00 \text{ in.}$$

This is a rather large camber for the average 80-ft 0-in. span bridge girder especially in a multispan bridge on which an automobile would rise and fall 3 in. on every span. Five methods of reducing camber are discussed in Step 10 of Chap. 10. The first, a deeper section, and the fifth, a larger prestressing force, are the only two that are applicable to this particular bridge member.

CHAPTER 5

MATERIALS

CONCRETE

5-1. Properties. In reinforced concrete structures the usable concrete strength is limited by the behavior of the member. When the tensile stresses in the reinforcing steel exceed 18,000 or 20,000 psi, the member begins to show excessive cracks and deflection. Since 3,000-psi concrete is strong enough to develop these stresses in the reinforcing, higher strengths are seldom specified.

The concrete used in prestressed concrete, although made of the same basic ingredients, is much stronger, since its full strength can be utilized.[1]* In this case the governing factor is economical fabrication. A majority of members are made of 5,000-psi concrete, although some fabricators use appreciably higher strengths and most specifications permit a minimum of 4,000 psi.

High-strength concrete has several advantages:

1. A smaller cross-sectional area can be used to carry a given load. This means less dead weight and in many instances shallower members, giving more clearance.

2. Its higher modulus of elasticity E_c decreases camber, which is frequently a problem in prestressed concrete because of the relatively high negative moment that exists under the dead-load condition. The high E_c also reduces deflection and in pretensioned members cuts down the stress loss due to elastic shortening. The Joint ACI-ASCE Committee on Prestressed Reinforced Concrete suggests the following formula for E_c in their Recommended Practice for Prestressed Concrete:

$$E_c = 1,800,000 + 500f'_c \tag{5-1}$$

Actual values can vary as much as 25 per cent from Eq. (5-1), and it does not apply to lightweight concrete (see Sec. 203.2a in Art. 8-2).

3. Members can be prestressed and equipment released for the next pour in minimum time because the required f'_{ci} is reached sooner. In

---

* Superscript numbers indicate references listed in the Bibliography at the end of the chapter.

some cases fabricators of pretensioned members use a mix which gives a higher f'_c than required by specifications in order to reach f'_{ci} in time to maintain their pouring schedule.

4. In bridges and other members exposed to freezing or salt spray the combination of high strength and density plus freedom from cracks makes prestressed concrete virtually maintenance-free.

5-2. Placing. Prestressed concrete fabricators employ several aids for handling the high-strength low-slump concrete to achieve satisfactory placement and rapid curing.

Internal vibrators are standard equipment for all work of this type. Vibrating screeds are frequently used on area-type members such as double T's and channels.

Air entraining cement and admixtures such as Plastiment are employed to increase the workability of the mix. Use of additional cement to increase workability while maintaining the water-cement ratio and ultimate strength is avoided because the extra cement paste in the rich mix is a source of additional shrinkage.

5-3. Curing. Rapid curing to permit frequent reuse of equipment is an important factor in the economical production of prestressed concrete and especially of the pretensiond type. Figure 5-1 illustrates the curing speed obtained by steam curing on a typical pretensioned project.[2] Some casting yards accelerate curing by circulating hot oil through pipes located under and beside the curing concrete. Many use high-early-strength cement.

Calcium chloride is not used to accelerate curing. Existing data suggest that its action is damaging to the properties of the highly stressed tendons (see Sec. 302.2.4 in Art. 8-2).

5-4. Lightweight Concrete. Prestressed concrete members both pretensioned and post-tensioned can be fabricated satisfactorily from lightweight concrete with the proper type of aggregate.

The chief differences between regular-weight concrete and lightweight concrete of the same strength are in the elastic properties. For lightweight concrete the E_c is usually smaller and the total creep larger than for the corresponding regular-weight concrete. When proper allowance for these factors is included in the calculations for stress loss and camber, and when aggregates which develop sufficient ultimate strength are used, lightweight prestressed concrete members often prove more economical than those of regular weight.

All specifications mentioned herein permit the use of lightweight concrete with the provision that E_c and stress losses are to be based on tests performed on concrete of the strength and type of aggregate being used. Such a provision is necessary because these properties vary considerably with different aggregates.

5-5. Grout. This section refers to the grout used around post-tensioned tendons to protect them and to bond them to the concrete of the member. It does not apply to grout used to connect precast units to each other.

Since the grout must completely fill the enclosure around the tendon, it is made to the consistency of thick paint and pumped into the enclosure at pressures of 75 to 100 psi. Typical proportions by volume are 1

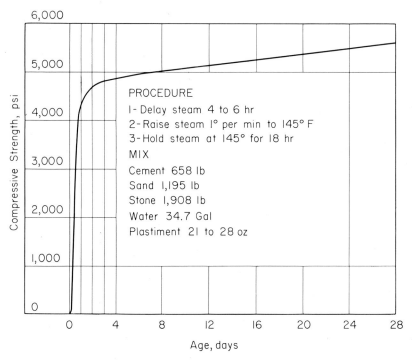

PROCEDURE
1- Delay steam 4 to 6 hr
2- Raise steam 1° per min to 145° F
3- Hold steam at 145° for 18 hr
MIX
Cement 658 lb
Sand 1,195 lb
Stone 1,908 lb
Water 34.7 Gal
Plastiment 21 to 28 oz

FIG. 5.1.   Time-strength curve for steam cured concrete.   (*By permission of Sika Chemical Corporation.*)

part cement, 0.75 part fine sand, and 0.75 part water. All sand must pass a No. 30 sieve, and many designers and fabricators require that at least half of it pass a No. 50 sieve. Admixtures to increase fluidity are permitted as long as they are not detrimental to the steel tendons. The sand can be reduced or completely eliminated if there is reason to believe that a more fluid grout is required to fill the enclosures completely in a specific structure (see Section 303 in Art. 8-2).

TENDONS

5-6. General Properties. The need for high-strength tendons to minimize the drop in prestressing force due to stress losses was discussed at the end of Chap. 2. Satisfactory tendons are made from wire or combinations of wires and from high-strength bars, all of which are fabricated with special prestressed concrete properties. These tendons differ from most other steels in several ways in order to meet the particular requirements of prestressed concrete.

Uniform elongation to initial tension is essential in obtaining an accurate prestressing force. Figure 5-2 is the stress-strain curve of a 0.196-

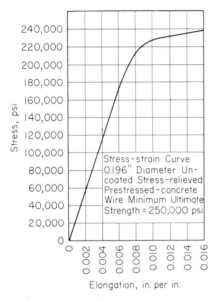

Stress-strain Curve 0.196" Diameter Uncoated Stress-relieved Prestressed-concrete Wire Minimum Ultimate Strength = 250,000 psi

FIG. 5-2. Stress-strain curve for 0.196-in.-diameter uncoated stress-relieved prestressed concrete wire.

in.-diameter uncoated stress-relieved prestressed concrete wire. (Its general shape is typical of all types of prestressed concrete tendons.)

For all practical purposes this curve is a straight line to a point above the initial tension of 165,000 to 175,000 psi normally used for 0.196-in. wire. Tendons do not have a yield point like that of ordinary steel where elongation continues without increase of stress. They do reach a point where the ratio of strain to stress increases rapidly and remains large until the tendon fails. This change in slope of the curve is also a necessary property. When a beam is overloaded and the stress in a tendon approaches ultimate, the tendon elongates, causing a visible deflection which warns of impending failure.

In addition to high strength and special elastic properties a tendon must have a low coefficient of relaxation at the high stresses used.

5-7. Wire. Table A-1* gives physical properties of the wires common to prestressed concrete work. The chief use of wire is for making post-tensioned cables which are composed of a number of parallel wires assembled in a flexible metal hose or inserted in a cavity left in the concrete.

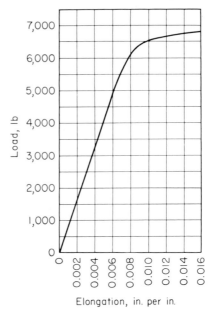

Fig. 5-3. Load-elongation curve for 0.196-in.-diameter uncoated stress-relieved prestressed concrete wire. (*By permission of John A. Roebling's Sons Corporation.*)

Figure 5-3 is a load-elongation curve for 0.196-in.-diameter uncoated stress-relieved prestressed concrete wire. This curve differs from Fig. 5-2 in that load is plotted against elongation instead of stress against elongation. This is done for the convenience of the fabricator so that, knowing the elongation, he can read the load directly from the curve without going through a calculation involving area and unit stress. Curves similar to this and plotted to a large scale for easy reading are available from the steel fabricators for each size and type of tendon.

*In Appendix A.

Prestressed concrete wire is made by drawing a high-carbon hot-rolled round steel rod through several conical dies. As the rod passes through each die, its diameter is decreased and its length is correspondingly increased. In the process the crystals that made up the rod are drawn out into the long parallel fibers which give wire its extremely high tensile strength. Figure 5-4 is a microphotograph showing the crystalline structure of the hot-rolled rod. Figure 5-5 is a microphotograph showing the fibers in a completed wire. After the wire has passed through the last die, it is called "cold drawn" wire.

FIG. 5-4. Microphotograph showing crystalline structure of hot-rolled rod. (*By permission of John A. Roebling's Sons Corporation.*)

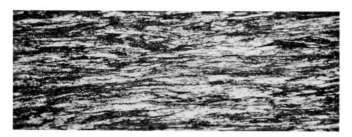

FIG. 5-5. Microphotograph showing fibers in a completed wire. (*By permission of John A. Roebling's Sons Corporation.*)

Cold drawn wire does not have the uniform elastic properties needed in prestressed concrete. As the crystals elongate into fibers, they develop stresses in excess of their yield point. The resulting wire is made up of fibers which are full of internal stresses. When a tensile load is applied to the wire, each fiber elongates the same amount. The stress due to this elongation is added to the internal stress, and soon the fiber with the highest internal stress reaches the point where its ratio of strain to stress increases rapidly. From here on this fiber will elongate with the others but its stress will not increase so rapidly. Since the internal stresses in the various fibers are not uniform, first one fiber, then another, then another will reach the yield point. The resulting load-elongation curve of the wire is not uniform.

The internal stresses in the cold drawn wire are eliminated by subjecting it to a stress-relieving process in which it is raised to a moderate temperature (750 to 850°F) for a short period of time (15 to 30 sec.). This is not a heat-treatment and does not change the ultimate strength of the wire to any noticeable degree. It does create a wire which has the desired uniform elastic properties because it is free of internal stresses.

At stresses up to 70 per cent of its ultimate strength the modulus of elasticity E_s of uncoated stress-relieved prestressed concrete wire is approximately 29,000,000 psi. While this value is sufficiently accurate for design calculations, it is recommended that the steel fabricator's load-elongation curve for the particular wire be used in computing the elongation required in jacking wires to a specified tension.

FIG. 5.6. Seven-wire strand. (*By permission of John A. Roebling's Sons Corporation.*)

Although oil-tempered wire has many of the properties desired in a prestressed concrete tendon, it also has other properties which make its desirability questionable (see Sec. 304.2 in Art. 8-2).

5-8. Seven-wire Strand. Table A-2 gives physical properties of seven-wire uncoated stress-relieved prestressed concrete strands. These strands are normally used in pretensioned bonded members. Figure 5-6 is a photograph of a seven-wire strand, and Fig. 5-7 is the load-elongation curve.

Each strand is made up of seven cold drawn wires. The center wire is straight, and the six outside wires are laid helically around it. All six outside wires are the same diameter, and the center wire is slightly larger. The difference in diamter is sufficient to guarantee that each of the outside wires will bear on and grip the center wire. This is an important detail in members where the tension in the strand is developed through bond. The six outer wires are bonded to the concrete both by adhesive bond and by mechanical bond of the concrete in the valleys between the wires. Under tension each of the outer wires bears on the center wire, and the resulting friction makes the center wire elongate with the outer wires. If the center wire were too small, the outer wires would bear against each other to form a pipe through which the center wire would slip without carrying any load.

The "lay" of the outer wires is the distance along the strand in which an outer wire makes one complete turn around the center wire. Each strand fabricator chooses the lay best suited to his production and within the limits of not less than twelve and not more than sixteen times the strand diameter. Since a strand with a long lay will have an appreciably

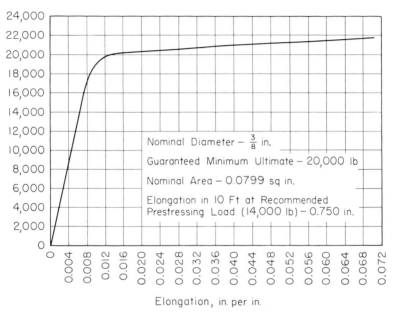

Nominal Diameter — $\frac{3}{8}$ in.

Guaranteed Minimum Ultimate — 20,000 lb

Nominal Area — 0.0799 sq in.

Elongation in 10 Ft at Recommended
Prestressing Load (14,000 lb) — 0.750 in.

Elongation, in. per in.

FIG. 5-7. Load-elongation curve for seven-wire uncoated stress-relieved prestressed concrete strand. (*By permission of John A. Roebling's Sons Corporation.*)

higher E_s than a strand with a short lay, specifications require that the "strand have a uniform lay"; i.e., the lay shall be constant for the full length of the strand.

After the seven wires are formed into a strand, the strand is subjected to a stress-relieving process like that described in Art. 5-7 for wire. The result is a strand with ideal elastic properties and free of internal stresses. Stress-relieving the individual wires before stranding does not produce a satisfactory strand because the outer wires are subjected to severe twisting in the stranding operation, which creates internal stresses. These are removed only when the stress-relieving operation follows the strand-ing operation.

5-9. Large Strands. Table A-3 gives physical properties of galvanized prestressed concrete strands, and Fig. 5-8 is a photograph of a 1-in.-diameter 19-wire strand. These strands are used entirely for post-tensioned work.

A galvanized prestressed concrete strand is composed of seven or more hot-dip galvanized wires. Here again the cold drawn wire is the basic unit. In this case the cold drawn wire is passed through a bath of molten zinc and emerges as a galvanized wire with an outer coating of pure zinc plus a hard zinc-steel alloy between the zinc and the steel. The tem-perature of the zinc bath and the speed of the wire passing through it are regulated so that the wire is stress-relieved as it is galvanized.

The smallest galvanized strand listed in Table A-3 is 0.600 in. diameter. This strand is composed of a center wire plus six outer wires assembled

FIG. 5-8.   One-inch-diameter prestressed concrete strand.   (*By permission of John A. Roebling's Sons Corporation.*)

in the same manner as the strands described in Art. 5-8. Larger strands are made by adding extra layers of wire. A 1-in.-diameter strand is a 0.600-in-diameter 7-wire strand with one more layer composed of 12 wires for a total of 19 wires. A 1⅜-in.-diameter strand is a 1-in.-diameter 19-wire strand with one more layer composed of 18 wires for a total of 37 wires. Intermediate sizes are made by varying either the number or size of the wires or both to produce the most economical strand.

Although strands well over 2 in. in diameter have been produced on existing equipment, the largest listed in Table A-3 and recommended for use in prestressed concrete is 1¹¹⁄₁₆ in. diameter. Beyond this size the problems of strand stiffness, heavy jacking equipment, etc., more than offset any saving due to handling fewer strands. In those few cases where larger strands must be used to get a large force into a small space, the strand fabricator should be consulted for advice on the best size to choose.

When the ultimate strengths given in Table A-3 are divided by the areas, it is found that the stresses at ultimate load are only 202,000 to 214,000 psi instead of the much higher stresses given for uncoated wire and strand. This is because it is standard practice to list the gross area of the strand including the zinc, even though the zinc carries practically no load.

In Art. 5-8 it was stated that the seven-wire strands are stress-relieved after stranding to eliminate internal stresses due to stranding. It is not practical to stress-relieve the larger strands because the outer wires would reach the critical temperature and revert to a crystalline structure before the inside wires were stress-relieved. To achieve uniform elongation characteristics the large strands are prestretched. In this operation a full shop length (usually 3,600 ft) is stretched in a tensioning rig to approximately 70 per cent of its ultimate and held at that load a short time. During this period of high stress the fibers which are stressed beyond their yield point because of the applied load added to internal stresses will continue to elongate until they reach a point of stability. After the load is released, the strand has good elastic properties up to its prestretching load. Figure 5-9 is the load-elongation curve of a $1^{11}/_{16}$-in.-diameter strand after the prestretching operation.

Ungalvanized strands having the same areas as the galvanized strands listed in Table A-3 can be made to order. Since their entire area is steel, their ultimate strength is approximately 10 per cent greater than that of the galvanized strands. Ungalvanized strands of this type are seldom used because they are more expensive than the parallel-wire cables mentioned in Art. 5-7 but have no particular advantage over them.

5-10. High-strength Steel Bars. Table A-4 gives physical properties of Stressteel bars, the first high-strength bars to be made in the United States in quantity for use in prestressed concrete work. Figure 5-10 is the stress-strain curve of a Stressteel bar.

The high strength needed for prestressed concrete tendons is achieved by using a specially selected hot-rolled alloy steel. In their hot-rolled state the alloy bars have neither the uniform elastic properties nor the ductility required. These properties are obtained by subjecting the bars to a stress-relieving treatment at 600°F for 8 hr in a furnace. They are then left closed in the furnace until cooled to approximately room temperature.

After stress-relieving, the bar has all the desirable properties except the stress-strain curve and high yield point typical of prestressed concrete tendons. These are developed by cold-stretching each bar to at least 90 per cent of its ultimate strength. The cold-stretching process also serves as a proof-stressing which eliminates any bars having surface imperfections or metallurgical defects.

5-11. Splices. Manufacturing and/or shipping conditions are often such that some tendons must be spliced. All splices have certain disadvantages, but they cannot be eliminated, so an understanding of the reasons for and conditions of their use is important.

Splices are not permitted in the wires of parallel-wire cables. There are two reasons for this. Since these wires are manufactured in lengths of 1,800 to over 7,000 ft, it is a simple matter to make a cable without splices. When wires are spliced, they are spliced by welding, which damages the fibers and therefore lowers the strength of the wire. In a parallel-wire cable each individual wire must carry its full share of the tension at all times. It cannot distribute part of its load to adjacent wires

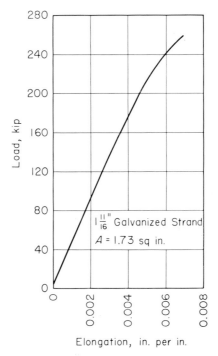

FIG. 5-9. Load-elongation curve for 1 $1\frac{11}{16}$-in.-diameter galvanized prestressed concrete strand (*By permission of John A. Roebling's Sons Corporation.*)

at a point where it is weak. As a result if a welded wire is used in a parallel-wire cable, it usually fails during the tensioning operation.

Seven-wire strands are produced in endless lengths and are most often shipped on reels containing 8,000 to 15,000 ft. In use the full length required is cut from the reel in one length and no splice is needed. When the last length on the reel is not long enough to reach the full length of the casting bed, some operators find it desirable to salvage this length by splicing it to another short length. Splicing two short lengths of strand together in this manner is permissible if the coupling used will develop the full strength of the strand, will not cause failure of the strand under the fatigue loadings which will be applied to the structure being fabricated, and does not weaken the member by replacing too much of the concrete in the cross section. The engineer must determine whether or not a particular splice has the necessary qualifications. Information on this subject is also available from some of the fabricators of seven-wire strands.

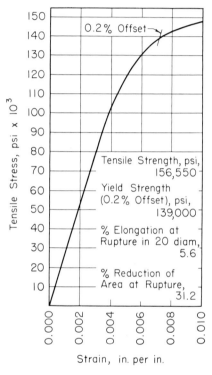

FIG. 5-10. Stress-strain curve of Stressteel bar. (*By permission of Stressteel Corp.*)

Splices are used in the individual wires of seven-wire strands during shop fabrication. ASTM Specification A 416-57T shown in Appendix F says "During fabrication of the strand, butt-welded joints may be made in the individual wires, provided there is not more than one such joint in any 150 foot section of the completed strand." Although the strength of the welded wire is reduced in the vicinity of the weld, the total strength of the strand is not seriously reduced. The welded wire is treated in the vicinity of the weld so that part of its load is transferred to the six other wires.

High-strength bars are spliced at the job site with couplers when necessary. Bars are fabricated in maximum lengths of about 80 ft and are sometimes furnished in shorter lengths with splices because of shipping difficulties. The couplers are larger in diameter than the bar and are tapped to take a threaded bar in each end. They develop the full strength of the bar. The disadvantage in the use of couplers is the large hole which must be cored in the concrete at the location of the coupler. If concrete stresses are high, the net section should be checked with the area of the hole deducted.

Large strands are never spliced, since they can be supplied in any length required without splices. They do have occasional splices in individual wires similar to the seven-wire strands.

5-12. Anchorages for Post-tensioned Tendons. The various types of anchor fittings used in the United States are illustrated in Chap. 7 in conjunction with the discussion of the tendons used with them.

Analysis of the stresses in anchor fittings for most post-tensioned tendons is a very specialized procedure and varies with the type of fitting. Responsibility for proper design of a fitting rests with the fabricator of that fitting.

An anchor fitting should be capable of developing the full strength of the tendon under static or fatigue loading. The prestressed concrete designer can safely accept types of fittings whose strength has been proved by years of actual use. When a new type is offered, it should be accompanied by sufficient test data to satisfy experienced prestressed concrete engineers that it will perform satisfactorily.

In addition to anchoring the tendon, the anchor fitting must spread the load to the concrete in the end block or it must be anchored against a bearing plate which will spread the load. Section 207.3.4 of the Practice in Art. 8-2 gives a formula for the allowable pressure under an anchor fitting or bearing plate. It is the author's experience that this formula is quite conservative. Where past experience with a particular fitting shows that it works satisfactorily even though the stresses computed by this formula are too high, the evidence of experience should be accepted and the use of the fitting permitted.

5-13. Flexible Metal Hose. Post-tensioned tendons are frequently encased in flexible metal hose. For large strands and bars the inside diameter of the hose is ¼ to ⅜ in. larger than the diameter of the tendon. For parallel-wire cables the diameter is selected to provide sufficient room for grouting the wires in the cable.

The purpose of the metal hose is to keep the tendon from bonding to the concrete until the concrete has cured and the tendon has been tensioned. After tensioning, the metal hose is pumped full of grout, which bonds the tendon to the hose. Since the hose is already bonded to the concrete, the grout actually bonds the tendon to the concrete.

Flexible metal hose is available in various thicknesses, profiles, degrees of watertightness, etc. Experience indicates that it should be made of metal having a minimum thickness of 0.011 in. Hose made of lighter metal is easily damaged. Special packings to make the hose absolutely watertight are not necessary. Properly formed hose without packing will be tight enough to prevent any leakage from the low-slump concrete into the hose.

Choice of uncoated metal hose or galvanized hose depends upon its use. Uncoated hose is satisfactory when it is to be used in a reasonably short time and will not be left exposed to the weather for more than a few days. Galvanized hose is used when exposure is expected to be severe enough to rust the light metal seriously in an uncoated hose. Galvanized hose is also used when friction between tendon and hose is a problem, because the galvanized hose gives a lower coefficient of friction.

The profile of the hose is an important factor. Profile refers to the shape into which the flat wire is bent as it is formed into the hose. The crushing strength of the hose, its ability to resist tearing as it is handled, and the radius to which it can be bent without damage are all functions of the profile.

Many fabricators of flexible metal hose have developed hoses especially for use with prestressed concrete and can refer designers to previous users of this material if necessary. They can also furnish hose with attachments for grout connections at specified locations.

5-14. Standard Materials. Cement, aggregate, water, reinforcing bars, etc., are of the same types and specifications as those used in ordinary reinforced concrete. References to the specifications applicable to these materials are found in Chap. III of the Practice in Art. 8-2.

BIBLIOGRAPHY

1. Klieger, Paul: Early High-Strength Concrete for Prestressing, *Research and Develop. Labs., Portland Cement Assoc. Research Dept. Bull.* 91, Chicago, Ill., March, 1958.
2. Schmid, Emil, and Raymond J. Schutz: Steam Curing, *J. Prestressed Concrete Inst.*, September, 1957, pp. 37–42.

CHAPTER 6

PRETENSIONED METHOD

6-1. Basic Operation. Pretensioning is defined by the ACI-ASCE Committee on Prestressed Concrete as "a method of prestressing reinforced concrete in which the reinforcement is tensioned before the concrete has hardened." Applied to standard practice in the United States, a more specific definition would be "a method of prestressing reinforced concrete in which the reinforcement is tensioned before the concrete is placed."

Basically, one complete cycle on a casting bed has five steps:

1. Tendons are placed on the bed in the specified pattern. They are tensioned to full load and attached to anchors at each end of the bed so that the load is maintained.

2. Forms, reinforcing bars, wire mesh, etc., are assembled around the tendons.

3. Concrete is placed and allowed to cure. In many cases curing is accelerated by the use of steam or other similar methods.

4. When the concrete reaches the strength specified for f'_{ci}, the load in the tendons is released from the anchors. Since the tendons are now bonded to the concrete, they cannot move independently of the concrete. As they try to shorten, their load is transferred to the concrete by bond. This load is the prestressing force in the concrete member.

5. The tendons are cut at each end of each prestressed concrete member, and the members are moved to a storage area so the bed can be prepared for the next cycle.

6-2. Tendons. The standard tendon for pretensioned members in the United States is the seven-wire uncoated stress-relieved prestressed concrete strand illustrated in Fig. 5-6 and covered by ASTM Specification A 416-57T which appears in Appendix F. These strands have proved superior to single wires because they have much better bonding properties, they take up less space for a given prestressing force, and they can be placed and tensioned with less labor.

In a pretensioned member the load in the tendon is transferred to the concrete by bond. This transfer of load takes place in a short distance, called the transfer length, at each end of the member. For example, test data show that the full initial tension in a $\frac{7}{16}$-in.-diameter strand is transferred to the concrete in a distance which varies from 15 to 30 in. depending upon the conditions in the particular member. Between the two transfer lengths the only transfer of load from the strand to the concrete is the small amount due to changes in bending moment. If a member is loaded to failure, the bond between strand and concrete must be sufficient to develop the ultimate strength of the strand. Prestressed concrete members fabricated in accordance with standard requirements have the necessary bond properties.

Seven-wire strands develop both adhesive and mechanical bond. The heat of the stress-relieving process burns off oil, grease, and other foreign materials which might impair the adhesion between concrete and the wires in the strand. In many cases "on-the-job" conditions make it difficult to keep the strand entirely free of rust. Rust is not harmful as long as it is within the limits permitted by ASTM A 416-57T; in fact a small amount of rust actually improves bond. Mechanical bond is developed by the concrete in the valleys between the wires of the strand.

All requirements affecting the bond of the seven-wire strand in prestressed concrete are based on test results. Procedures for computing the effective bond as a function of concrete strength, strand diameter, etc., have been suggested, but none has been considered accurate enough to be adopted by the writers of prestressed concrete specifications. Numerous comprehensive tests have been conducted to establish the bonding properties of seven-wire strand. They include everything from simple pull-out tests to full-size bridge girders subjected to millions of cycles of repeated loadings.[1-4]* Pull-out tests seldom give accurate results because the full advantage of the mechanical bond is not obtained. As shown by Fig. 5-6 the seven-wire strand looks something like a stud on which the threads have a very long pitch. When subjected to a pull-out test, the strand rotates or unscrews so that only the adhesive bond is effective. The mechanical bond is effective in a typical beam or girder because the strand is encased in concrete for its full length and cannot unscrew.

Single wires are used for pretensioned structures in Europe and were tried in this country when prestressed concrete fabricators were looking for the most efficient combinations of materials and production methods. Tests comparing the bonding properties of wires and seven-wire strands soon demonstrated the superiority of the strands. The full ultimate strength of 0.196-in.-diameter or smaller stress-relieved wires is developed in prestressed concrete beams statically loaded to failure. However, after such beams have been loaded to design load a million or more times,

---

*Superscript numbers indicate references listed in the Bibliography at the end of the chapter.

they fail under static test at loads as low as 60 per cent of their computed ultimate strength, and the failure is due to failure of bond between the concrete and the wires.   Beams pretensioned with seven-wire strands have just as high an ultimate strength after millions of cycles of loading as they have when loaded only once.   This leads to the conclusion that smooth wires undergo a progressive loss of bond while strands with the additional advantage of mechanical bond are not subject to this type of bond failure.   Since a typical highway bridge can be subjected in its lifetime to over a million cycles of full load plus numerous severe overloads, use of single wires anchored only by bond is not recommended.

For members not subjected to repeated loads, development of satisfactory bond limits wire sizes to about 0.196 in. maximum diameter.   A single 0.196-in.-diameter wire in a pretensioned member has a final tension of 4,000 lb.   Comparing this to 11,200 lb for a ⅜-in. strand and 15,120 lb for a ⁷⁄₁₆-in. strand we see that the number of wires needed is three to four times the number of strands needed.   In many members the space between strands is the minimum permitted by the size of the aggregate being used.   If the number of tendons were increased three or four times, a much larger concrete section would be needed to accommodate them. Since the labor required to place and tension a single wire is practically the same as that for a seven-wire strand, use of strands saves labor.

Although 0.196-in.-diameter stress-relieved wire is readily available as a standard item used in post-tensioned cables, it has almost completely disappeared from pretensioned work.

The first seven-wire strands used in pretensioned bonded work were ¼ in. diameter.   These were followed closely by ⁵⁄₁₆ and ⅜ in. diameters before the question of bond was raised.   Thorough tests of concrete members prestressed with ⅜-in. strands proved that these strands had the necessary bonding properties.   As the prestressed concrete industry grew, the size of the members being fabricated by the pretensioned method grew too and a point was reached where it was difficult to crowd enough ⅜-in. strands into the space available in some of the longer members. Although the obvious solution was ⁷⁄₁₆-in.-diameter strands, lack of data on bond discouraged their use until test programs verified their satisfactory bonding properties.   Once proved, they soon became the standard tensioning element for most large pretensioned members.   The 1957 edition of Specifications for Pre-Tensioned Prestressed Concrete by PCI approves the use of ⁷⁄₁₆-in.-diameter strands.

It appears that the maximum strand diameter approved for use will increase gradually until some limiting factor is reached.   Unless bond or some other property intervenes, the limiting factor may be the properties and production of the strand itself.   While existing equipment can produce larger seven-wire strand, the maximum size produced economically is about 0.600 in. in diameter. Since a 0.600-in. strand is quite stiff, handling at the casting bed will be another factor.

6-3. The Casting Bed. Figure 6-1 is a line drawing showing the basic elements of a casting bed on which three pretensioned members are curing. Figure 6-2 is an over-all view of a casting yard.[5-9]

The anchor posts must carry the full load of the tendons until the concrete has cured to the specified strength, f'_{ci}. Since the tendons are placed above the surface of the concrete slab, they create a bending moment as well as a horizontal force which must be resisted by the anchor posts. Details of the anchor posts depend upon soil conditions. Some are prestressed concrete piles like those shown in Fig. 6-1, some are gravity blocks similar to those used to anchor suspension bridge cables, and in some cases the concrete slab is made heavy enough to carry the load in compression without anchor posts. Anchor posts strong enough to hold the tendons of a large bridge girder are often one of the most expensive items in a casting bed. For this reason casting yards with more than one bed usually have just enough beds with heavy anchor posts to meet their

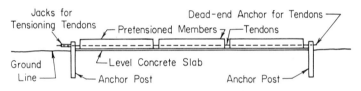

Fig. 6-1. Basic elements of a casting bed.

requirements for production of heavy members. They have additional beds with smaller anchor posts for the lighter members.

The concrete slab between the anchor posts serves as the pallet on which the members are cast. It is usually equipped with insets to which the forms can be fastened. When a bed is to be used for casting members with deflected strands as discussed in Art. 6-8, the slab is also equipped with inserts for holding the strands down at deflection points.

Casting beds have been built in lengths from under 100 to over 600 ft, but the efficient length for most installations seems to be in the neighborhood of 300 to 400 ft. No matter what bed length is chosen, there will be occasions when the total length of members to be cast is appreciably less than the distance between end anchor posts. In these cases the strand between the end of the last member cast and the end anchor post is wasted. Casting yards deal with this waste in various manners.

When the quantity is small, the waste strand can be cast into concrete members in loops that serve as lifting hooks or it can be used in the unstressed condition to replace small reinforcing bars. Some casting beds are designed with intermediate anchor posts. Intermediate posts help to reduce strand waste, but they are so expensive that there is some question as to whether or not the value of the strand saved justifies the initial investment in the additional posts. Other casting yards have various arrangements of strands or long bars that can be used as tag lines between the anchor post and the end of the last member.

FIG. 6-2. Over-all view of R. H. Wright and Son, Inc., casting yard at Dania, Fla. Overhead crane runway services casting beds, storage, and loading areas.

Lengths of strand too short to reach the full distance between anchor posts are frequently salvaged by splicing to a length long enough to complete the distance. A popular splice for this purpose is the PLP splice for prestressed concrete strands made by Preformed Line Products Co. of Cleveland, Ohio. These splices shown in Fig. 6-3 and 6-4 not only develop the full ultimate strength of the strand, they are small in diameter and can be cast into the concrete member.

The details of a casting bed are determined by the members it is to produce. Even the largest casting yards have at least one universal-type bed. A universal bed can be used to fabricate any pretensioned member that has a prestressing force within the capacity of the anchor posts. It is composed of anchor posts, a level concrete slab between the posts, and jacking equipment. In addition it usually has inserts in the slab for supporting forms, steam, or other curing facilities and inserts for strand deflection. Forms for the members to be cast are placed on the concrete slab. Templates for spacing and holding strands at the anchor

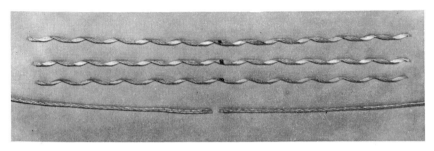

FIG. 6-3. Preformed Line Products Co. splice for seven-wire strand showing strands ready for splicing and the splice subsets to be used. The splice subsets are made of high-strength wires which have their contact surfaces with the strand coated with a gripping compound.

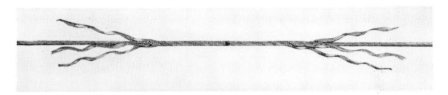

FIG. 6-4. Preformed Line Products Co. splice partially assembled on seven-wire strands.

posts have uniform spacings for strand patterns, and every effort is made to design members with strand patterns that can be worked into the standard templates. Jacking equipment is designed to accommodate any strand pattern within the capacity of the bed. Universal beds permit small yards to produce all types of members, and they are essential to any yard in the production of a complete line of prestressed concrete members. They are not quite so efficient in the production of standard members as a standard bed.

A standard bed is designed to produce a specific member in permanent forms. One of the most versatile and popular standard forms is the double T. Figure 6-5 shows the various sections which can be made in a double-T bed. The deepest double T is cast in the permanent form. Shallower double T's are cast by placing fillers in the legs of the form to the desired height. Channels are formed by using fillers which block out the overhanging portions of the top slab. Two rows of joists can be cast at one time by placing a divider of the desired width along the center line of the slab portion of the form. Depth of channels and joists can be varied by using fillers in the legs of the forms.

Some projects are large enough to justify the construction of custom-made beds for the one job. These beds are very efficient because each detail can be chosen to suit the members to be made. For instance, the length between anchor posts can be set to leave a minimum of strand waste.

6-4. Handling Strands. As seven-wire strands emerge from the stress-relieving process, they are wound onto reels for storage or shipment. The majority of strand fabricators use reel details the same as or close

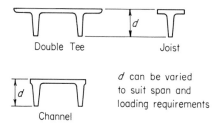

Fig. 6-5. Sections which can be cast in a standard double-T form.

to those shown in Fig. 6-6. Reels with the following standard lengths of strand are available:

Strand diameter, in.	Lineal feet of strand per reel	
	Small reels	Large reels
$\frac{1}{4}$	25,000	
$\frac{5}{16}$	15,000	
$\frac{3}{8}$	10,000	15,000
$\frac{7}{16}$	8,000	12,000
$\frac{1}{2}$	6,000	9,000

Although special lengths can be made to order, they are seldom used because the extra charge for nonstandard lengths offsets any saving in material.

It is standard practice with some strand fabricators to wrap a layer of VPI paper (vapor phase inhibitor) around the strand between the flanges of the reel and then cover it with a layer of waterproof paper The VPI paper creates a rust-preventing atmosphere around the strand which lasts, under reasonable conditions, for several months.

Seven-wire strands can also be made to order in coils to a length specified by the purchaser. There is no extra cost if the coil length is within certain limits. Although coils were quite popular when pre-stressed concrete was first starting in the United States, they are seldom used with newer casting-bed methods.

Reasonable care should be exercised in handling and storing strand to avoid mechanical damage, corrosion, excessive rust, and injurious temperatures. When reels of strand must be kept for any length of time,

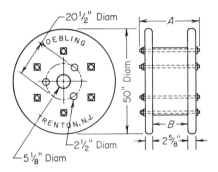

	Dimension *A*, in.	Dimension *B*, in.	Approx. empty reel wt, lb
Large reels....	36¾	30	300
Small reels....	30	23¼	280

Fig. 6-6. Standard reel dimensions. (*By permission of John A. Roebling's Sons Corporation.*)

they should be stored indoors if possible. Reels stored outdoors should be supported a few inches above the ground on timbers and covered with tarpaulins.

Strands, being made of high-carbon steel, are susceptible to mechanical damage. A nick or kink can be enough of a stress raiser to cause failure when the strand is tensioned to the high stresses normally used. All lifting and handling equipment should be attached to the flanges of the reel, never around the strand itself. Mechanical damage occurs most frequently when the strand has been pulled into the bed but not tensioned. It is caused by the edges of carelessly handled steel tools, wheelbarrow wheels, etc. Damage from vibrators during placing of concrete does not seem to be a problem.

Improper handling of welding equipment can be a cause of strand failure. A single drop of molten weld metal on a strand will raise the temperature of several wires to the point where the fibers return to crystals, thus losing more than half of their strength. The same change in structure will result when an electric arc jumps to or from the strand. If the strand is under tension when the high temperature occurs, failure will be instantaneous. If it is not under tension, the change in structure will still take place and failure will occur during the tensioning operation.

The foregoing comments may give the impression that prestressed concrete strands are extremely delicate. This is not the case. Properly organized casting yards seldom have trouble with strand damage, but

FIG. 6-7.   Stand for four reels in plant of Jackson Ready-Mix Concrete, Jackson, Miss.

the problems connected with handling these strands must be pointed out for the benefit of new operators.

6-5. Placing and Tensioning Strands. Reels of strand are placed on a stand at one end of the casting bed, and strands are pulled simultaneously from each reel to the far end of the bed. Some reel stands have as many reels as there are strands in the member to be cast so that all the strands can be pulled into the bed in one operation. With smaller reel stands it is necessary to make two or more passes to get the required number of strands into the bed. Figure 6-7 shows one type of small reel stand. When a casting yard has several beds, the reel stand is usually set up so that it can serve all the beds. Power equipment such as a tag line from a winch at the far end of the bed is used to pull the strands into the bed. Sometimes a heavy block is hung from a crane, the strands are attached to the block, and the crane moves along the bed pulling out the strands.

When the proper length has been pulled into the bed, the strand is cut from that remaining on the reel. The cut is made with welding equipment or with a shear. The high temperature needed to sever the strand with welding equipment returns the fibers to a crystalline structure, but only a few inches of strand are damaged, and the damaged portion will not be under tension.

A thick steel plate which serves as a combination anchor plate and template is provided at each end of the bed. The plate has holes, slightly larger than the strand diameter, which are spaced in the pattern

Size of Barrels

5/16 and 3/8 in.—1¼ in. OD by 1½ in. long

7/16 and ½ in.—1⅝ in. OD by 1½ in. long

FIG. 6-8. Prestressing anchor grips for holding seven-wire strands under tension in casting bed. Distributed by International Prestressing Corporation, Los Angeles, Calif.

the strands are to have in the concrete member. At one end of the bed each strand is threaded through its hole in the template and anchored on the far side by a temporary grip. Typical grips are shown in Figs. 6-8 to 6-10. When the concrete member is completed and removed from the bed, the grips are recovered for reuse.

Details and sequence of the following operations will vary for different conditions and specifications. Some specifications require that each strand be tensioned to a specific low tension and anchored against the anchor plate before all are jacked simultaneously from the low load to full tension. Others permit pulling each strand hand-tight for anchoring before jacking the entire group. We shall consider a group of 3/8-in.-diameter strands to be tensioned to a total load of 14,000 lb per strand with the requirement that each strand be tensioned and anchored at a load of 1,000 lb before the group is tensioned to full load. Distance between anchor plates before tensioning is 350 ft. The strands will be kept at a constant elevation for the entire length of the bed.

Each strand has already been anchored at one end of the bed. At the other end it is threaded through its hole in the anchor plate, and the tem-

FIG. 6-9. Supreme Chuck (anchor grip) in place on a seven-wire strand. Made by Supreme Products Corporation, Chicago, Ill.

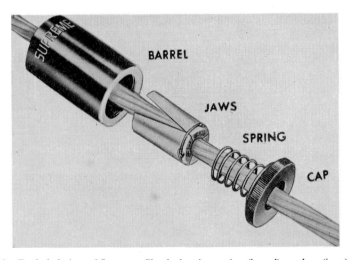

FIG. 6-10. Exploded view of Supreme Chuck showing casing (barrel), wedges (jaws), spring, and cap.

porary grip is threaded over it and pushed up to the anchor plate. The end of the strand is gripped by a "come-along" which is coupled through a calibrated dynamometer to a light tensioning device. The tensioning device stretches the strand until the dynamometer reads 1,000 lb; the temporary grip is then pushed along the strand until it is tight against the face of the anchor plate. As load is released from the tensioning device, the temporary grip holds the tension in the strand.

After each strand has been anchored at 1,000-lb tension, form diaphragms which act as strand spacers are assembled. Form diaphragms between the ends of beams are detailed so they can be slipped over the strand pattern after the strands are in place. It is not necessary to thread the strands through them. Figure 6-11 shows one end of a bed casting I-shaped bridge girders with a form diaphragm in place.

We are now ready to tension the entire group of strands to a total load of 14,000 lb per strand. In discussing "Measurement of Prestressing," Sec. 404.2.2 of the Recommended Practice in Art. 8-2 says "Measurement of elongation will usually give more consistent results." In Art.

FIG. 6-11. Casting pretensioned I-section bridge girders at plant of Formigli Brothers, Inc., Berlin, N.J. Form diaphragm is shown in place around strands. Metal side forms are arranged along ground on each side of bed ready for assembly around strands. Pairs of vertical steel wide-flange sections projecting from the bed permit variation in location of anchor plate to save strand when members being cast do not fill full length of bed.

5-7 we were told that the load-elongation curve of a wire rather than a modulus of elasticity should be used in computing the elongation required to reach a specified tension. The same statement applies to strand. Figure 5-7 is the load-elongation curve of the ⅜-in.-diameter strand which we are using in this example. The values used in the following calculations were read from a large-scale curve of the type available from strand fabricators. In Art. 5-8 it was explained that the load-elongation properties of strands were not the same for all fabricators. It is therefore recommended that all the strands to be tensioned at one time be made by one fabricator and that his curve be used in computing the required elongation.

Each strand has been tensioned by a calibrated dynamometer to a load of 1,000 lb. Reading from the curve, the elongation at 1,000 lb is 0.0005 in. per in. Also from the curve the elongation at 14,000 lb is 0.00625 in. per in. Thus the elongation from 1,000 to 14,000 lb is $0.00625 - 0.0005 = 0.00575$ in. per in. The total elongation in 350 ft is $350 \times 12 \times 0.00575 = 24.15$ in.

As tension is applied, the wedges in the temporary grips move a short distance into their casings and the strand moves with them. The actual elongation of the strand is thereby decreased an amount equal to the motion of the wedges seating in their casings, and this amount should be added to the distance the anchor plate on the jacking end is moved. The amount to be added can be measured during the jacking operation. When the strand is tensioned to 1,000 lb, the seating which takes place on the anchor end is ignored because it takes place before the 1,000-lb load is measured. On the jacking end the wedges are not seated when the 1,000-lb load is measured. As the load is released from the tensioning device, the wedges and strand move into the casing until the wedges are seated. The amount of this motion is measured by making a mark on the strand and measuring its distance from a reference point before and after releasing the load. The difference is the amount of motion. We shall assume that this motion was measured as ⅛ in. Additional seating may take place at both ends of the bed as the load is raised from 1,000 to 14,000 lb. It is measured in the same way. We shall assume that this was measured as ¹⁄₁₆ in. at each end. The total loss is ⅛ + ¹⁄₁₆ + ¹⁄₁₆ = ¼ in., so the anchor plate on the jacking end should be moved an additional ¼ in. The amount of seating needs to be measured only once. The value obtained the first time can be used in future operations, using the same tensioning procedure and the same make of temporary grip.

Before the strands are tensioned, the position of the jacking end anchor plate is measured with respect to a stationary reference point. The jacks are operated to move the anchor plate 24.15 in. plus ¼ in., struts are placed and adjusted, and the pressure in the jacks is released, leaving the struts to hold the load.

Figure 6-12 is a picture of the jacking end of a universal bed. The casting bed itself is outside the picture on the left. The vertical structural steel section near the left of the picture which looks like a wide-flange member with stiffeners in the web is the stationary anchor post which resists the load in the strands. The moving crosshead is just to the right of the center of the picture. It is made up of two vertical wide-flange sections and two horizontal wide-flange sections. The template anchor plate bears against the two horizontal wide-flange sections. The crosshead assembly is supported on steel wheels which run on short lengths of railroad rail as elongation of the strands takes place. On this bed four hydraulic jacks are used to push the crosshead away from the anchor post, thus elongating the strands, and four struts are used to hold the crosshead in position after the elongation is completed. The upper and lower cylindrical members in the center of the picture are hydraulic jacks which have completed the tensioning operation. The two center cylindrical members are struts which have just been adjusted

Fig. 6-12. Jacking end of a universal casting bed in plant of Schuylkill Products, Inc., Cressona, Pa. See text for description.

to the length between the anchor post and the crosshead. The next step will be to retract the jacks, leaving the load in the struts. The other two jacks and struts are located between the anchor post and crosshead on the far side of the group of strands.

When full elongation has been reached, the jack pressures should be read and converted to total load as a check on the load specified. Jack pressures are not a 100 per cent accurate method of measuring load because their friction factor varies, but they do provide a reasonable check.

The jacking arrangement shown in Fig. 6-12 is well designed for a universal bed. On a universal bed the elevation of the center of gravity of the strand group will vary as different members are fabricated. With some jacking units the jacks would have to be raised or lowered to match the c.g.s. in each new member. With this unit the top jack is well above the highest possible elevation of the c.g.s. and the bottom jack is well below the lowest possible elevation. When the c.g.s. is not exactly halfway between the two jacks, there will be a difference in the oil pressure required in each, but it will not be too great because the space between the jacks is large in comparison with the amount the c.g.s. can move. The problem of the difference in oil pressure is eliminated by using a special pump which supplies an equal volume of oil to each of the four jacks regardless of pressure. Since each jack gets the same volume of oil and oil is noncompressible, all the jacks have equal run-out.

A number of casting-yard operators prefer to tension one strand at a time to full tension instead of using the method just described. The cost of equipment is less, and they believe that the total elapsed time and the total labor required are no greater. This procedure should definitely be given consideration when jacking equipment is being designed for a casting bed.

Some designers feel that overtensioning is necessary to reduce stress losses from relaxation. Overtensioning is tensioning to a load greater than the specified initial tension and holding for a few minutes before relaxing to initial tension. This procedure was originally developed in Europe for wire which had a 12 per cent stress loss when tensioned to 57 per cent of its ultimate. When this wire was overtensioned to 63.5 per cent of its ultimate for 2 min and then relaxed to 57 per cent of ultimate as an initial tension, its stress loss was cut to 4 per cent. Such an operation was obviously worth the trouble. All the tests which have been run on the high-quality stress-relieved wire and seven-wire strand made in the United States show that the stress loss from relaxation when tensioned to 70 per cent of ultimate without overtensioning does not exceed 4 per cent. Tests on seven-wire stress-relieved strand show that the stress loss in an overtensioned strand can be cut to as low as one-half the stress loss in a strand not overtensioned when the comparison is made after the relatively short time of 100 hr. Long-time comparative test data on stress-relieved materials are not available. The little data available from European tests on non-stress-relieved material indicate that the initial advantage shown by overtensioned wire is lost after several years as it continues to relax. Whether or not the same condition would exist with stress-relieved material, we do not know. Since our specifications say nothing about overtensioning, any benefits to be obtained from this extra operation are questionable.

6-6. Deflected Strands. In Chap. 1 it was shown that a member with deflected tendons could be designed to carry a larger live-load moment than a like member with straight tendons and that the magnitude of the additional moment capacity was equal to the dead-load moment of the prestressed member. The advantages of deflected tendons are twofold. If a given member with straight tendons needs added capacity equal to its own dead-weight moment, this capacity can be gained by using deflected tendons without changing the original concrete section. If the additional capacity must be gained using straight tendons, a larger concrete section must be used. This not only uses more concrete, it creates additional dead weight requiring a still larger section to carry the extra dead-weight moment. It is apparent, therefore, that even though deflected strands are more expensive to install than straight ones, they can show a net saving in the finished member when the dead-weight moment is appreciable.

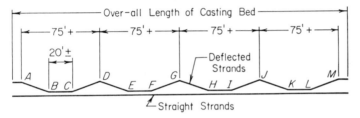

Fig. 6-13. Typical strand pattern for bed casting girders with deflected strands.

Placing and tensioning deflected strands present problems which are not met in working with straight strands. On a typical 300-ft bed with four 75-ft members the strands would be held down at eight points and held up at three intermediate points and at each end. Figure 6-13 shows the approximate path the strands would follow. The desired location of the c.g.s. can usually be attained by tensioning 50 to 70 per cent of the total number of strands in a straight line and deflecting the remaining strands.

There are two methods of installing deflected strands, and each has its drawbacks. One is to place the strands in their final path under no tension and then tension them. The other is to tension the strands in a straight line and then deflect them up or down to their final position.

When the strands are placed in their final position and then tensioned, the problem is friction. If the deflected strands in Fig. 6-13 are tensioned from one end, they must be pulled through 12 deflection points each of which is a source of loss in tension due to friction. Even if the strands are tensioned from both ends at one time, the tension at the middle of the bed is less than that at the jacks by the friction losses at 6 deflection points. In Fig. 6-13 points *A, D, G, J,* and *M* at which the strands are supported are located beyond the ends of the concrete members. Since these points are outside the concrete, the supports are reusable and it is feasible to use permanent roller bearings under the strands to minimize friction losses. The hold-down devices at points *B, C, E, F, H, I, K,* and *L* become a permanent part of the precast mem-

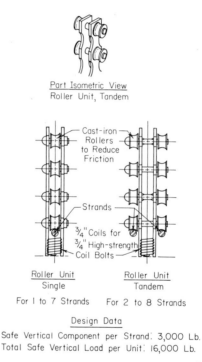

Part Isometric View
Roller Unit, Tandem

Cast-iron
Rollers
to Reduce
Friction

Strands

3/4" Coils for
3/4" High-strength
Coil Bolts

Roller Unit   Roller Unit
Single   Tandem

For I to 7 Strands   For 2 to 8 Strands

Design Data
Safe Vertical Component per Strand: 3,000 Lb.
Total Safe Vertical Load per Unit: 16,000 Lb.

FIG. 6-14. One type of hold-down for a group of seven-wire strands as made by Superior Concrete Accessories, Inc., Franklin Park, Ill. A ¾-in. high-strength bolt with a special "coil thread" projects up through the bottom of the form to hold the unit down.

ber. In many cases the device shown in Fig. 6-14, although not frictionless, gives usable performance at reasonable cost. When friction must be almost completely eliminated, roller bearings can be used at all hold-down as well as support points. After tensioning and before pouring concrete, the roller bearings at the hold-down points can be replaced with less expensive devices like those in Fig. 6-14. Figure 6-15 shows details of tendons and reinforcing at the end of a bridge girder with deflected strands.

When the strands are tensioned in a straight line and then deflected, losses due to friction are practically eliminated but the procedure is more complicated. One method used for heavy members is to tension the strands in a straight line at the lowest elevation they will have in the finished girder. Hold-downs similar to those shown in Fig. 6-14 are as-

FIG. 6-15. Details at end of bridge girder with deflected strands at plant of Consumers Company, Chicago, Ill. The sloping strands were placed in their deflected path and then tensioned. Support with roller bearings will be outside concrete beam on left of end form plate. Tin cans core holes in web for transverse steel in diaphragm. Six loops of seven-wire strand form lifting hook. Note that this member is an I section for its full length. There will be no end block. The closely spaced reinforcing used to prevent cracking when no end block is provided had not yet been placed when this picture was taken. See Art. 9-4.

sembled around the strands and attached to hold-down bolts. The strands are then raised simultaneously at all support points to their final elevation. Raising the strands increases their length, which, in turn, increases their tension. The amount of this increase in tension is computed before the tensioning operation and deducted from the specified initial tension to establish the tension placed in the strands in their straight-line position. Strands are jacked up at support points rather than down at hold-down points for several reasons:

1. The number of jacks required is kept to a minimum because the number of hold-down points is usually about double the number of support points.

2. The support points are outside the concrete members, so that all parts are reusable.

3. It is simpler to push up from the concrete slab than to pull down to the hold-down bolts.

The operation of raising the strands must be performed simultaneously at all support points in order to minimize friction.   Refer to Fig. 6-13. If the strands are raised simultaneously at each support point, there will be no motion of the strands through the support points.   There will be a small motion of the strands at the hold-downs.   In beam $DEFG$ part DE will increase in length and tension.   Since this makes the tension in DE greater than the tension in EF, there will be a small amount of motion of strand through E toward D until the two tensions are balanced. There is an equal motion through F toward G.   In this procedure the total effective friction is that at one hold-down; it is not cumulative as when tensioned from the ends.   Figure 6-16 shows equipment for raising a group of strands at a support point.

If the strands were raised at one support at a time, friction would accumulate.   The logical procedure would be to raise the strands first at G.   This would pull the strand through all the other deflection points toward G, creating friction at each one.   Raising the strand next at D would pull the strand through every deflection point toward D.   This adds to the friction at all points except E and F, where it is decreased. When this method is used, the resulting tensions will vary from one beam to the next.

Support points and hold-downs not properly detailed are potential sources of mechanical damage to the strand.   Deflecting the strand around a small-diameter pin sometimes creates enough additional stresses to cause a strand failure, especially if the strand slides across the pin while under a high tension.

The foregoing discussion refers chiefly to heavy girders in which a number of deflected strands are used to offset the dead-weight moment of the girder.   Deflected strands are sometimes used in lighter members such as double T's to offset the dead-load moment or to reduce excessive camber.   In these members the hold-down load is comparatively small because both the amount of deflection and the number of strands deflected are small.   This makes it feasible to deflect the strands by pushing them down after they have been tensioned, as shown in Fig. 6-17.

The more complicated procedure involved in placing deflected strands means that the load placed in the strands may not be quite so accurate as that in strands tensioned in a straight line. This does not affect the structural stability of the member.

6-7. Forms. Forms for pretensioned work are usually made of steel, which provides the durability needed to maintain accurate dimensions

FIG. 6-16. Equipment for raising a group of strands at a support point between girders at plant of Material Service Corp., Lyons, Ill.

during constant reuse. Standard forms that can be used on universal beds are available from fabricators specializing in prestressed concrete forms. Types of standard forms include I sections, double T's, square piles, octagonal piles, and Amdek bridge sections. Standard forms are made as versatile as possible so that one form can be used to cast members of several different depths and/or widths. The double-T form is particularly versatile, as illustrated by Fig. 6-5.

Permanent forms are popular for double-T sections. The steel form is set in concrete to the level of the top of the finished member. Since the stems of most double T's are tapered and must be drawn from the form, it is important to prevent dents or bulges in the sides of the forms which would bind as the double-T section is raised from the form. With a permanent form of this type anchor posts are unnecessary; the tension in the strands is carried by compression in the concrete under the form.

The initial tension of approximately 175,000 psi in the strands keeps them in their proper position, but it is not sufficient to prevent sagging in a 300- or 400-ft-long casting bed. Sag is eliminated by strand spacers which are incorporated in the form diaphragms at the ends of each precast member as shown in Fig. 6-11.

Fig. 6-17. Deflecting strands in a double-T member by pushing strands down after they have been tensioned at plant of R. H. Wright and Sons, Inc., Fort Lauderdale, Fla.

In rectangular prestressed concrete sections, concrete near the neutral axis of the section is undesirable because it not only adds unnecessarily to the volume of concrete used and to the dead weight of the member, it absorbs a lot of the prestressing force without appreciably increasing the load-carrying capacity of the member. The concrete in the center of the member is eliminated by casting in a paper tube. At first these were the readily available round cardboard tubes. As the sections became larger, round tubes left too much unnecessary concrete and specially shaped tubes of corrugated paperboard were developed. The Amdek bridge members discussed in Chap. 13 make use of this method. Figures 6-18 to 6-20 show a typical rectangular section, forms, and tube.

6-8. Completing the Member. Preparations for placing concrete are completed. Reinforcing bar cages, wire mesh, lifting hooks, and forms are assembled in their places. Concrete is placed using vibrators to ensure proper compaction of the low-slump mix.

Where live steam is used for accelerated curing, it is applied to the members through one or more pipes running the full length of the bed. An enclosure is placed around the concrete member and the steam pipe. Steam escapes through holes spaced along the pipe, filling the enclosure around the member, both raising the temperature and keeping it moist. On some beds pipes are placed in or around the forms to carry hot oil, hot water, or steam. These pipes raise the temperature of the concrete members through radiation. A steam pipe can be seen in Fig. 6-20. Rate of strength gain obtained by steam curing is shown by the chart in Fig. 5-1.

Since steam curing has been used for years to accelerate the curing of concrete and standard procedures for its application have been estab-

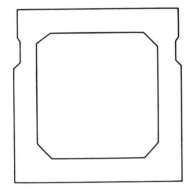

FIG. 6-18. Rectangular section with hole cored by specially shaped corrugated-paper tube.

lished, it will not be discussed at length here. Steam curing is not a simple matter of allowing some steam to flow around a concrete member. Time lapse between pouring concrete and turning on of steam, rate of temperature increase, maximum temperature reached, etc., must be determined to suit the conditions and then properly controlled. Improperly applied steam curing can damage the concrete in a member so that it will never reach its design strength. Reference to specifications and literature on this subject is recommended for those not already familiar with it.[10]

One of the big factors which makes pretensioned bonded prestressed concrete members so economical is the fact that a well-organized casting yard can be run on a production-line schedule. A bed casting small standard members such as double T's, joists, channels, or piles can be operated on a 24-hr cycle when curing is accelerated by steam or radiant

heat.   Larger and more complicated members are usually produced in a
48-hr cycle or more.

6-9. Removal from Bed. When the load in the strands is transferred
from the anchor posts to the concrete members, elastic shortening of the
members takes place.   This means that there is longitudinal motion of
the concrete member with respect to the bed.   Permanent forms are

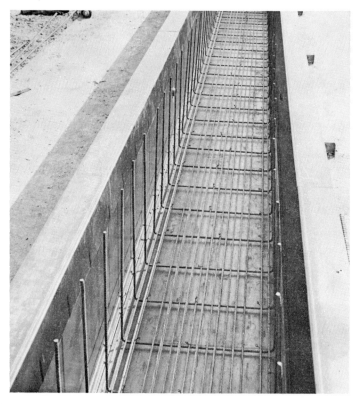

FIG. 6-19. Rectangular section showing strands and stirrups in place at plant of Crider and
Shockey, Inc., Winchester, Va.   Quick release and reset forms by Blaw-Knox Co.

designed so they will not restrict this motion.   Other types of forms are
removed before the strand load is transferred.

Most specifications contain a statement similar to "Pretension in the
strands or wires shall be transferred gradually to the concrete."   This
means that all strands shall be unjacked.   It prohibits severing the strands
while they are under tension because the impact from such a suddenly
applied load can damage bond (see Art. 15-2).

After the load has been transferred from the anchor posts to the concrete members, the strands are cut at each end of each member. This is usually done with welding equipment.

The foregoing applies to strands tensioned in a straight line. Deflected strands present an additional problem because of the hold-downs attached to the casting bed. If the strands are detensioned before the

Fig. 6-20. Fabricating rectangular section at plant of Crider and Shockey. Concrete has been poured to level of bottom of paper tube. Tube is being placed and will be held down while sides and top are poured. Pipe near bottom of form will supply steam for curing.

hold-downs are released, the longitudinal motion of the member can apply a large force to the hold-down, making it very difficult to release. When the hold-downs are released, the vertical load in the strand, which they were resisting, is applied to the concrete beam. If the strands have not been released from the anchor posts, the beam is not prestressed and the vertical loads will cause serious cracks in the top of the beam. At this writing, the use of deflected strands is relatively new and no ideal procedure for detensioning them has been developed.   In spite of the present rather makeshift detensioning procedures, deflected strands are proving economical.   Information on latest methods can be obtained from PCI, fabricators of materials for prestressed concrete, and engineers familiar with the subject (see Pretensioned Strands, Chap. 15).

After the strands have been detensioned and cut, the members are removed from the casting bed to a storage area.   In all members designed to resist bending such as girders, beams, and double T's the strands are located eccentrically to produce the maximum allowable negative bending moment under the dead load of the member.   When these members are handled, they must be picked at or near their normal support points to avoid creating additional negative moment.   They are often transported on equipment like that used for poles, as shown in Fig. 6-11. Symmetrically stressed members such as piles are lifted at points 21 per cent of their length from each end so that the positive moment at the center of the length is equal to the negative moment at the pickup points. Scrap lengths of seven-wire strand can be used for lifting loops, as shown in Fig. 6-15.

6-10. Economy. Pretensioned bonded prestressed concrete members are the most economical prestressed concrete members available when existing conditions are reasonably suited to their use.   Ideal conditions for pretensioned members are:

1. The casting plant is located within economical hauling distance.

2. Members used are standard with the casting plant, or enough similar members are needed to justify a setup.

3. Size and weight of members are within capacity of hauling equipment.

4. The design is adapted to make use of the properties of prestressed concrete members rather than simply trying to substitute prestressed concrete for another type of member.

Prestressed concrete members show a lower first cost for many structures than other materials.   In addition they offer greater durability, less maintenance, and fire resistance.

BIBLIOGRAPHY

1. Slutter, Roger G., and Carl E. Ekberg, Jr.: Static and Fatigue Tests on Prestressed Concrete Railway Slabs, *AREA Bull.* 544, June–July, 1958. Also printed as Special Report 6, Fritz Engineering Laboratory, Structural Concrete Division, Lehigh University, Bethlehem, Pa.
2. Ozell, A. M., and J. F. Diniz: Fatigue Tests of Prestressed Concrete Beams Pretensioned with ½ Inch Strands, *J. Prestressed Concrete Inst.,* June, 1958, pp. 79–88.

3. Ekberg, C. E., Jr.: The Characteristics of Prestressed Concrete under Repetitive Loading, *J. Prestressed Concrete Inst.,* December, 1956, pp. 7–16.

4. Ozell, A. M., and E. Ardaman: Fatigue Tests of Pretensioned Prestressed Beams, *J. Am. Concrete Inst.,* October, 1956, pp. 413–424.

5. PCI Standards for Prestressed Concrete Plants, *J. Prestressed Concrete Inst.,* September, 1956, pp. 36–45, or *PCI-STD-103-58*T.

6. Pretensioning Bed-assembly Line for Prestress Products, *Construct. Methods and Equipment,* February, 1957, pp. 138–154.

7. "Concrete Industries Yearbook," Pit & Quarry, Chicago, Ill., 1957, 1958, or later edition.

8. Peck, Roy L.: Largest Midwestern Prestresser [Photographs and discussion of casting yard operation], *Modern Concrete,* November, 1957.

9. Prestress Plant Turns out Piles Fast, *Construct. Methods and Equipment,* May, 1957, pp. 90–97.

10. Schmid, Emil, and Raymond J. Schutz: Steam Curing, *J. Prestressed Concrete Inst.,* September, 1957, pp. 37–42.

CHAPTER 7

POST-TENSIONED METHOD

7-1. Basic Operation. Post-tensioning is defined as "a method of pre-stressing reinforced concrete in which the reinforcement is tensioned after the concrete has hardened." Basically, the complete operation has six steps:

1. The tendon is assembled in a flexible metal hose, and anchor fittings are attached to the ends of the tendon.

2. The tendon assembly is placed in the form and tied in place in the same manner as a reinforcing bar. Reinforcing bars, wire mesh, etc., are placed.

3. Concrete is poured and allowed to cure to the strength specified for tensioning.

4. Tendons are elongated by hydraulic jacks, and the anchor fittings are adjusted to hold the load in the tendons.

5. The space around the tendon is pumped full of cement grout under pressure.

6. Anchor fittings are covered with a protective coating.

Although the foregoing procedure is the most common, others are used to suit various conditions. In some cases a hole is cored in the concrete and the tendon is threaded through the hole just before it is to be tensioned. Holes can be cored by casting in a rubber tube of the desired shape and then withdrawing it after the concrete has set. Holes can also be cored by casting in a flexible metal hose. The hose becomes a permanent part of the structure. Since the hose is not stiff enough to maintain its position while the concrete is placed, one or more steel bars are placed inside the hose and are withdrawn after the concrete has set.

In large hollow structures such as hollow-box bridges, the tendons are threaded through the hollow spaces and tensioned against anchor plates cast in the end block of the structure. Galvanized strands are used in these structures, and grouting is not required.

7-2. Combination of Pretensioned and Post-tensioned Methods. When the two methods are combined, pretensioned strands are tensioned in a straight line to provide as much of the prestressing force as possible and post-tensioned tendons are used in a deflected path to provide the remaining force and vary the location of the c.g.s. as required.

The pretensioned post-tensioned combination is used where some deflected tendons are needed and lack of facilities or other reasons prevent the economical use of deflected pretensioned strands. Under most conditions the combination of methods is more economical then an all-post-tensioned structure.

7-3. Systems. Several different systems or types of post-tensioned tendons are used in the United States. Procedure for fabricating a post-tensioned member is essentially the same with all systems except for the details of the tendons and their anchorages.

Most systems are patented to some degree, but there are seldom any royalty fees. Purchase of materials for a particular system from the patent holders who fabricate the parts includes permission to use the system.

Table 7-1. Properties of Freyssinet Cables

Type of unit	8 × 0.196″	10 × 0.196″	12 × 0.196″	18 × 0.196″	12 × 0.276″
Minimum guaranteed ultimate tensile strength for uncoated cables, lb	60,000	75,000	90,000	135,000	168,500
Recommended final prestress, lb	34,000	43,000	51,000	77,000	93,000
Steel area, sq in.........	0.241	0.302	0.362	0.543	0.723
Weight per lin ft, lb	0.82	1.03	1.23	1.85	2.45
OD metal hose, in.	1⅛	1⅛	1¼	1⅝	1⅝
ID metal hose, in.	1	1	1⅛	1½	1½
Dimensions of anchorage:					
A.............	3¹⁵⁄₁₆	3¹⁵⁄₁₆	3¹⁵⁄₁₆	4²³⁄₃₂	4²³⁄₃₂
B...	3²⁵⁄₃₂	3²⁵⁄₃₂	3²⁵⁄₃₂	4¹³⁄₁₆	4¹³⁄₁₆
C...	1⅞	1⅞	1⅞	2⁷⁄₁₆	2⁷⁄₁₆
D..................	1³⁄₃₂	1³⁄₃₂	1³⁄₃₂	1¹⁵⁄₃₂	1¹⁵⁄₃₂

Jacking equipment, grouting equipment, technical advice on use of the system, and any necessary field supervision are available from the suppliers of materials for the various systems.

7-4. Freyssinet System. A Freyssinet cable is composed of a number of parallel uncoated stress-relieved prestressed concrete wires. Table 7-1 lists the standard groups of wires and their properties. The top line indicates the number and size of wires in the cable. Thus 12 × 0.276 stands for 12 wires each 0.276 in. in diameter. Properties of the individual wires are given in Table A-1.

In a post-tensioned member the initial load in the tendon is transferred to the concrete through an anchor fitting at each end of the tendon. Figure 7-1 shows the two parts of a Freyssinet anchor fitting, and Fig. 7-2 shows a fitting in a completed member.

Freyssinet cables are made by pushing the wires into a flexible metal hose which has been cut to the proper length. The wires project about 2 ft beyond the ends of the hose so that they can be gripped by the tensioning jack. On small jobs the cables are assembled in a fabricating plant and shipped to the job site in coils. On large jobs it is sometimes more economical to set up equipment for assembling the wires in the

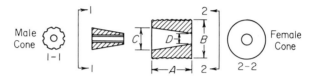

FIG. 7-1. Parts of a Freyssinet anchor fitting. Male cone shown is for an eight-wire cable. See Table 7-1 for dimensions.

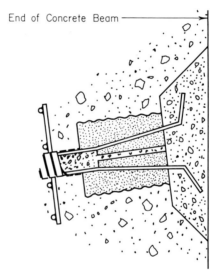

FIG. 7-2. Section through Freyssinet anchor fitting in a finished prestressed concrete member. See text for full description.

hose on the job. In this case the wire is shipped to the job site in coils.

The cable assembly is placed in the form and tied in place in the same manner as a reinforcing bar. The female cones of the anchor fittings are threaded over the wires at each end and anchored to the form in their final position. Various devices for anchoring the fittings to the form are available from the suppliers of the fittings. A grid of small reinforcing bars is placed in front of each fitting to help distribute the concentrated load the fitting will apply to the concrete. Freyssinet fittings are usually embedded in the concrete so that part of the load is distributed to the concrete by the corrugations on the side of the fitting, as shown in Figs. 7-2 and 7-3. Freyssinet engineers recommend the fol-

FIG. 7-3. Three Freyssinet cables assembled in forms with female cones attached to end of form and reinforcing grids in place. Note cones are in a recess several inches from end of girder.

lowing minimum dimensions for spacing and cover of their anchor fittings at the ends of prestressed concrete members:

Cable size	Center to center of fittings, in.	Center of fitting to face of concrete, in.
12 × 0.276 or 18 × 0.196	7	4
12 × 0.196 and smaller	6	3

After the cables are in place, any remaining reinforcing bars, wire mesh, etc., are installed, the forms are assembled, and concrete is placed. Forms are similar to those for reinforced concrete unless they will be reused enough to justify more expensive materials. Since many large prestressed concrete members have relatively thin webs and wide bottom flanges, vibrators are used to place the concrete satisfactorily. High-early-strength cement is normally used, but steam curing is omitted unless the members are being precast at a plant equipped for steam curing.

FIG. 7-4. Tensioning a Freyssinet cable. Operator is checking elongation before driving home the male cone. Wedges on jack which grip wire for tensioning are just to right of man's hands. On this member anchor fittings were not embedded.

When the concrete has cured to the specified strength, the tendons are tensioned. In his design calculations, as shown in Chap. 11, the engineer computes the loss of tension due to friction between the tendon and its enclosure to determine whether it should be jacked simultaneously from both ends or from one end only. If one-end jacking is sufficient, the male cone is tapped into the female cone at the anchor end of the tendon to grip the wires. As tension is applied, there may be a small motion of this cone as it seats itself under load.

The special Freyssinet jacking unit is illustrated by Figs. 7-4 to 7-7 and Table 7-2. The jacking unit is placed at the tensioning end, the wires are gripped by the wedges on the main piston, and the pump is operated to move the main piston and elongate the wires. Power pumps are normally used, although hand pumps are available for small jobs. When the specified elongation is reached, the jack pressure is checked in accordance with Sec. 404.3.4 of the ACI-ASCE Recommendations. The male cone is driven home by operating the inner piston, pressure is released from both pistons, and the jacking unit is removed.

A load-elongation curve like that in Fig. 5-3 is used to determine the required elongation. The motion of the wires measured with reference

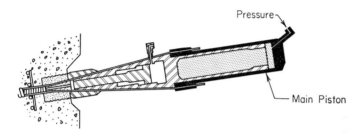

FIG. 7-5. Freyssinet jack at start of tensioning operation. Note that the jack base bears **only** on the fitting.

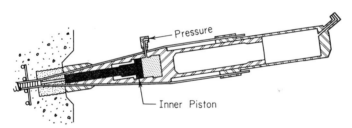

FIG. 7-6. Freyssinet jack at end of jacking operation. Inner piston is driving home the male plug.

to the end of the concrete girder will be greater than the actual elongation in the wires by the sum of four factors. As the cone seats itself in the anchor end, the wires move with it. This motion of the wires carries through the full length of the cable and is measured as part of the motion at the jacking end but does not represent any elongation of the wires.

The compressive force from the cables causes an elastic shortening of the girder which must be included when determining the elongation and initial tension of each cable. Consider a girder post-tensioned with three cables. As the first cable is tensioned, the girder will shorten an amount equal to ΔL, which means that the actual elongation of the wires will be ΔL less than the motion of the wires measured with respect to the end of the girder. This can be compensated by adding ΔL to the required motion of the wires.

When the required motion of the wires with respect to the end of the girder has been reached, the inner piston is operated to drive home the

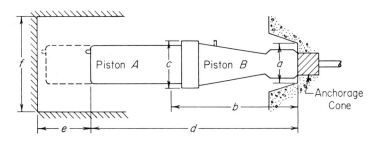

FIG. 7-7. Detail dimensions of Freyssinet jacks. See Table 7-2 for tabulation of dimensions.

Table 7-2. Dimensions of Freyssinet Jacks
(See Fig. 7-7.)

Jack type / Dimension	A, B, or C 8, 10, 12 × 0.196, in.	J* 12 × 0.196	E 18 × 0.196	F 18 × 0.196 12 × 0.276	H* 12 × 0.276
a	6½	5	7	7	6
b†	24	18	24	24	18
c	8	7½	8	12	12
d	36	24	38	38	30 or 34
e	12	8	12	8	8 or 12
f	17	17	18	22	22

* Equipped with hydraulic return and automatic dewedging. All other jacks have spring returns.

† Length required for attaching wires to jack.

NOTE: These dimensions indicate the minimum spacing which must be allowed around the jacks to permit them to operate properly. In the event such spacing cannot be provided, consult the Freyssinet Company to study the special provisions to be made.

male cone and then the pressure on both pistons is released. As the load in the wires is transferred from the jack to the cones, there is a small motion of the male cone in seating itself. The wires move with the cone and therefore shorten an amount equal to its motion.

Tensioning the second cable causes the girder to shorten an additional amount equal to ΔL. As the girder shortens, the wires in the first cable (which is now achored to the girder) shorten with it and lose some of their tension. The same process occurs when the third cable is tensioned.

Before tensioning can begin, the required motion of the wires with respect to the end of the girder must be determined such that the wires will have their proper elongation and load after all cables have been tensioned. The load in the jacks at the required motion must also be determined for use as a check.

For the first cable the required motion will be the sum of the motions of the two male cones in seating themselves plus $3\Delta L$ plus the elongation measured from the load-elongation curve for the specified tension. The load in the cable at this point will be the specified initial tension plus the load due to an elongation of $2\Delta L$ and the motion of the cone on the jacking end. The motion of the cone on the anchor end and the shortening ΔL from the load in the first cable are part of the measured motion but are not part of the actual elongation of the wires.

For the second cable the required motion will be the sum of the motions in the two cones plus $2\Delta L$ plus the elongation for the specified tension. Load in the cable will be the specified tension plus load due to an elongation of ΔL and the motion of the cone on the jacking end.

For the third and last cable the required motion will be the sum of the motions of the two cones plus ΔL plus the elongation for the specified tension. Load in the cable will be the specified tension plus load due to an elongation equal to the motion of the cone on the jacking end.

Friction between the tendon and its enclosure was not mentioned in the foregoing discussion. When the required motion and corresponding jack load have been determined, the friction should be computed and added to the jack load. If the resulting jack load is larger than the allowable tension in the tendon for the jacking condition, the tendon should be tensioned from both ends at one time.

After all cables have been tensioned and anchored, the wires are cut off and their remaining projections are bent as shown in Fig. 7-2.

Each cable is grouted by pumping grout through the hole in the center of the male cone at one end until it flows smoothly from the other end. The discharge end is then closed, and pressure is applied by the pump to fill any voids. One or more intermediate grout connections will be used for long cables (approximately 90 ft and over) or for cables with curvatures that can cause air pockets. A grout connection is usually a ⅜-in. pipe leading from the enclosure around the cable to the top or side of the concrete member where the grout pump connection can be attached. See also Sec. 405 of Recommendations in Art. 8-2 for grouting procedures.

7-5. High-strength Bars. Each high-strength bar is used as a single tendon complete in itself. Table A-4 lists the properties of Stressteel bars.

Anchor fittings are the wedge type, Fig. 7-8, or the threaded type, Fig. 7-9. Details of wedge fittings and plates are shown in Fig. 7-10, and dimensions in Table 7-3. Figure 7-11 shows two types of detail of end fittings in place in a finished member.

At the job site a flexible metal hose is assembled on the bar, and the assembly placed in the form or reinforcing bar cage and tied in place as

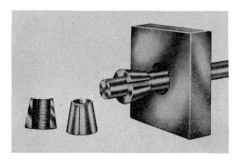

FIG. 7-8. Wedge-type anchor fitting and bearing plate for Stressteel bar.

FIG. 7-9. Threaded type anchor fitting and bearing plate for Stressteel bar.

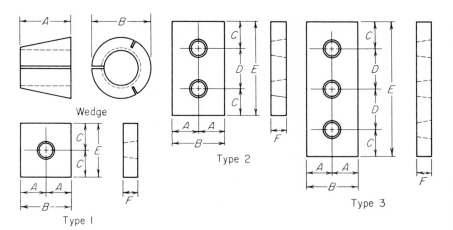

FIG. 7-10. Details of wedge-type fitting and bearing plates for Stressteel bars.

a reinforcing bar would be. Bearing plates are assembled as shown in Fig. 7-11*b*, forms are completed, and concrete is placed.

When the concrete has cured to the specified strength, the tendons are tensioned. At the anchor end a temporary clamp, Fig. 7-12, is attached to the bar to seat the wedges when the jacking operation begins. The

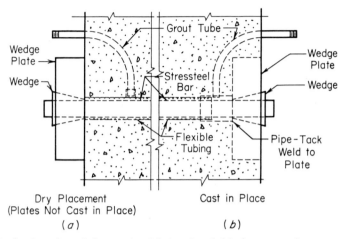

Dry Placement
(Plates Not Cast in Place)
(*a*)

Cast in Place
(*b*)

FIG. 7-11. Sections through Stressteel end fittings in a finished prestressed concrete member. See text for full description.

Table 7-3. Dimensions of Stressteel Anchorages

Part No.	Bar ϕ, in.	No. of holes	Dimensions, in.						Wt, lb each
			A	B	C	D	E	F	
Wedges									
W-6	¾	...	1³⁄₁₆	1¼	...	...	...	...	0.22
W-7	⅞	...	1½	1½	...	...	...	...	0.32
W-8	1	...	1½	1¾	...	...	...	...	0.50
W-9	1⅛	...	1¾	2	...	...	...	...	0.70
W-10	1¼	...	2	2¼	...	...	...	...	0.80
Wedge plates									
WP6	¾	1	2	4	2	...	4	1	4.5
WP7	⅞	1	2½	5	2½	...	5	1½	10.6
WP8	1	1	2½	5	2½	...	5	1½	10.6
WP9	1⅛	1	3	6	3	...	6	1¾	17.8
WP10	1¼	1	3	6	3½	...	7	2	23.8
WP6-2	¾	2	2	4	2	4	8	1	9.1
WP7-2	⅞	2	2½	5	2½	4	9	1½	19.1
WP8-2	1	2	2½	5	2¾	4½	10	1½	21.2
WP9-2	1⅛	2	3	6	3	4½	10½	1¾	31.2
WP10-2	1¼	2	3½	7	3½	5	12	2	47.6
WP6-3	¾	3	2	4	2	4	12	1	13.6
WP7-3	⅞	3	2½	5	2½	4	13	1½	27.6
WP8-3	1	3	2½	5	2¾	4½	14½	1½	30.8
WP9-3	1⅛	3	3	6	3	4½	15	1¾	44.6
WP10-3	1¼	3	3½	7	3½	5	17	2	67.4

jacking unit, Figs. 7-13 and 7-14, is assembled on the bar at the jacking end. Note that the bar projects far enough beyond the end of the concrete member to permit attachment of the pulling wedge. The bar is tensioned to its required elongation, and the load in the jacks is checked in accordance with Sec. 404.3.4 of ACI-ASCE Recommendations. When the required motion of the bar with respect to the end of the member

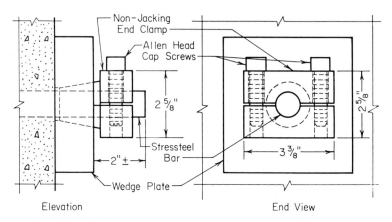

FIG. 7-12. Clamp for seating wedges on nonjacking end of Stressteel bar.

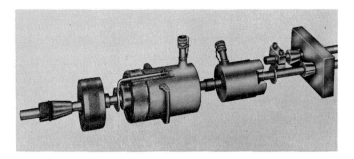

FIG. 7-13. Exploded view of jacking unit for Stressteel bar.

and the required jack load is determined, the seating of wedges, elastic shortening of concrete member, and friction of tendon in its enclosure must be considered as described in Art. 7-4. When the proper motion and load are reached, the wedges are set by operating the wedge seating ram and then the hydraulic pressure is released from both rams. The temporary clamp should be removed from the anchor end during the tensioning operation when the load on the jack is about 20 per cent of the specified initial tension. That portion of the bar projecting more than ½ in. beyond the wedges and plates can be removed by flame cutting. Grout is placed.

Alternate details are used to suit varying conditions. The wedge plate can be assembled against the face of the member after the concrete has

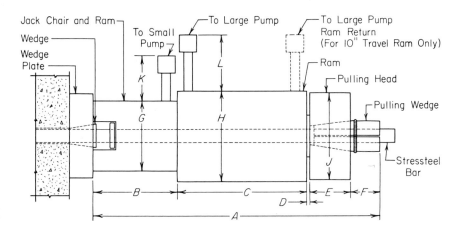

Type	Dimensions, in.											Weight, lb. each
	A^*	B	C	D Closed-ext.	E	F	G	H	J	K	L	
60-ton— 3-in. travel...	21⅜	6¼	9⅝	¼	3	3	2¼	5	6½	6¼	3¼	4	114
60-ton—10-in. travel...	30¼	6¼	18½	¼	10	3	2¼	5	6½	6¼	3¼	4	173
100-ton— 3-in. travel...	26¼	9¼	10½	¼	3	3½	2¾	4½	7½	6¼	3¼	4	159
100-ton—10-in. travel...	32¼	9¼	16½	¼	10	3½	2¾	4½	7½	6¼	3¼	4	249

* Minimum bar length necessary for jacking, outside of plate.
NOTE: Bushings are provided to center pulling head and rams.
   10-in. travel rams have hydraulic return; 3-in. travel rams have spring return.

FIG. 7-14. Details of Stressteel jacking unit.

cured, Fig. 7-11*a*. Bars can be threaded through cored holes after the concrete has cured.

The foregoing applies to bars which are shipped in one length. When the length required is too great for the available manufacturing or transporting facilities, bars are shipped in two or more lengths and spliced at the job site. Bars can be fabricated in single lengths up to 83 ft.

At splice points and at threaded anchors Stressteel bars have a special thread. This is a full-depth thread for a short distance from the end of the bar and then tapers to no thread. The nut or coupling has a matching taper. When the nut or coupling is turned tight on the bar, load transfer from the bar to the nut or coupling begins at the point where the depth of the tapered thread is minimum and there is very little loss of net section in the bar. By the time the full-depth thread is reached, enough load has been transferred to permit the net section of the bar to

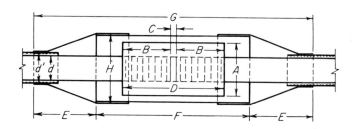

| Part No. | | Bar φ | Flex. tube | Dimensions, in. | | | | | | | | Weight each |
Coupler	Coupler shield	d, in.	ID d′, in.	A	B	C	D	E	F†	G	H	coupler, lb
HC-6	CS-6*	¾	1	1½	1⅜	¼	3	. .	. .	. . .	. . .	1.1
HC-7	CS-7	⅞	1⅛	1¾	1⅝	¼	3½	2	10	14	2½	1.8
HC-8	CS-8	1	1¼	1¾	1¾	¼	3¾	2	10	14	2½	1.9
HC-9	CS-9	1⅛	1⅜	2	1⅞	½	4¼	2	10	14	2½	2.5
HC-10	CS-10	1¼	1½	2¼	2⅛	½	4¾	3	10	15½	3	3.8

* CS-6 on special request only.

† Standard—can be made any length required for coupler movement.

FIG. 7-15. Details of couplers and coupler shields used at splice points in Stressteel bars.

carry the remaining load. These threaded connections develop the minimum guaranteed ultimate strength of the bar.

The coupler itself is a short length of steel bar of a larger diameter than the tendon and is tapped each end to match the special thread on the tendons. Figure 7-15 shows details of couplers and coupler shields. To permit the coupler to move longitudinally as the bar elongates during the tensioning operation, the flexible metal hose is terminated a distance either side of the coupler and a large-diameter coupler shield is placed around the coupler and tapered to connect to the ends of the flexible metal hose. The hole cored by a coupler shield may be large enough to affect the section modulus of the concrete cross section.

Couplers should be staggered where it is feasible, and the provisions of PCI Specification for Post-tensioned Prestressed Concrete, Sec. 3 (C) (2) (3) and (4), in Appendix B and Sec. 206.3 of ACI-ASCE Recommendations in Art. 8-2 should be considered.

7-6. Large Strands. Galvanized strands are shipped from the fabricator's plant as complete assemblies. The strand is cut to length, flexible metal hose is assembled on the strand if it is required, and the anchor fittings are attached. Each strand assembly is shipped as a separate coil except for special conditions. When the length is especially long or the shipping conditions severe, several assemblies are shipped on one large reel. Unspliced lengths up to 3,600 ft can be fabricated.

Table A-3 lists properties of galvanized strands, and Figs. 7-16 to 7-18 give details of anchor fittings, bearing plates, and their application.

At the casting site the strand assembly in flexible metal hose is placed in the form and tied in place. The bearing plates are positioned and clipped or bolted to the form. In some instances the end fittings are secured to the bearing plates.

Figure 7-19 shows the tensioning operation for a strand with fitting type SDS 35. The stud on the fitting projects through the bearing plate, and the permanent nut is turned up snugly against the plate before concrete is poured. When the concrete has been placed and allowed to cure, the jacking rod is attached to the stud on the fitting through a threaded coupling. The jacking unit consists of a steel chair with an opening for access to the permanent nut and a center-hole ram. This unit is slipped over the jacking rod, and a nut is placed on the jacking rod and turned down snugly against the plunger of the center-hole ram. When the hydraulic pump operates the ram, the jacking rod moves away from the end of the beam, elongating the strand. As the tensioning operation proceeds, a worker turns the permanent nut by hand to keep it near the bearing plate. At the end of the operation he sets it by hand tight against the bearing plate, jack pressure is released, and the jacking unit removed. The projecting portion of the permanent stud on the fitting can be severed ½ in. from the nut by flame cutting if desired. Grout is installed through the grout tubes, and the permanent nut and stud are painted or coated with a bitumastic material if they are not encased in concrete. Figure 7-20 shows the tensioning of a 1%16-in.-diameter galvanized strand.

Fittings types SDS 34 and SS 2 do not have permanent studs. Before the tensioning operation begins, these fittings are often recessed in the pipe attached to the bearing plate. These fittings have a tapped hole as well as an outside thread. The jacking rod is threaded into the tapped hole in the fitting, the permanent nut is slipped over the rod, and the jacking unit is placed. As the jacking operation progresses, the fitting

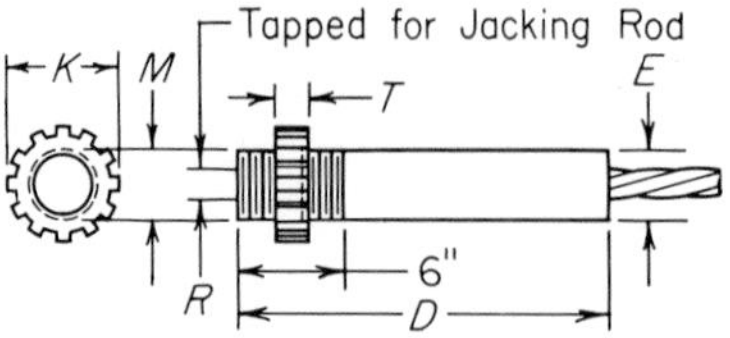

Type SDS 34

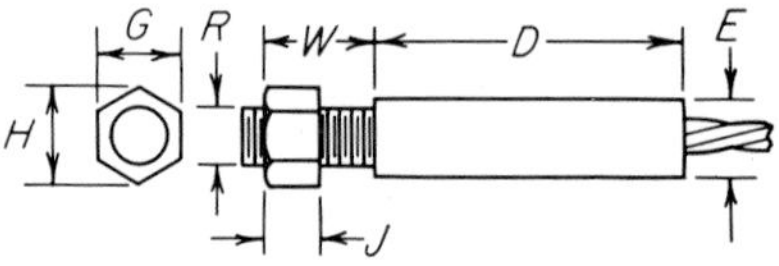

Type SDS 35

Strand diameter, in.	Measurements, in.										Total weight, lb	
	D	*W*	*E*	*M*	*R*	*G*	*H*	*J*	*K*	*T*	Type SDS 34	Type SDS 35
0.600	7	8	1 5/8	....	1 1/4—12N	1 13/16	2 1/16	1 3/16	...	...	....	9 1/4
0.835	12 1/2	10	2 1/4	12N	1 5/8—12N	2 1/4	2 9/16	1 5/16	3 3/4	1	16 1/2	21
1	13	11	2 3/4	8N	2 — 8N	3	3 7/16	1 3/4	4 3/8	1 1/4	24 3/4	32 1/2
1 1/8	16 1/2	11	3	8N	2 1/4— 8N	3	3 7/16	1 3/4	4 3/4	1 1/2	39 1/2	50

For fittings type SDS 35, standard studs having dimension *W*, shown above, are carried in stock.

Other stud lengths must be fabricated to order. All SDS 34 and 35 fittings are proof-loaded. to a stress in excess of the recommended design stress after being attached to the strand.

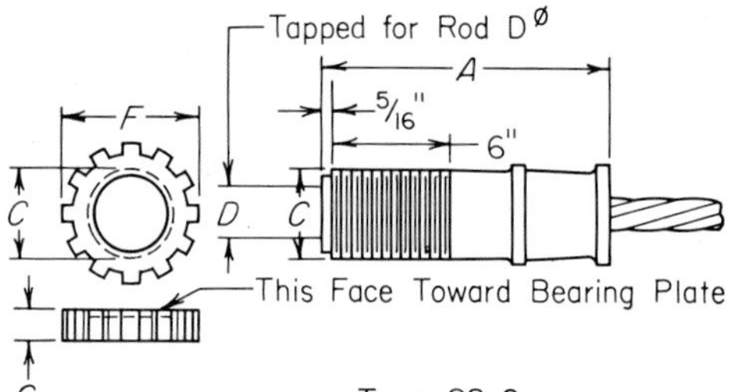

Type SS 2

Strand diameter, in.	Measurements, in.					Total weight, lb
	A	*C*	*D*	*F*	*G*	
1	10	3 1/2—4N	2—4 1/2NC	5 3/8	1 1/4	29
1 1/8	10 3/4	4—4N	2 1/4—4 1/2NC	6	1 3/8	38
1 1/4	11 3/8	4 3/8—4N	2 1/2—4NC	6 1/2	1 5/8	45
1 3/8	11 3/4	4 7/8—4N	3—4NC	7	1 5/8	54
1 1/2	12 3/8	5 1/4—4N	3—4NC	7 5/8	1 3/4	74
1 9/16	12 3/4	5 1/2—4N	3 1/2—4NC	7 7/8	1 3/4	77
1 5/8	13	5 5/8—4N	3 1/2—4NC	8	1 3/4	84
1 11/16	13 1/4	5 7/8—4N	3 1/2—4NC	8 3/8	1 3/4	88

Fittings type SS 2 can also be supplied with permanent studs and no external threads when necessary.

FIG. 7-16. Details of Roebling anchor fittings for galvanized strands.

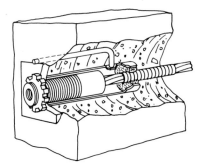

FIG. 7-17. Roebling fitting type SDS 34 and bearing plate after stand has been tensioned but before grouting. The packing of crumpled paper around the metal hose at the end of the pipe keeps the concrete out of the pipe during pouring. The metal hose projects into the pipe through the packing to receive the grout.

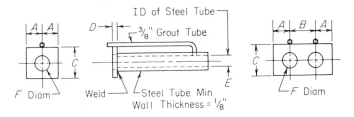

Type of fitting	Strand φ, in.	A*	B*	C*	D	E		F
						Min	Max	
SDS 34	0.835	3	5¼	6	⅞	2⅜	2½	E + ¹⁄₁₆
	1	3	5½	6	⅞	2⅞	3	E + ¹⁄₁₆
	1⅛	3½	6¼	7	1	3⅛	3¼	E + ¹⁄₁₆
SDS 35	0.600	2	3¼	4	⅝	1¾	1⅞	1½
	0.835	3	4½	6	⅞	2⅜	2½	1⅞
	1	3	4⅞	6	⅞	2⅞	3	2¼
	1⅛	3½	5½	7	1	3⅛	3¼	2½
SS 2	1	4	7	8	⅞	3¾	3⅞	E + ¹⁄₁₆
	1⅛	4¼	7½	8½	1	4¼	4⅜	E + ¹⁄₁₆
	1¼	4½	8	9	1¼	4⅝	4¾	E + ¹⁄₁₆
	1⅜	4¾	8½	9½	1¼	5⅛	5¼	E + ¹⁄₁₆
	1½	5⅜	9½	10¾	1⅜	5½	5⅝	E + ¹⁄₁₆
	1⁹⁄₁₆	5⅞	10¼	11¾	1⅜	5¾	5⅞	E + ¹⁄₁₆
	1⅝	5⅞	10¼	11¾	1½	5⅞	6	E + ¹⁄₁₆
	1¹¹⁄₁₆	6	10½	12	1½	6⅛	6¼	E + ¹⁄₁₆

* These are standard minimum dimensions. They can be reduced slightly by using special jack bases. Bearing pressure under above plates does not exceed 2,500 psi.

FIG. 7-18. Details of bearing plates recommended by Roebling.

emerges from the pipe and the permanent nut can be turned onto the outside thread, Fig. 7-17. At the end of the jacking operation, the permanent nut is turned hand-tight against the bearing plate, jack pressure is released, and the jacking unit removed. Fittings of this type never project more than 6 in. beyond the face of the bearing plate. They cannot be cut off.

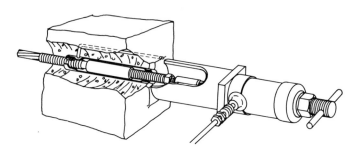

FIG. 7-19. Roebling fitting type SDS 35 and jacking unit. See text for description.

FIG. 7-20. Tensioning a Roebling strand on post-tensioned pile caps at Pier A, Hoboken, N.J.

As described in Art. 7-4, friction of the strand in its enclosure and shortening of the concrete member must be considered. With fittings type SS 2 there is a small amount of seating of the strand into its fitting during the tensioning operation which is treated in the same manner as the seating of wedges in the Freyssinet cones. There is no seating with fittings type SDS 34 and SDS 35, since they are proof-loaded after they are attached.

When galvanized strands are used in hollow structures, they are not encased in flexible metal hose and they are not grouted. They are often painted with a bitumastic paint.

7-7. Button-head System. A button-head cable is composed of a number of parallel uncoated stress-relieved prestressed concrete wires. The wires are usually the ¼-in. size listed in Table A-1.

Button-heads, Fig. 7-21, or nailheads as they are sometimes called, are formed by upsetting the end of the wire. Button-heads at each end of

FIG. 7-21. Button-head on ¼-in.-diameter wire.

the cable transfer the load in the wire to steel fittings. The wire passes through a hole only slightly larger than itself in the fitting. Since the button-head is larger than the hole, it cannot pull through and therefore transfers its load to the fitting.

There are several types of button-head systems in use in the United States, but they can be divided into two basic groups: single button-head and double button-head. For the single button-head group the cable is tensioned by pulling on the steel fitting. For the double button-head group two button-heads are placed a short distance apart. The cable is tensioned by pulling on the button-heads at the ends of the wires, and the button-heads farther down the wires serve as the permanent anchors against steel fittings.

In forming a button-head the end of the wire is cut perfectly square and smooth with a special shear. The wire is placed in a heading machine which grips it near the end and holds it while a piston exerts enough force against the end to upset it.

The length between button-heads must be the same for all the wires in a cable if each wire is to carry the same load. When one wire is shorter than another, the button-heads on the short wire will seat against the fittings first, so that the short wire undergoes the greatest elongation and develops the largest load. Equal lengths are achieved by use of a measuring jig, which is usually a long structural steel member such as a channel. A steel block with a slot slightly wider than the wire is attached to one end of the jig as a base point. The special shear is clamped to the structural member at the proper distance from the base point for the cable being made. One end of the wire is button-headed and dropped into the slot of the block at the base point; a come-along and dynamometer are used at the other end to pull the wire to a predetermined low tension; it is cut by the shear and then button-headed. Since the shear is left clamped at the same point until all the wires for one cable are made, they will all be the same length. In some systems the wires must be threaded through the fitting before they are headed, while in others the fittings are in segments which can be assembled on the finished cable. Cables are fabricated at a plant or at the job site, depending upon the particular conditions.

Figures 7-22 to 7-28 and Tables 7-4 and 7-5 illustrate the Prescon system which uses a single button-head at each end of each wire. Prescon uses two types of button-head cables. Their type G cables are encased in flexible metal hose and are grouted after the tensioning operation has been completed. Their type M cables are covered with a thick layer of rust-preventing greaselike material and then spiral-wrapped with waterproof paper. Type M cables are not grouted after tensioning and are therefore in the unbonded category.

7-8. General Considerations. Proper placement of end bearing plates or cones is important. The plate must be perpendicular to the actual slope of the tendon at the end of the member. If it is not, the tendon will be on an angle with its anchor fitting and can develop severe stresses.

Jacks must be centered on the hole in the bearing plate through which the tendon is being pulled so that the tendon will not be scraped along the plate.

The entire inside face of the bearing plate should bear against the concrete unless the engineer's drawings specifically state otherwise. If a rag is wrapped around the flexible metal hose as a seal where it meets the bearing plate, it will also keep the concrete from touching the plate in that area. When load is applied to the plate, the rag will compress and all the load will be distributed to the outer edges of the plate, causing excessive bending in the plate and excessive pressure in the concrete at the point where it is in contact with the plate.

Details should be arranged so that elastic shortening of the member can take place during the tensioning operation, or allowance must be made for any part of the prestressing force that is dissipated to the sup-

Fig. 7-22. End view of girder using Prescon button-head cables. Cable in upper left-hand corner has not been tensioned. Cable in upper right-hand corner is being held under tension by jack while shim is inserted to keep it at the desired elongation. Cables in the bottom row have been tensioned and anchored with permanent shims.

porting structure. When one end of a bridge girder rests on a rocker, the rocker is tilted in the unstressed condition so that it will rotate to the desired angle as a result of elastic shortening. There is no loss of prestress to the supporting structure in this case. If one end of a prestressed member is lifted from the support, dissipation of prestress will be eliminated.

Placing and tensioning of post-tensioned tendons are relatively simple operations. In most cases a competent job superintendent with no previous prestressed concrete experience can direct his crew from the in-

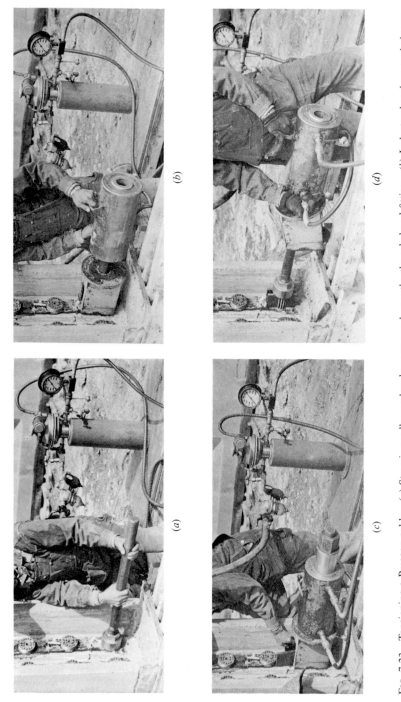

Fig. 7-23. Tensioning a Prescon cable. (*a*) Stressing collar and rod are screwed over the threaded end fitting. (*b*) Jack stand and center-hole ram are placed over pull rod. (*c*) Shims are placed under fitting of stressed tendon. Note the nut at end of stressing rod bearing on piston of center-hole ram. (*d*) Removing jacking equipment after shims have been placed and jack load released.

98

structions furnished by the supplier of the tendons.   The supplier of the tendons should be consulted as to whether or not specialized supervision is needed on a particular project.   When a supervisor is needed, it is usually for only one or two days.

Grouting is also a simple operation but one whose importance is not always appreciated.   Grout not only bonds the tendons to the member, it protects them from corrosion.   The grouting operation must expel all the air and water from the space around the tendon and replace it with grout.   This can be done satisfactorily if instructions from the suppliers of the tendons are followed correctly.   Any free water remaining in the cavity can also freeze and split the concrete member.

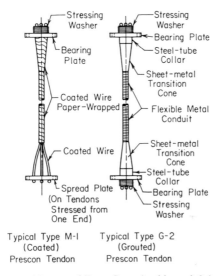

FIG. 7-24.   Typical Prescon cable assemblies.   Coated cable on left has jacking end at top and anchor end at bottom.   Grouted cable at right has fittings for jacking from both ends.

7-9. Economy.   Properly designed post-tensioned structures are more economical than reinforced concrete or structural steel under many conditions.   They are seldom competitive with pretensioned members where conditions are suitable to pretensioned design.   When some of the tendons must be deflected and a casting bed is available, the combination of pretensioned and post-tensioned methods often proves economical.

One of the biggest uses of post-tensioned tendons is in members which are too large to be transported or which for some other reasons must be cast in place.   This group includes long, continuous members.

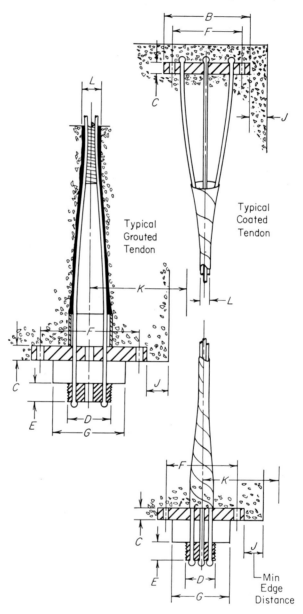

Typical
Grouted
Tendon

Typical
Coated
Tendon

Min
Edge
Distance

Fig. 7-25. Enlarged details at ends of Prescon cables. See Table 7-4 for dimensions represented by letters.

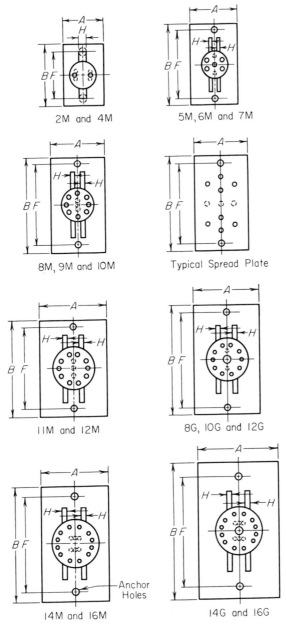

FIG. 7-26. Bearing-plate details for Prescon cables. See Table 7-4 for dimensions represented by letters.

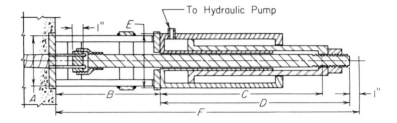

Table of Jack Clearances

Ram capacity, tons	Ram extension, in.	Base size A, in.	Base length B, in.	With ram closed C, in.	With ram open D, in.	Ram base ϕ D, in.	Fully extended clearance, in.	Ram wt, lb
30	6	3½	11	14	20	5	32	25
60	3	4 × 6	12	13	16	6½	29	60
60	6	4 × 6	12	23	29	6½	42	90
60	10	4 × 6	12	23	33	6½	46	120
100	10	5½ × 7	11	22	32	7½	44	180

NOTE: Consult Prescon where above clearances are not possible and special equipment is indicated.

FIG. 7-27.   Jack dimensions and clearances for Prescon equipment.

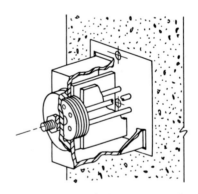

FIG. 7-28.   Grout attachment for jacking end of Prescon type G cable.   Other types of end grout connections are also available.

The most economical results are obtained when the drawings and specifications are adapted to permit quotation of all recognized systems of post-tensioning. The drawings show the magnitude and location of the final prestressing force, and the specifications cover the various types of tendons that may be used. This procedure permits unrestricted competitive bidding within the limits of proper materials.

Table 7-4. Details of Prescon Tendons

Prescon prestressing tendons are identified as indicated below:

6M1: 6—Number ¼-in.-diameter wires per tendon; M—coated wires wrapped in paper; 1—stressed from one end only.

10G2: 10—Number ¼-in.-diameter wires per tendon; G—wires enclosed in flexible metal conduit for grouting; 2—stressed from both ends.

Type tendon	*A*	*B*	*C*	*D*	*E*	*F**	*G*	*H*	*J*	*K*†	*L*	A_s	P_{ult}	P_{final}
2M	2½	3	½	1½	1		2½	⅜	1	3¾	½	0.098	23.5	14.1
4M	3	4½	⅝	2	1¼	3½	3½	⅝	1¼	5	⅝	0.196	47.0	28.2
5M	3	5½	⅝	2	1¼	4½	4	¼	1¼	5½	¾	0.245	58.8	35.3
6M	3½	6	¾	2	1¼	5	4	¼	1¼	5½	¾	0.295	70.8	42.5
7M	4	6	¾	2½	1¼	5	4	⅜	1¼	5¾	¾	0.344	82.6	49.5
8M	4	7	¾	2½	1¼	6	5	⅜	1¼	6¾	⅞	0.393	94.3	56.6
9M	4	7½	¾	2½	1¼	6	5	⅜	1¼	6¾	1	0.442	106.1	63.6
10M	4	8½	¾	2½	1¼	7	5	⅜	1¼	6¾	1	0.491	117.8	70.7
11M	5	7½	1	3	1¼	6½	5	⅜	1¼	7	1⅛	0.540	129.6	77.8
12M	5	8	1	3	1¼	7	5	⅜	1½	7	1⅛	0.589	141.4	84.8
14M	6	8½	1¼	3½	1¼	7	6	½	1½	8¼	1⅛	0.687	164.9	98.9
16M	6	9½	1¼	3½	1¼	7	6	½	1½	8¼	1¼	0.785	188.4	113.0
8G	5	7	1	3	1¼	6	5	⅜	1½	7	1⅝‡	0.393	94.3	56.6
10G	5	8	1	3	1¼	7	5	⅜	1½	7	1⅝‡	0.491	117.8	70.7
12G	5	9½	1	3	1¼	7	6	⅜	1½	8	1⅝‡	0.589	141.4	84.8
14G	6	9	1¼	3½	1¼	7	6	½	1½	8¼	1⅞‡	0.687	164.9	98.9
16G	6	10	1¼	3½	1¼	7	6	½	1½	8¼	1⅞‡	0.785	188.4	113.0

* Anchor holes are ⅝ in. for 14- and 16-wire tendons, ½ in for all others.

† Clear dimensions required on one side only for inserting shims, measured in the direction of the long dimension of the plate.

‡ ID of tubing is ⅛ in. less than this value.

Table 7-5. Estimated Field Labor for Prescon Tendons

Member	Type tendon	Average length, ft	Man-hours to place	Man-hours to stress	Man-hours to grout
Channel deck	4M1	25–40	0.30	0.30	
Double-T deck	5M1-7M1	25–40	0.55	0.50	
	8M1-10M1	25–50	0.75	0.60	
Slabs	5M2-7M2	50–85	0.95	0.90	
	8M2-10M2	50–85	1.20	1.00	
Joists	4M1	25–45	0.45	0.35	
	5M1-7M1	25–45	0.75	0.50	
	5M2-7M2	45–75	0.90	0.75	
	8M2-10M2	75–110	1.35	1.10	
Beams and girders	8M1-10M1	25–45	0.90	0.60	
	8M2-10M2	45–75	1.10	0.85	
	8M2-10M2	75–110	1.30	1.00	
	12M2-14M2	75–110	1.60	1.30	
	16M2	75–110	1.75	1.45	
	8G2-10G2	40–60	1.25	0.95	0.30
	12G2	40–60	1.30	1.00	0.35
	12G2	60–80	1.70	1.30	0.45
	12G2	80–150	1.80	1.45	0.75
	14G2	60–80	1.75	1.40	0.45
	14G2	80–150	2.00	1.60	0.75
	16G2	60–80	1.80	1.45	0.50
	16G2	80–150	2.25	1.80	0.80

CHAPTER 8

SPECIFICATIONS

8-1. Using Prestressed Concrete Specifications. Prestressed concrete will be a comparatively new type of building material for years to come. Once the use of this material began to spread, development of techniques, equipment, and procedures was rapid, but final standardization of all factors is still in the future.

A number of specifications dealing with prestressed concrete and the materials used therein are presented in this chapter and in the Appendix. Note that each one is called "tentative." The engineers who wrote them realized that future developments would make changes desirable. Designers of prestressed concrete structures should make sure that they have the latest revision of any specifications they are using.

After studying the preceding chapters the reader should have an understanding of the properties of a prestressed concrete structure and the materials and methods used in fabricating it. This knowledge must be used to interpret and apply the specifications.

8-2. ACI-ASCE Recommendations. The Joint ACI-ASCE Committee on Prestressed Reinforced Concrete has prepared a report entitled Tentative Recommendations for Prestressed Concrete. These Recommendations constitute the most comprehensive coverage of prestressed concrete available. The report, which took more than five years to complete, was prepared by a group of experts in the prestressed concrete field representing both the ACI and the ASCE.

As pointed out in its own Sec. 101: "This report constitutes a Recommended Practice, not a Building Code or Specification." In other words, the engineer should be a competent structural designer and he must go beyond the simple process of applying the formulas presented. He must learn as much as he can about the materials and processes of prestressed concrete, and he must, as he should in design with any material, consider such factors as partial continuity not used in the design but resulting from the method of erection, temperature effect, etc.

It is recommended that the ACI-ASCE Recommendations be used as the basis of all prestressed concrete structures composed of linear members. The complete Recommendations are presented herewith. The author's explanatory comments and suggestions are shown immediately following the section to which they refer. These Recommendations should be studied carefully.

TENTATIVE RECOMMENDATIONS FOR PRESTRESSED CONCRETE*

Report of the Joint ACI-ASCE Committee on Prestressed Reinforced Concrete

SYNOPSIS

A guide to design and construction of safe, serviceable, linear structural members prestressed with high strength steel. Emphasis is on flexural members—beams, girder, and slabs. Most of the recommendations are applicable to both buildings and bridges. Design chapter treats: loading; allowable stress; prestress loss; flexure and shear; bond and anchorage; composite construction; continuity; end blocks; fire resistance; and cover and spacing of prestressing steel. Concrete, grout, prestressing steel, anchorages, and splices are covered in the section on materials. Construction section includes: transportation, placing, and curing of concrete; forms, shoring, and falsework; placement of prestressing steel and application of the prestressing force; grouting; and handling and erection.

CONTENTS

Chapter 1—Introduction

Section 101–Objective; 102–Scope; 103–Acceptance tests; 104–Notation.

Chapter 2—Design

Section 201–General considerations; 202–Special considerations; 203–Assumptions; 204–Loading stages; 205–Load factors; 206–Repetitive loads; 207–Allowable steel and concrete stresses; 208–Loss of prestress; 209–Flexure; 210–Shear; 211–Bond and anchorage; 212–Composite construction; 213–Continuity; 214–End blocks; 215–Fire resistance; 216–Cover and spacing of prestressing steel.

Chapter 3—Materials

Section 301–Introduction; 302–Concrete; 303–Grout; 304–Prestressing steel; 305–Anchorages and splices.

---

* Tentative Recommendations for Prestressed Concrete has been included by permission of the American Concrete Institute and the American Society of Civil Engineers. It first appeared in *Journal of the American Concrete Institute*, January, 1958, and *Journal of the Structural Division, American Society of Civil Engineers*, Paper 1519, January, 1958. This report is subject to revision whenever the studies of the committee responsible indicate that developments in prestressed concrete design and construction warrant change. Inquiries concerning revision should be made periodically to the American Concrete Institute, P.O. Box 4754, Redford Station, Detroit 19, Mich., or to the American Society of Civil Engineers in New York, N.Y. Readers' comments on this report and the Committee Closure are printed in Appendix E.

Chapter 4—Construction

Section 401–Introduction; 402–Transporting, placing, and curing concrete; 403–Forms, shoring and falsework; 404–Placement of prestressing steel and application of prestressing force; 405–Grouting; 406–Handling and erection.

Chapter 1—INTRODUCTION

101—OBJECTIVE

The objective of this report is to recommend those practices in design and construction which will result in prestressed concrete structures that are comparable both in safety and in serviceability to constructions in other materials now commonly used.

This report constitutes a recommended practice, not a building code or specification. Since it was not written as a code, its use or interpretation as one will not serve the best interests of either the public or the engineering profession. Recommendations contained in the report are presented solely for the guidance and information of professional engineers. Safety and economy of structures in prestressed concrete will depend as much on the intelligence and integrity of engineers preparing the design and supervising or carrying out the construction as on the degree to which these recommendations are followed.

102—SCOPE

102.1—Linear Prestressing

This report is confined in scope to linear structural members involving prestressing with high strength steel; circularly prestressed members such as tanks or pipes are not covered. These types of construction have been excluded for two reasons. They have been designed and constructed in this country for a great number of years and procedures have been developed on the basis of research and experience which have proved successful in practice. Design and construction of tanks and pipes in prestressed concrete are confined to a relatively small group of specialists and are not likely to be attempted by persons outside that group. For these reasons there seems to be no immediate need for recommendations regarding circularly prestressed structures.

102.2—Flexural Members

For the most part, recommendations in this report relate to flexural members—beams, girders, and slabs. Other structural forms, such as columns, ties, arches, shells, trusses, pavements, etc., are treated only briefly or not at all. In some of these cases, such as columns or ties, the principles involved in design are essentially simple and no need was felt to include them in this report. In other cases, insufficient information was available either from research or experience to permit recommendations to be made at this time. This lack of information is due in some instances to the complexity of the type of structure involved and in others to the infrequency of its use in this country.

102.3—Buildings and Bridges

These recommendations are intended to apply to both buildings and bridges. The form and nature of this report are such that almost all recommendations made apply without differentiation to both types of structures. Where this is not the case, separate recommendations are made for buildings and bridges.

103—ACCEPTANCE TESTS

It is recognized by the committee that unusual types of construction, design, or materials may be used in such a manner that these recommendations are not applicable or may not have been complied with. Such structures may be adequate for the purpose intended. In these cases it is recommended that tests be made to verify design.

104—NOTATION

104.1—General

Symbols are assembled into sections pertaining to groups of associated terms. The list comprises only the symbols in this report. No attempt is made to present a complete notation for design of prestressed concrete.

The notations listed in Sec. 104 are used throughout the book with the exception of A_c and e. The definition of A_c in Sec. 104-2 is used only in connection with bearing-plate computations, and the definition of e in Sec. 104.5 is used only in connection with friction computations. For all other computations, the definitions of A_c and e given in Notations apply.

104.2—Dimensions and Cross-sectional Constants

A_b = bearing area of anchor plate of post-tensioning steel

A_c = maximum area of the portion of the anchorage surface that is geometrically similar to and concentric with the area of the bearing plate of post-tensioning steel

A_s = area of main prestressing tensile steel

A'_s = area of conventional tensile steel

A_{sf} = steel area required to develop the ultimate compressive strength of the overhanging portions of the flange

A_{sr} = steel area required to develop the ultimate compressive strength of the web of a flanged section

A_v = area of web reinforcement placed perpendicular to the axis of the member

b = width of flange of a flanged member or width of a rectangular member

b' = width of web of a flanged member

d = distance from extreme compressive fiber to centroid of the prestressing force

I = moment of inertia about the centroid of the cross section

j = ratio of distance between centroid of compression and centroid of tension to the depth d

$p = A_s/bd$; ratio of prestressing steel

p' = ratio of conventional reinforcement

pf'_s/f'_c = percentage index

s = longitudinal spacing of web reinforcement

t = average thickness of the flange of a flanged member

Q = statical moment of cross section area, above or below the level being investigated for shear, about the centroid

104.3—Loads

D = effect of dead load

L = effect of design live load including impact, where applicable

W = effect of wind load, or earthquake load, or traction forces

V_c = shear carried by concrete

104.4—Stresses and Strains

E_c = flexural modulus of elasticity of concrete

E_s = modulus of elasticity of prestressing steel

f'_c = compressive strength of concrete at 28 days

f'_{ci} = compressive strength of concrete at time of initial prestress

f_{cp} = permissible compressive concrete stress on bearing area under anchor plate of post-tensioning steel

f'_s = ultimate strength of prestressing steel

f_{se} = effective steel prestress after losses

f_{si} = initial stress in prestressing steel after seating of the anchorage

f_{su} = stress in prestressing steel at ultimate load

f_{sy} = nominal yield point stress of prestressing steel

f'_t = flexural tensile strength of concrete; modulus of rupture

f'_y = yield point stress of conventional reinforcing steel

k_2 = ratio of distance between extreme compressive fiber and center of compression to depth to neutral axis

k_1k_3 = ratio of average compressive concrete stress to cylinder strength, f'_c

n = ratio of E_s/E_c

u_d = strain in concrete due to creep

u_e = strain in concrete due to elastic shortening

u_s = strain in concrete due to shrinkage

v = shearing stress

δ_1 = ratio of loss in steel stress due to relaxation of prestressing steel

δ_2 = ratio of loss in steel stress due to friction during prestressing

104.5—Friction during Prestressing

e = base of Naperian logarithms

K = friction wobble coefficient per ft of prestressing steel

T_o = steel stress at jacking end

T_x = steel stress at any point x

μ = friction curvature coefficient

α = total angular change of prestressing steel profile in radians from jacking end to point x

L = length of prestressing steel element from jacking end to point x

Chapter 2—DESIGN

201—GENERAL CONSIDERATIONS

201.1—Purpose

The purpose of design is to define a structure that can be constructed economically, that will perform satisfactorily under service conditions, and will have an adequate ultimate load capacity.

201.2—Mode of Failure

Ultimate strength should be governed preferably by elongation of the prestressing steel rather than by shear, bond, or concrete compression.

There is a specific reason for this preference. The high-strength steels used in prestressed concrete develop large elongations at loads of 90 to 95 per cent of their actual ultimate strengths. This elongation causes marked deflection of the structure, warning of impending failure. Failure by shear, bond, or concrete compression can be instantaneous and therefore much more dangerous.

201.3—Design Theory

The elastic theory should be used at design loads with internal stresses limited to recommended values. The ultimate strength theory also should be applied to insure that ultimate capacity provides the recommended load factors.

202—SPECIAL CONSIDERATIONS

202.1—Loading Conditions

Consideration should be given to all critical loading conditions in design including those that occur during fabrication, handling, transportation, erection, and construction.

202.2—Deflections

Camber and deflection may be design limitations and should be investigated for both short and long time effects.

202.3—Length Changes

Length changes of concrete due to prestress and other causes should be investigated for both short and long time effects.

202.4—Reversal of Loading Effects

Where reversal of moment or shear may occur it should be considered in the design.

202.5—Buckling

General buckling due to prestressing can occur only over the length between points of contact of the prestressing steel with the concrete.

General buckling of an entire member or local buckling of thin webs and flanges under external loads may occur in prestressed concrete as in members made of other materials and should be provided for in design.

A more complete discussion of this subject is given in Art. 1-5.

203—ASSUMPTIONS

203.1—Basic Assumptions

The following assumptions may be made for design purposes:
a. Strains vary linearly over the depth of the member throughout the entire load range.
b. Before cracking, stress is linearly proportional to strain.
c. After cracking, tension in the concrete is neglected.

203.2—Modulus of Elasticity

When accurate values for modulus of elasticity are not available, the following values may be used as a guide:
a. Flexural modulus of elasticity of concrete E_c, in psi, may be assumed to be 1,800,000 plus 500 times the cylinder strength at the age considered. Actual values may vary as much as 25 per cent from those given by the foregoing expression. This expression is not applicable to lightweight concrete, for which E_c should be determined by test.
b. Modulus of elasticity of steel, in psi, may be assumed to be 29,000,000 for cold drawn wire, 27,000,000 for 7-wire strand, 25,000,000 for strand with more than 7 wires, and 27,000,000 for alloy steel bars.

203.3—Deflections

Deflection or camber under short time loading may be computed using values of E_c obtained as described in Section 203.2.a.

Deflection associated with dead load, prestress, and live loads sustained for a long time may be computed on the assumption that the corresponding concrete strains are increased as a result of creep. The increase in strain may vary from 100 per cent of the elastic strain in very humid atmosphere to 300 per cent of the elastic strain in very dry atmosphere. These values may not pertain to concrete made with lightweight aggregates.

204—LOADING STAGES

204.1—Loading

Loading stages listed in the following sections should be investigated. No attempt is made to list all significant loading stages that may occur. Stages listed are those that normally affect the design.

204.2—Initial Prestress

Prestressing forces are applied in prearranged sequence and sometimes in stages. If prestressing forces are not counteracted by the effect of the dead load of the member, or if the stressing operation is accompanied by temporary eccentricities, concrete stresses should be investigated.

204.3—Initial Prestress Plus Dead Load of Member

For determination of concrete stresses at this stage, losses in prestress are those which occur during and immediately after transfer of prestress.

204.4—Transportation and Erection

Support conditions for precast members during transportation and erection may differ from those during service loads. Handling stresses should be included together with prestress and dead load. Losses in initial prestress up to time of handling should be considered.

204.5—Design Load

This stage includes stress due to effective prestress after losses, dead loads, and maximum specified live load.

204.6—Cracking Load

Complete freedom from cracking may or may not be necessary at any particular loading stage. Type and function of the structure and type, frequency, and magnitude of live loads should be considered.

204.7—Temporary Overload

This stage refers to any large live load in excess of design load, which is of short-time duration and expected to occur infrequently during life of structure. For such a load, stresses may exceed those recommended for design load but elastic recovery must be assured.

204.8—Ultimate Load

Ultimate load is that load which applied statically in a single application causes failure. Such a large load would never intentionally be placed on the structure, but it is used as a measure of safety. In statically determinate structures, failure will occur at a single cross section. In statically indeterminate structures, the load which causes moment in one section to reach its ultimate value may not be sufficient to cause failure of the structure because of moment redistribution. Since it is not always possible to predict that full redistribution will take place in accordance with limit design, it is suggested for the time being that moments be determined by elastic analysis.

205—LOAD FACTORS

205.1—General

A load factor is a multiple of the design loads used to insure safety of the structure.

205.2—Cracking Load Factors

If cracking of concrete is undesirable, load factors for cracking load should be chosen to reflect the greatest load that can be expected during life of structure.

Formation of a crack under temporary overload may not be objectionable. If reopening such a crack under subsequent design load is objectionable it may be avoided by proper choice of concrete stress permitted for cracking load.

If a load sufficient to crack the structure has been applied just once, the crack will open up every time the stress goes into tension. On this basis the only sure way to avoid cracks would be to design to zero tension under the specified load.

205.3—Ultimate Load Factors

The ultimate load capacity should be computed since stresses are not linearly proportional to external forces and moments throughout the entire load range. For the present, it is recommended that moments, shears, and thrusts produced by external loads and prestressing forces be investigated by elastic analysis.

The load factors recommended are believed to be consistent with current viewpoints. It may be desirable to modify or expand the load factor formulas to fit special conditions that may occur in unusual structures, extremely long spans, or for unique loadings. Deviations from the recommended values should be substantiated by suitable investigations.

205.3.1—Buildings

For the present, to correlate prestressed concrete with reinforced concrete practice in current use, the committee recommends that ultimate load capacity be investigated to insure meeting the following requirements:

$$1.2D + 2.4L$$
or $$1.8\,(D + L)$$
or $$1.2D + 2.4L + 0.6W$$
or $$1.2D + 0.6L + 2.4W$$
or $$1.8\,(D + L + \tfrac{1}{2}W)$$
or $$1.8\,(D + \tfrac{1}{2}L + W)$$

whichever is greater.

205.3.2—Highway bridges

The following load factors for highway bridges are recommended by a subgroup appointed by American Association of State Highway Officials, Committee on Bridges and Structures.*

$$1.5D + 2.5L$$

The committee is not prepared at this time to make recommendations for load factors involving the effect of lateral loads on bridges.

---

* These load factors are considered adequate for spans of moderate length, simply supported. For exceptionally long spans and for continuous members special investigation to consider a possible increase in load factors is recommended.

205.3.3—Railway bridges

Ultimate load factors for railway bridges are currently being studied by the American Railway Engineering Association. The committee is not prepared to recommend such factors at this time.

206—REPETITIVE LOADS

206.1—General

Ultimate strength of concrete or steel subjected to repetitive loading may be less than static strength because of the phenomenon of fatigue. Full importance of fatigue in prestressed concrete members has not yet been determined. Fatigue failure may occur in concrete, steel, anchorages, splices, or bond.

206.2—Concrete

Fatigue strength of concrete in both tension and compression depends on magnitude of stress, range of stress variation, and number of loading cycles. Since high stresses and stress ranges are common, fatigue should be considered when repetition of loading cycles may occur.

Fatigue failure is unlikely if the allowable stresses of Section 207.3.2 are not exceeded and there is no reversal of stress. If a large number of overloads are anticipated a reduction in the safety factor may occur.

206.3—Prestressing Steel

Fatigue strength of prestressing steel depends on magnitude and range of stress, and number of cycles of loading. Minimum stress is the effective prestress. Maximum stress and range of stress depend on magnitude of live loads or overloads that may be repeated. Range of stress under service loads will usually be small unless concrete is cracked. Cracking may occur if tension is permitted in concrete. Fatigue failure of steel should be considered in such cases, especially when a high percentage of ultimate strength is used for prestress.

Devices for splicing steel may contain strain concentrations that lower fatigue strength. Consideration should be given to fatigue whenever splices are used.

206.4—Anchorages

If steel is fully bonded, no difficulty should be expected in the anchorage or end bearing as the result of repetitive loads. With unbonded steel, fluctuations in stress due to repeated service loads or overloads are transmitted directly to anchorages and fatigue strength of the anchorage will require special consideration.

206.5—Bond

Failure of bond under repetitive loading is unlikely unless the member is cracked under design loads or a significant number of repetitions of overload. High bond stresses adjacent to cracks may be a source of progressive failure under repeated loads.

206.6—Shear and Diagonal Tension

Since inclined cracks may form under repetitive loading at appreciably smaller stresses than under static loading, web reinforcement should always be provided in members subjected to repetitive loading.

206.7—Design Recommendations

Fatigue should not result in a reduction of strength if the following recommendations are observed. When the recommendations cannot be followed, fatigue strength of all elements comprising the prestressed member should be considered.
   a. Flexural compressive concrete stress should not exceed $0.4f'_c$ under either design load or an overload that may be repeated many times.
   b. Tension should not be permitted in concrete at the critical cross section under either design load or overloads that may be repeated a large number of times.
   c. Reversal of stress should not occur under repeated loads.
   d. Prestressing steel should be bonded.
   e. Web reinforcement should be provided.

207—ALLOWABLE STEEL AND CONCRETE STRESSES

207.1—Prestressing Steel

207.1.1—Temporary stresses

Under normal design loads stress in prestressing steel will almost always be less than stress at initial prestress. Stress at the anchorage immediately after seating has been effected should not exceed $0.70f'_s$ for material having stress-strain properties defined in Chapter 3. Overstressing for a short period of time to $0.80f'_s$ may be permitted provided the stress, after seating of anchorage occurs, does not exceed $0.70f'_s$.

For discussion of overstressing, see the last paragraph of Art. 6-5.

207.1.2—Stress at design loads

Effective steel stress after losses described in Section 208 should not exceed:

$$0.60f'_s \text{ or } 0.80f_{sy}$$

whichever is smaller.

207.2—Non-prestressed Reinforcement

Non-prestressed reinforcement provided to resist tension in conformance with requirements of Section 207.3.1.b.2 may be assumed stressed to 20,000 psi.

207.3—Concrete

207.3.1—Temporary stresses

Concrete stress in psi before losses due to creep and shrinkage should not exceed the following:
   a. Compression
      For pretensioned members.................................... $0.60f'_{ci}$
      For post-tensioned members............. .... $0.55f'_{ci}$

b. Tension
  1. For members without non-prestressed reinforcement:
     Single element . . . . $3\sqrt{f'_{ci}}$
     Segmental element . . . . zero
  2. For members with non-prestressed reinforcement provided to resist the tensile force in the concrete, computed on the basis of an uncracked section:
     Single element . . . . $6\sqrt{f'_{ci}}$
     Segmental element . . . . $3\sqrt{f'_{ci}}$

Single element refers to a monolithic member. Segmental element refers to a member composed of precast blocks assembled and then prestressed. In some segmental elements the blocks bear against each other, and in some there is a mortar joint between the blocks.

207.3.2—Stresses at design loads

After full prestress losses, stresses in psi should not exceed the following:
a. Compression
  1. Single element
     a. Bridge members . . . . $0.40f'_c$
     b. Building members . . . . $0.45f'_c$
  2. Segmental elements
     a. Bridge members . . . . $0.40f'_c$
     b. Building members . . . . $0.45f'_c$
b. Flexural tension in the precompressed tensile zone
  1. Single element
     a. Bridge members . . . . zero
     b. Pretensioned building elements not exposed to weather or corrosive atmosphere . . . . $6\sqrt{f'_c}$
     c. Post-tensioned bonded elements not exposed to weather or corrosive atmosphere . . . . $3\sqrt{f'_c}$
  2. Segmental elements
     a. Bridge members . . . . zero
     b. Building members . . . . zero

Allowable flexural tension of $6\sqrt{f'_c}$ in Section 207.3.2.b.1.b may be exceeded provided it is shown by tests that the structure will behave properly under service conditions and meet any necessary requirement for cracking load or temporary overload.

Item 207.3.2.b specifies allowable tensile stresses in the "precompressed tensile zone," but no mention is made of allowable tensile stresses in the compressive zone (i.e., the top fibers of a simple span member). It is suggested that the PCI Specifications, Appendix B, be followed in this matter. See Sec. 4(B)(2) of the PCI Specifications.

207.3.3—Stress at cracking load

Flexural tensile strength (modulus of rupture) should preferably be determined by test. When test data are not available the ultimate flexural tensile stress in psi may be assumed as:

$$f'_t = 7.5\sqrt{f'_c}$$

For lightweight concrete, f'_t should be determined by tests.

207.3.4—Anchorage bearing stresses

The maximum allowable stress at post-tensioning anchorage in end blocks adequately reinforced in conformance with Section 214.4 may be assumed as:

$$f_{cp} = 0.6f'_{ci}\sqrt[3]{A_c/A_b}$$

where A_b = bearing area of the anchor plate.

$\quad A_c$ = maximum area of portion of the member that is geometrically similar to and concentric with the area of bearing plate.

The allowable value of f_{cp} should not exceed f'_{ci}.

The provisions of this item should not be construed as prohibiting the use of time-tried special anchors such as those used on Freyssinet cables.

208—LOSS OF PRESTRESS

208.1—Introduction

Initial prestress is that stress in steel which exists immediately after seating of anchorage. Stress diminishes with time and finally reaches a stable condition of effective prestress assumed to be permanent.

208.2—Sources of Prestress Loss

208.2.1—Friction loss in post-tensioned steel

If post-tensioned steel is draped, or irregularities exist in alignment of ducts, steel stress will be less within the member than at the jack because of friction between prestressing steel and duct. Magnitude of this friction should be estimated for design and verified during stressing operation.

Friction loss may be estimated from an analysis of forces exerted by prestressing steel on duct. One method for determination of friction loss at any point is given below.

$$T_o = T_x e^{(KL + \mu\alpha)}$$

where T_o = steel stress at jacking end

$\quad T_x$ = steel stress at point x

$\quad e$ = base of Naperian logarithms

$\quad K$ = friction wobble coefficient per ft of prestressing steel

$\quad L$ = length of prestressing steel element from jacking end to point x in ft

$\quad \mu$ = friction curvature coefficient

$\quad \alpha$ = total angular change of prestressing steel element in radians from jack to point x

For small values of KL and $\mu\alpha$ the following formula may be used:

$$T_o = T_x(1 + KL + \mu\alpha)$$

The following values of K and μ are typical and may be used as a guide. They may vary appreciably with duct material and method of construction. Values of K and μ used in design should be indicated on the plans for guidance in selection of materials and methods that will produce results approaching the assumed values.

Type of steel	Type of duct or sheath	Usual range of observed values		Suggested design values	
		K	μ	K	μ
Wire cables	Bright metal sheathing	0.0005–0.0030	0.15–0.35	0.0020	0.30
	Galvanized metal sheathing			0.0015	0.25
	Greased or asphalt-coated and wrapped	0.0030	0.25–0.35	0.0020	0.30
High strength bars	Bright metal sheathing	0.0001–0.0005	0.08–0.30	0.0003	0.20
	Galvanized metal sheathing			0.0002	0.15
Galvanized strand	Bright metal sheathing	0.0005–0.0020	0.15–0.30	0.0015	0.25
	Galvanized metal sheathing			0.0010	0.20

Workmanship in placing, supporting, tying, and fabricating prestressing elements and ducts influences the magnitude of wobble factor, K. The larger the sheath or duct in relation to the size of prestressing steel element, the smaller K will be. With normal placing tolerances wobble effect may be neglected if sheath is 1″ greater in diameter than prestressing steel element.

Effect of overestimating friction loss should be considered since excessive prestress may cause undesirable permanent stress conditions. Underestimating friction loss may result in an error in computing cracking load and deflection.

208.2.2—Elastic shortening of concrete

Loss of prestress caused by elastic shortening of the concrete occurs in prestressed concrete members. This loss equals $n(\Delta f_c)$. For pretensioned concrete, Δf_c is the concrete stress at the center of gravity of the prestressing steel for which the losses are being computed. For post-tensioned concrete where the steel elements may not be tensioned simultaneously, Δf_c is the average concrete stress along one prestressing element from end to end of the beam caused by subsequent post-tensioning of adjacent elements.

208.2.3—Shrinkage of concrete

Shrinkage depends on many variables. Unit shrinkage strain may vary from near 0 to 0.0005. A value between 0.0002 and 0.0003 is commonly used for calculation of prestress loss. Shrinkage loss may be greater in pretensioned members where the prestress is transferred to the concrete at an earlier age than is usual for post-tensioned members. Shrinkage of lightweight concrete may be greater than the values obtained with the above factors

208.2.4—Creep of concrete

Creep is the time-dependent strain of concrete caused by stress. For pretensioned and post-tensioned bonded members, concrete stress is taken at center of gravity of prestressing steel under effect of prestress and permanent loads (normal conditions of unloaded structure).

In post-tensioned unbonded members, stress is the average concrete stress along the profile of center of gravity of prestressing steel under the effect of prestress and permanent loads. Additional strain due to creep may be assumed to vary from 100 per cent of elastic strain for concrete in very humid atmosphere to 300 per cent of elastic strain in very dry atmosphere.

Creep of some lightweight concretes may be greater than indicated above.

208.2.5—Relaxation of steel stress

Loss of stress due to relaxation of prestressing steel should be provided for in design in accordance with test data furnished by the steel manufacturer. Loss due to relaxation depends primarily on properties of the steel and initial prestress. This loss is generally assumed in the range of 2 to 8 per cent of initial steel stress.

208.3—Alternate Procedures for Estimating Prestress Losses

Two methods are suggested for estimating prestress losses. Method 1 should be used when individual losses may be predicted with reasonable accuracy. Method 2 applies when specific loss data are lacking.

The ultimate strength is not significantly affected by the magnitude of steel stress loss. An error in choosing the loss is reflected in the cracking load and amount of camber.

208.3.1—Method 1

The total stress loss in prestressing steel:

$$\Delta f_s = (u_s + u_e + u_d) E_s + \delta_1 f_{si} + \delta_2 f_{si}$$

208.3.2—Method 2

Loss in steel stress not including friction loss may be assumed as follows:

Pretensioning	35,000 psi
Post-tensioning	25,000 psi

For camber calculations these values may be excessive.

208.4—Lightweight Concrete

Losses due to concrete shrinkage, elastic shortening, and creep should be based on results of tests made with the lightweight aggregate to be used.

209—FLEXURE

209.1—Stresses due to Dead, Live, and Impact Loads

Prestressed concrete members may be assumed to function as uncracked members subjected to combined axial and bending forces provided stresses do not exceed those given in Section 207.

In calculations of section properties prior to grouting, areas of the open ducts should be deducted unless relatively small. The transformed area of bonded reinforcement may be included in pretensioned members and post-tensioned members after grouting.

For calculations of stress due to prestress in T-beams no definite recommendations are made at this time, but attention should be given to the possibility that the entire available flange width may be included in calculation of section properties.

Eliminating part of the flange in computing the section properties of a T beam is not necessarily on the safe side. The value of F/A_c is normally a function of the area of the entire concrete cross section. If part of the flange is ignored, the value of A_c used in the computation is decreased and the computed value of F/A_c will be greater than the actual value. This means that the computed compressive stress due to F will be larger than the actual value, and as a result the member is underprestressed.

209.2—Ultimate Flexural Strength

209.2.1—General method

(a) Rectangular sections—For rectangular sections or flanged sections in which the neutral axis lies within the flange, ultimate flexural strength may be expressed as:

$$M_u = A_s f_{su} d \left(1 - \frac{k_2 p f_{su}}{k_1 k_3 f'_c} \right) \dots \dots \dots \dots \dots (a)$$

where f_{su} = average stress in prestressing reinforcement at ultimate load
d = depth to centroid of force
k_2 = ratio of distance between extreme compressive fiber and center of compression to the depth to neutral axis
$k_1 k_3$ = ratio of average compressive concrete stress to the cylinder strength, f'_c

The results of numerous tests have shown that the factor $k_2/k_1 k_3$ may be taken equal to 0.6 for members and materials considered in this report. Determination of the value of f_{su} requires knowledge of the stress-strain characteristics of the prestressing steel, effective prestress and crushing strain of the concrete. Assumptions must be made regarding the relation between steel and concrete strains. These assumptions will be different for bonded and unbonded construction.

The ultimate moment may be computed from Eq. (a) whenever sufficient information is available for the determination of f_{su}. The approximate method of Section 209.2.2 may be used if the required conditions are satisfied.

(b) Flanged sections—If a flange thickness is less than $1.4dpf_{su}/f'_c$, the neutral axis will usually fall outside the flange and the following approximate expression for ultimate moment should be used:

$$M_u = A_{sr}f_{su}d\left(1 - 0.6\frac{A_{sr}f_{su}}{b'df'_c}\right) + 0.85f'_c(b - b')t(d - 0.5t)\ldots\ldots(b)$$

where $A_{sr} = A_s - A_{sf} =$ the steel area required to develop the ultimate compressive strength of the web of a flanged section

$A_{sf} = 0.85f'_c(b - b')t/f_{su} =$ steel area required to develop the ultimate compressive strength of the overhanging portions of the flange.

$t =$ average thickness of flange

The expressions for f_{su} given in Section 209.2.2 may be used if the required conditions are satisfied.

209.2.2—Approximate method

The following approximate expressions for f_{su} may be used in Eqs. (*a*) and (*b*) of Section 209.2.1 provided the following conditions are satisfied:

1. The stress-strain properties of the prestressing steel are reasonably similar to those described in Section 304.
2. The effective prestress after losses is not less than $0.5f'_s$.
   (a) Bonded members

$$f_{su} = f'_s\left(1 - 0.5\frac{pf'_s}{f'_c}\right)$$

   (b) Unbonded members—Ultimate flexural strength in unbonded members generally occurs at lower values of steel stress than in bonded members. Wide variations between stress levels reported by different investigators reflect the fact that several factors influence the stress developed by unbonded steel at ultimate moment. These factors include: magnitude of effective prestress, profile of the prestressing steel, shape of the bending moment diagram, length/depth ratio of the member, magnitude of the friction coefficient between the prestressing steel and duct, and amount of bonded nonprestressed supplementary steel.

Unless the proper value of f_{su} is known from tests of members closely approximating proposed construction with respect to the several factors listed in the preceding paragraph, it is recommended that:

$$f_{su} = f_{se} + 15,000$$

209.2.3—Maximum steel percentage

To avoid approaching the condition of over-reinforced beams for which the ultimate flexural strength becomes dependent on the concrete strength, the ratio of prestressing steel preferably should be such that pf_{su}/f'_c for rectangular sections and $A_{sr}f_{su}/b'df'_c$ for flanged sections are not more than 0.30.

If steel ratio in excess of this amount is used, the ultimate flexural moment shall be taken as not greater than the following values when either the general or approximate method of calculation is used.

(a) Rectangular sections

$$M_u = 0.25f'_c bd^2$$

(b) Flanged sections—If the flange thickness is less than $1.4dpf_{su}/f'_c$ the neutral axis will usually fall outside the flange and the following formula is recommended.

$$M_u = 0.25b'd^2f'_c + 0.85f'_c(b - b')t(d - 0.5t)$$

209.2.4—Non-prestressed reinforcement in conjunction with prestressing steel

209.2.4.1—Conventional reinforcement—Non-prestressed conventional reinforcement may be considered to contribute to the tensile force in the beam at ultimate moment an amount equal to its area times its yield point provided that

$$\frac{pf_{su}}{f'_c} + \frac{p'f'_y}{f'_c} \text{ does not exceed 0.3}$$

where f'_y = yield point of conventional reinforcement
p' = ratio of conventional reinforcement

209.2.4.2—High tensile strength reinforcement—If untensioned prestressing steel or other high tensile strength reinforcement is used in conjunction with prestressed reinforcement, the ultimate moment should be calculated by means of the general method of Section 209.2.1.

210—SHEAR

210.1—General

210.1.1—Ultimate strength

It is essential that shear failure should not occur before ultimate flexural strength required in Section 209.2 is developed. If this condition is satisfied, it is unnecessary to investigate shear or principal tensile stresses at design loads.

For some time it was standard procedure to check principal tensile stresses at design loads and also at ultimate load. Since the stirrups required for ultimate load always prove more than sufficient for design loads, only the ultimate load condition need be calculated.

210.1.2—Inclined cracking

Formation of inclined cracks precedes failure in shear. They are caused by inclined principal tensile stresses that are the resultant of shearing stresses and normal bending stresses. Compressive prestress reduces the principal tensile stress thereby increasing the load necessary to cause inclined cracks. The use of thin webs will increase inclined stresses.

210.1.3—Conditions for shear failure

The resistance to formation of inclined cracks is greater with larger prestress and increasing web thickness. The significance of inclined cracks is less with low ultimate flexural strength caused by low ratio of reinforcement. Their significance is also less with low shear/moment ratios. If inclined cracks occur in an unreinforced web, sudden failure by shear is almost certain. If the web is adequately reinforced, ultimate flexural strength can be developed.

210.2—Web Reinforcement

210.2.1—Critical percentage of tensile steel

Experimental data, although limited, indicate that inclined tension cracks will not form and web reinforcement will not be required if the following condition is satisfied:

$$\frac{pf'_s}{f'_c} \lessgtr 0.3 \frac{f_{se}b'}{f'_s b}$$

where b' = thickness of web
b = width of flange corresponding to that used in computing p

This expression may be conservative for members having span/depth ratios greater than about 15 or for uniformly loaded members. In such cases, web reinforcement may not be required even though the percentage index, pf'_s/f'_c, exceeds that given in the above expression. The omission of web reinforcement in such members may be allowed when justified by tests.

210.2.2—Design of web reinforcement

The amount of web reinforcement necessary to develop required ultimate flexural capacity is a function of the difference between inclined cracking load and ultimate load in flexure. This difference varies rather widely as a function of prestress force, web thickness, amount of tensile reinforcement, and shear/moment ratio but is usually smaller for prestressed concrete than for conventional reinforced concrete. Current design procedures for web reinforcement in reinforced concrete are conservative for prestressed concrete.

Available test data indicate that the following expression for area of web reinforcement, with its factor of ½, will give reasonably conservative results for prestressed members of usual dimensions and properties. Since the formula does not involve the prestress force it may not be conservative for very low prestress or where only a portion of the reinforcement is stressed. For such cases it may be necessary to increase the factor of ½ as the member approaches the condition of conventionally reinforced concrete.

$$A_v = \tfrac{1}{2} \frac{(V_u - V_c)s}{f'_v jd}$$

where A_v = area of web reinforcement at spacing s, placed perpendicular to the axis of the member
V_u = shear due to specified ultimate load and effect of prestressing
$V_c = 0.06f'_c b'jd$ but not more than $180b'jd$
s = longitudinal spacing of web reinforcement
f'_v = yield strength of web reinforcement

210.2.3—Minimum quantity of web reinforcement

Because of the nature and limited knowledge of shear failures, it is suggested that some web reinforcement be provided even though the criterion of Section 210.2.1 is satisfied.

Where the web reinforcement is designed by Section 210.2.2, the minimum amount of web reinforcement should be $A_v = 0.0025b's$. This requirement may be excessive for members with unusually thick webs and the amount of web reinforcement may be reduced if tests demonstrate that the member can develop its required flexural capacity.

Heavily loaded members with thin webs and relatively small span/depth ratios such as highway bridge girders and crane girders should have web reinforcement (see Section 206.6).

210.2.4—Spacing of web reinforcement

The spacing of web reinforcement should not exceed three-quarters the depth of the member. In members with relatively thin webs, spacing should preferably not exceed the clear height of the web.

210.2.5—Critical sections for shear

Because formation of inclined cracks reduces flexural capacity the critical sections for shear will usually not be near the ends of the span where the shear is a maximum but at some point away from the ends in a region of high moment.

For the design of web reinforcement in simply supported members carrying moving loads, it is recommended that shear be investigated only within the middle half of the span length. The web reinforcement required at the quarter-points should then be used throughout the outer quarters of the span.

For simply supported members carrying only uniformly distributed load, the maximum web reinforcement may be taken as that required at a distance from the support equal to the depth of member. This amount of web reinforcement should be provided from this point to the end of member. In the middle third of the span length, the amount of web reinforcement provided should not be less than that required at third-points of the span.

211—BOND AND ANCHORAGE

211.1—Pretensioning

211.1.1—Prestress transfer bond

Bond between the pretensioned steel and concrete is necessary to establish a prestress in the concrete. The transfer of force from the steel to the concrete takes place in a finite length in the end region of a member and the function of the resulting bond, termed "prestress transfer bond," is anchorage of prestressing steel. Prestressing force varies from near zero at the end to a maximum value some distance from the end.

Transfer length will generally be of minor significance in long members, but it should be considered for short members or those in which the loading conditions may cause cracking in or near the region of prestress transfer.

211.1.2—Flexural bond

Flexural bond is the bond stress developed as a consequence of flexure. Bond stress at design loads in uncracked members is usually not critical since the increase in steel stress resulting from flexure is usually not significant. If cracking is anticipated under design loads, bond stress should be given special consideration.

211.1.3—Significance of bond stress at ultimate load

Bond failure should not occur prior to the development of the required ultimate flexural capacity.

For span lengths usually associated with prestressed concrete, bond failure is not a significant design factor. Bond adequacy in extremely short members should be investigated by test.

The factors affecting bond are concrete strength, perimeter shape, area and surface condition of prestressing steel, stress in the steel at ultimate strength, length of transfer zone, and superimposed load pattern.

212—COMPOSITE CONSTRUCTION

212.1—Introduction

Prestressed concrete structures of composite construction are comprised of prestressed concrete elements and plain or conventionally reinforced concrete elements interconnected in such a manner that the two components function as an integral unit. The prestressed elements may be pretensioned or post-tensioned and may be precast or cast in place. The plain or reinforced concrete elements are usually cast in place.

212.2—Interaction

212.2.1—Shear connection

To insure integral action of a composite structure at all loads, a connection should be provided between the component elements of the structure capable of performing two functions:
(1) To transfer shear without slip along the contact surfaces, and
(2) To prevent separation of the elements in a direction perpendicular to the contact surfaces.

212.2.2—Transfer of shear

Slip may be prevented and shear transferred along the contact surfaces either by bond or by shear keys. It should be assumed that the entire shear is transferred either by bond or by shear keys.

212.2.3—Anchorage against separation

Mechanical anchorage in the form of vertical ties should be provided to prevent separation of the component elements in the direction perpendicular to the contact surfaces. Web reinforcement or steel dowels adequately embedded on each side of the contact surface will provide satisfactory mechanical anchorage.

212.3—Design of Shear Connection

212.3.1—Loading stage

The shear connection should be designed for ultimate load.

212.3.2—Magnitude and transfer of ultimate shear

The shear at any point along the contact surface may be computed by the usual method as $v = (V_u Q)/I$. If the bond capacity is less than the computed shear, full width shear keys should be provided throughout the length of the member. Keys should be proportioned according to concrete strength of each component of the composite member.*

212.3.3—Capacity of bond

The following values are suggested for ultimate bond resistance of the contact surfaces.

When minimum steel tie requirements of Section 212.3.4 are followed . .   75 psi
When minimum steel tie requirements of Section 212.3.4 are followed and
the contact surface on the precast element is artificially roughened. . . . 150 psi
When additional steel ties in excess of the requirements of Section
212.3.4 are used and the contact surface of the precast element is arti-
ficially roughened. . . . . 225 psi

212.3.4—Vertical ties

In the absence of experimental information on the capacity of vertical ties it is recommended that all web reinforcement be extended into the cast-in-place concrete.

Spacing of vertical ties should not exceed four times the minimum thickness of the composite elements, or 24 in., whichever is less. The total area of vertical ties should not be less than that provided by two #3 bars spaced at 12 in.

For light pretensioned members such as those used for building floors not subjected to repetitive loads the above minimum requirements may be too severe. The committee is not prepared to recommend an amount or spacing of steel for this type of member.

212.4—Design of Composite Structures

212.4.1—Design of composite section

Physical properties of the composite section should be computed on the assumption of complete interaction between component elements. For structures composed of concretes of different qualities, the area of one of the component elements should be tranformed in accordance with the ratio of the two moduli of elasticity.

---

* Lack of experimental data makes the committee hesitate to recommend a shear stress at the root of a key. Indications are that for keys on bridge girders in current use shear stress at the root of a key as high as $0.3f'_c$ would sometimes be required to transmit ultimate shear force.

212.4.2—Beam and slab construction

If the structure is composed of beams with a cast-in-place slab placed on top of the beams, effective slab width should be computed in the same manner as for integral T-beams.

212.4.3—Allowable stress with different concrete strengths

In structures composed of elements with different concrete strengths, the allowable stresses should be governed by strength of the portion under consideration.

212.4.4—Superposition of stress

Stresses may be superposed in design calculations that involve elastic stresses. Superposition of stresses should not be used in computing ultimate strength since inelastic action of the material is involved.

212.4.5—Stress after structure becomes integral

The properties of the composite cross section should be used in computing stresses due to loads applied after the structure becomes integral.

212.4.6—Shrinkage stresses

In structures with a cast-in-place slab supported by precast beams, the differential shrinkage tends to cause tensile stresses in the slab and in the bottom of precast beams. Stresses due to differential shrinkage are important only insofar as they affect cracking load. When cracking load is significant, such stresses should be added to the effects of loads.

212.4.7—Ultimate strength

Ultimate strength of a composite section should be computed in the same manner as ultimate strength of an integral member of the same shape.

213—CONTINUITY

213.1—Determination of Moments, Shears, and Thrusts

Moments, shears, and thrusts produced by external loads and prestressing force should be determined by elastic analysis. Effects of axial deformation should be considered. Determination of effects produced by the prestressing forces should take into account the restraint of attached structural elements and supports.

213.2—Stresses

Allowable stresses are those recommended in Section 207.

213.2.1—Prestress

When prestressing is to be applied in more than one stage, the internal stresses should be investigated at each stage.

213.3—Frictional Losses

Frictional losses in continuous post-tensioned steel may be more significant than in simply supported members.

213.4—Ultimate Strength

The ultimate strength of a continuous member should be evaluated not only at points of maximum moment, but also at intermediate points. In applying ultimate load factors where dead load causes effects opposite to those of live load, consideration should be given to load factor combinations in which dead load factor may equal one. It is recommended that moment redistribution not be considered in design at the present time.

214—END BLOCKS

214.1—Purpose

An enlarged end section, called an end block, may be required to transmit concentrated prestressing forces in a shaped member from the anchorage area to the basic cross section.

End blocks may be required to provide sufficient area for bearing of anchorages in post-tensioned design. They may be needed to transmit vertical and lateral forces to supports and to facilitate end detailing.

214.2—Requirements

In pretensioned members with large concentrated eccentric prestressing elements, end blocks should be used. For lightly pretensioned members, or members of approximately rectangular shape, end blocks may be omitted. However, reinforcement should always be provided in the anchorage zone.

In post-tensioned, shaped members, end blocks should be provided.

214.3—Proportioning

End blocks are usually proportioned by experience. Depending on the degree of concentration and eccentricity of the prestressing force at the end surface, the length of the end block should be from one-half the depth of the member to the full depth. In general, shallow members should have an end block length equal to the depth, and deep beams should have an end block length equal to three-quarters of the depth. Length of an end block can be considered as the distance from beginning of anchorage area to the point where the end block intersects the narrowest width of member.

214.4—Reinforcement

Reinforcing is necessary to resist tensile bursting and spalling forces induced by the concentrated loads of the prestressing steel. A reinforcing grid with both vertical and horizontal steel in the plane of the cross section should be provided directly beneath anchorages to resist spalling forces. Closely spaced reinforcement should be placed both vertically and horizontally throughout the length of the end block to resist tensile forces.

215—FIRE RESISTANCE

215.1—General

The fire resistance of both prestressed concrete and reinforced concrete is subject to the same general limitations. One is the rate of heat transmission through the concrete from the surface exposed to fire to the unexposed surface. The other is the reduction of steel strength at the temperatures induced in the steel during the test. Either limitation may govern.

215.2—Heat Transmission

Since the rate of heat transmission through prestressed concrete is similar to that of reinforced concrete of the same composition, the critical dimensions to control temperature rise at the unexposed surface will be the same in prestressed or reinforced concrete members.

215.3—Load-carrying Capacity

The ability of the structure to carry required loads during fire test depends largely on thickness of cover over prestressing steel. The following minimum thicknesses of concrete cover on prestressing steel and end anchorages are recommended for various fire ratings:

Hour rating...................	1 hr	2 hr	3 hr	4 hr
Minimum concrete cover........	1½ in.	2½ in.	3 in.	4 in.

Data now available are insufficient to make recommendations for such factors as shape of cross section, type and arrangement of prestressing steel. The cover thicknesses recommended are believed to be conservative.

216—COVER AND SPACING OF PRESTRESSING STEEL

216.1—Cover

The following minimum clear concrete covers are recommended for prestressing steel, ducts, and non-prestressed steel.

Minimum concrete cover

Concrete surfaces exposed to weather............................ 1½ in.
Concrete surfaces in contact with ground........................ 2   in
Beams and girders not exposed to weather
    Prestressing steel, and main reinforcing steel................. .. 1½ in.
    Stirrups and ties....................   .... 1 in.
Slabs and joists not exposed to weather.... ... . ¾ in.

216.2—Spacing at Ends

216.2.1—Spacing of pretensioning steel

Minimum horizontal or vertical clear spacing between pretensioning steel elements at ends of members should be three times the diameter of the steel or 1⅓ times the maximum size of coarse aggregate, whichever is greater.

This is the same as saying "Minimum distance center to center of pretensioning steel elements should be four times the diameter of the steel or 1⅓ times. . . ."

216.2.2—Spacing of post-tensioning ducts

The clear space between conduits at the ends should be a minimum of 1½ in. or 1½ times the maximum size of coarse aggregate, whichever is greater.

216.2.3—Dimensions of post-tensioning ducts

When steel is placed inside conduits which are to be filled with cement grout, such conduits should have a minimum inside diameter ¼ in. larger than the diameter of the prestressing steel.

216.3—Draped Prestressing Steel

When prestressing steel is placed in a curved or deflected position, steel or conduits may be bundled together in the middle third of the span length provided the minimum spacing recommended in Section 216.2.1 and 216.2.2 is maintained for a minimum distance of 3 ft at each end of member. The committee is not prepared to suggest limits for the number of conduits or prestressing steel elements that may be bundled horizontally and vertically. Excessive bundling may lead to insufficient bond capacity in pretensioned members, resulting in bond slip.

Chapter 3—MATERIALS

301—INTRODUCTION

The nature and economics of prestressed concrete construction require the use of high strength materials. Ability to sustain high stresses with a minimum of time-dependent change in stress or strain is essential.

These requirements are more severe than those for conventionally reinforced concrete. Highest standards of manufacture and construction should be observed. Prior to adoption of new materials, sufficient test data should be obtained to verify properties assumed in design.

302—CONCRETE

302.1—Scope

Particular attention should be given to properties of individual materials used in prestressed concrete and their effect on compressive strength, modulus of elasticity, drying shrinkage, creep, bond strength, and uniformity of concrete in place.

When new materials and methods are employed, trial mix investigations should include tests for drying shrinkage, creep, and modulus of elasticity.

302.2—Materials

302.2.1—Portland cement

Portland cement should conform to one of the following:
  Specifications for Portland Cement (ASTM C 150)
  Specifications for Air-Entraining Portland Cement (ASTM C 175)
  Specifications for Portland Blast Furnace Slag Cement (ASTM C 205)
  Specifications for Portland-Pozzolan Cement (ASTM C 340)

302.2.2—Concrete aggregates

Concrete aggregates should conform to one of the following:
Specifications for Concrete Aggregates (ASTM C 33)
Specifications for Lightweight Aggregates for Structural Concrete (ASTM C 330)

Mineral composition and soundness of aggregates may have a marked influence on compressive strength, modulus of elasticity, drying shrinkage, and creep.

Concretes made with some lightweight aggregates may exhibit a lower modulus of elasticity, greater creep and drying shrinkage than do concretes of the same strength made with aggregates of normal weight.

The range of properties possible in the same concrete mix with different lightweight aggregates may be large. Therefore, it is recommended that test data should be obtained for compressive strength, modulus of elasticity, drying shrinkage, creep, modulus of rupture, and bond.

302.2.3—Water

Water for mixing concrete should be clean and free of injurious quantities of substances harmful to concrete or to prestressing steel. Sea water should not be used for making prestressed concrete.

302.2.4—Admixtures

Certain admixtures may be beneficial to fresh or hardened concrete. However, admixtures should not be used until shown by test to have no harmful effect on the steel or concrete.

The use of calcium chloride or an admixture containing calcium chloride is not recommended where it may come in contact with prestressing steel.

302.3—Proportioning, Batching and Mixing

The proportioning of materials, batching, and mixing of concrete for prestressing should be done in accordance with the ACI *Manual of Concrete Inspection,* the U. S. Bureau of Reclamation *Concrete Manual,* or other comparable regulations including ACI Standards "Recommended Practice for Winter Concreting (ACI 604-56)," "Recommended Practice for Selecting Proportions for Concrete (ACI 613-54)," "Recommended Practice for Measuring Mixing and Placing Concrete (ACI 614-42)," and "Standard Specifications for Ready-Mix Concrete (ASTM C 94).

Available materials should be proportioned to produce concrete meeting specification requirements with a minimum water content. Slump of fresh concrete should be as low as feasible. Cement, sand, and narrow-size ranges of coarse aggregate should be separately batched by weight. Water and some liquid admixtures may be batched by volume with accurate measuring equipment. Close control of all materials and operations is essential.

302.4—Strength

The strength required at given ages should be specified by the designer. Controlled concrete should be used and tested in accordance with Section 304 as modified by Section A602 (f) of "Building Code Requirements for Reinforced Concrete (ACI 318-56)."

303—GROUT

303.1—General

When required by job specifications, post-tensioned steel should be grouted to completely fill the void surrounding the prestressing steel with a portland cement grout to insure high flexural bond strength and provide permanent protection for the steel.

303.2—Materials

Grout should be made of either (a) cement and water or (b) cement, fine sand, and water. Mix (a) should be used where the cavity is very small. Either Mix (a) or Mix (b) may be used where the cavity is relatively large. Admixtures should conform to recommendations of Section 303.2.4.

303.2.1—Portland cement

Same as Section 302.2.1.

303.2.2—Sand

Sand should preferably be a natural quartz sand meeting "Tentative Specification for Aggregate for Masonry Mortar (ASTM C 144)," except for gradation requirements. The sand should pass a No. 30 sieve, about 50 per cent should pass a No. 50 sieve, and about 20 per cent should pass a No. 100 sieve.

303.2.3—Water

Same as Section 302.2.3.

303.2.4—Admixtures

Certain admixtures may be beneficial to fresh or hardened grout. However, no admixture should be used until shown by test to have no harmful effect on the steel or grout.

Calcium chloride or an admixture containing calcium chloride is not recommended for use in grouting post-tensioned members.

303.3—Proportioning

Proportions of grouting materials should be based on results of tests made on fresh and hardened grout prior to beginning work. Grout should have the consistency of thick cream or heavy paint. When permitted to stand until setting takes place, grout should neither bleed nor segregate.

304—PRESTRESSING STEEL

304.1—General

High tensile strength steel is required in prestressed concrete to provide necessary internal concrete stresses after losses have occurred. The following four types are in common use:

(a) High tensile strength single wire, applied in the form of assemblies made up of two or more substantially parallel wires. They may be used for either pretensioning or post-tensioning purposes.

(b) Small diameter, high strength strand, shop fabricated, is usually made up of six wires spiraled around a center wire. Small diameter strand is normally, though not exclusively, used for pretensioning purposes.

(c) Large diameter high strength strand is usually shop fabricated with factory attached end fittings for post-tensioned construction. It has 7, 19, 37, or more individual wires.

(d) High strength alloy steel bars are produced by a cold stretching or drawing process. They are currently available in diameters ranging from ½ to 1⅛ in. Alloy steel bars are used principally for post-tensioned construction.

Each type of prestressing steel should be made to distinctly separate specifications, of which the following sections give a general description.*

When an ASTM specification for a type of tensioning element becomes available it should be used instead of the data in the recommendations. For uncoated seven-wire stress-relieved strand use ASTM Designation A 416-57T, shown in Appendix F. For uncoated stress-relieved wire use ASTM Designation A 421-58T shown in Appendix F.

304.2—High Tensile Strength Single Wire

High tensile strength single wire is generally made from high carbon steel hot rolled into rods. It is then heat treated by a process termed "patenting" and cold drawn to produce the required final tensile strength. In its most commonly used form the wire is then stress relieved by a controlled time-temperature treatment that improves elastic properties within the tensile range usually employed in prestressing concrete. It also produces a straighter, more easily handled wire.

High tensile strength wire produced by the oil tempering process is not recommended for use in prestressed concrete.

304.2.1—Ultimate tensile strength

High tensile strength wire for prestressed concrete is made to minimum tensile strengths as high as 250,000 psi for a diameter of 0.196 in. Higher tensile strengths are available at smaller diameters and lower tensile strengths at larger diameters.

304.2.2—Shape of stress-strain curve

Stress relieved wire for prestressing should display a high yield strength and a reasonable elongation before rupture. Minimum yield strength at 1 per cent elongation under test load should be equal to 85 per cent of specified ultimate tensile strength. Minimum elongation after rupture should be 4 per cent in 10 in. Elongation tests should conform to "Specification for Mechanical Testing of Steel Products" (ASTM A 370-54T).

304.2.3—Ductility

Wire for prestressing should be capable of a reasonable amount of cold deformation without failure. It should have a minimum reduction in cross-sectional area of 30 per cent at rupture.

---

* The American Society for Testing Materials is currently formulating specifications for prestressing steels.

304.2.4—Creep and relaxation

Data concerning typical creep and stress relaxation properties of the material should be obtained from the manufacturer. Special acceptance tests for individual lots are usually expensive and unnecessary.

Creep tests and short-term relaxation tests do not necessarily represent long-time stress relaxation characteristics.

304.3—Small Diameter High Strength Wire Strand

Small diameter high strength strand is normally made of seven wires. A straight center wire is enclosed tightly by six spirally wound outer wires. Because of its small diameter, strand can be given a final stress-relieving treatment similar to that for single wires. This treatment improves elasticity and handling characteristics. Acceptance tests, when required, should be made on the strand rather than single wires.

Physical properties should be based on the total metallic area of all the individual wires. Ultimate tensile strength, shape of stress-strain curve, ductility, creep and relaxation should be the same as described in Section 304.2 (high tensile strength single wire) except as follows:

(a) Minimum elongation at rupture, 3.5 per cent in 24 in.

(b) Minimum yield strength at 1 per cent elongation under test load equal to 85 per cent of specified ultimate tensile strength.

304.4—Large Diameter High Strength Wire Strand

Large strand may be made of 7, 19, 37, or more galvanized or uncoated hard-drawn wires, spirally wound. Galvanized strand is most commonly used.

Because large diameter strand cannot be given a final stress-relieving treatment, some of its physical properties differ from those of wire or small strand. Acceptance tests, when required, should be based on properties of the strand rather than individual wires.

304.5—Cold Stretched High Strength Alloy Steel Bars

These bars are usually made from alloy steel designated AISI 5160 or AISI 9260. After hot rolling, the bars are either heat treated or cold worked. Each bar is then cold stretched to a minimum of 90 per cent of the specified ultimate strength.

304.5.1—Ultimate tensile strength

High strength alloy steel bars are produced with a minimum tensile strength of 145,000 psi for all diameters.

304.5.2—Shape of stress-strain curve

High strength bars for prestressing should have a minimum yield strength at 0.2 per cent permanent strain equal to 90 per cent of the specified ultimate tensile strength. Minimum elongation after rupture should be 4 per cent in a length of 20 diameters.

304.5.3—Ductility

Bars for prestressing should be capable of a reasonable amount of cold deformation without failure. The bar should have a reduction of area of not less than 15 per cent at rupture.

304.5.4—Creep and relaxation

Data concerning typical creep and stress relaxation properties of the material should be obtained from the manufacturer. Special acceptance tests for individual lots are usually expensive and unnecessary.

Creep tests and short-term relaxation tests do not necessarily represent long-time stress relaxation characteristics.

304.6—Corrosion

Since prestressing steels are susceptible to corrosion, they should be protected during storage, transit and construction.

The term stress corrosion is applied to the embrittlement of steel that occurs under the combined effects of high stress and some corrosive environments. It may take place without apparent surface impairment.

Normally, steel cast in concrete or properly grouted will not be subject to such corrosion. When post-tensioned steel is not grouted, special precautions should be taken to protect the steel (see Section 404.3.2).

305—ANCHORAGES AND SPLICES

305.1—General

Anchorages for post-tensioning elements now in general use consist of:
Threaded ends and wedge anchors for bars; factory attached end fittings for large diameter strand; button-head, sandwich plate, and conical wedges for parallel lay wire systems; and conical wedges for small diameter strand.
Splices are used primarily for bars and consist of threaded couplings.

305.2—Ultimate Strength

Anchorages and splices should be capable of developing the ultimate strength of attached steel elements without excessive deformation.

305.3—Anchorage Set

Movement of prestressing steel in anchorage during seating should be stated by the manufacturer and substantiated by test data.

Chapter 4—CONSTRUCTION

401—INTRODUCTION

This chapter outlines construction procedures that should result in sound and durable structures.

Prestressed concrete members are composed of high strength concrete and steel. Design stresses are closely controlled, but behavior in service depends upon the specified concrete being properly placed in forms of the correct dimensions around accurately positioned prestressing steel or ductwork for steel. Construction requires accuracy and care. Deviation from careful workmanship may result in an unsafe structure and should not be condoned.

402—TRANSPORTING, PLACING, AND CURING OF CONCRETE

402.1—General

Quality of the finished concrete members depends on care used in transporting, placing, and curing. Recommended practice is outlined in "Building Code Requirements for Reinforced Concrete (ACI 318-56)," Sections 403-406, and "Recommended Practice for Measuring, Mixing and Placing Concrete (ACI 614-42)."

402.2—Placing

Low slump, high cement content mixes should be placed in the shortest possible time after mixing is completed to prevent loss of workability.

Concrete should be deposited close to its final position. The method of placement should be such that segregation will not occur.

402.3—Vibration

Internal or external vibration or both are usually necessary to produce dense, well-compacted concrete.

Vibrators should not be used to move concrete horizontally in the form. Over-vibration should also be avoided.

When internal vibration is used, vibrator heads should be smaller than the minimum distance between ducts or prestressing steel. Care must be exercised to avoid damage to or misalignment of ducts for post-tensioning steel.

Vibration is not a substitute for workability. Judgement should be used in specifying slump, and approved methods of vibration used to achieve maximum compaction.

402.4—Construction Joints

In long cast-in-place members the use of construction joints is recommended (1) to reduce cracking near columns caused by settlement or movement of shoring and falsework, and (2) to allow for shrinkage. In general, joints should be placed near falsework supports.

Construction joints preferably should be perpendicular to prestressing steel. Joints should not be made parallel to prestressing steel unless the provisions of Section 212 (composite construction) are followed.

402.5—Curing

Curing should start soon after finishing. If high temperature curing is used, an initial setting time prior to application of heat should be required. Curing should continue until the required strength for application of the prestress force is reached. Fresh concrete should be protected from rain or the rapid loss of moisture prior to the curing period. Rapid drying should be prevented until the final design strength is obtained.

When high temperature curing is used, the rate of heating and cooling should be controlled to reduce thermal shock to the concrete.

Where identical precast members are required, curing conditions should be uniform to maintain proper quality control.

402.6—Protection from Freezing

During periods of freezing temperatures, ungrouted ducts should be blown clear of water or protected against freezing.

403—FORMS, SHORING, AND FALSEWORK

403.1—General

Quality of concrete members depends on the care used in constructing forms and falsework. Correct practices outlined in "Building Code Requirements for Reinforced Concrete (ACI 318–56)" Sections 501 and 502 are recommended.

403.2—Special Requirements

Forms for pretensioned members should be constructed to permit movement of the member without damage during release of the prestressing force.

Forms for post-tensioned members should be constructed to minimize restraint to elastic shortening during prestressing and shrinkage. Deflection of members due to the prestressing force and deformation of falsework should be considered in design. Form supports may be removed when sufficient prestressing has been applied to carry dead load, formwork carried by the member, and anticipated construction loads.

404—PLACEMENT OF PRESTRESSING STEEL AND APPLICATION OF PRESTRESSING FORCE

404.1—General

The location of the center of gravity of the prestressing steel, initial and final prestressing force, and the assumed losses due to creep, shrinkage, elastic shortening, and friction shown on the plans are based on the use of specified materials. Other materials not specified but capable of producing the same results may be used with approval of the engineer.

Unless tolerances for location of the prestressing steel are shown, a variation of $\pm\frac{1}{8}$ in. to $\pm\frac{1}{4}$ in., depending on size of the member, is suggested as maximum permissible.

404.2—Pretensioning Steel

404.2.1—General

Steel should be kept clean and dry. Foreign matter, grease, oil, paint, and loose rust should be removed prior to casting concrete. A light coat of rust is permissible and sometimes preferable provided loose rust has been removed and the surface of the steel is not pitted.

404.2.2—Measurement of prestressing force

Pretensioning force should be determined by measuring elongation and checking jack pressure on a calibrated gage. Measurement of elongation will usually give more consistent results. When there is a difference of over 5 percent between the steel stress determined from elongation and from the gage reading, the cause of the discrepancy should be ascertained and corrected.

If several wires or strands are stretched simultaneously, provision must be made to induce the same initial stress in each.

404.2.3—Transfer of prestressing force

The force in the prestressing steel should be transferred to the concrete smoothly and gradually. If the force in the wires or strands is transferred individually, a sequence of release should be established by the engineer to avoid subjecting the member to unanticipated stresses. Any variation in this sequence should be submitted to the engineer for approval.

404.2.4—Protection

Ends of pretensioning steel exposed to weather or corrosive atmosphere should be protected by a coating of asphaltic material. They should preferably be recessed in the member, coated with asphaltic material and covered with mortar.

404.3—Post-tensioning Steel

404.3.1—General

The steel should be kept clean and dry. For bonded construction, foreign matter, grease, oil, paint, and loose rust should be removed prior to placing steel in ducts. A light coat of rust is permissible provided loose rust has been removed and the surface of the steel is not pitted.

404.3.2—Protection

For general use in unbonded construction, galvanizing may be considered to protect the steel from corrosion when coated with grease or asphalt-impregnated material and enclosed in a sheath. Uncoated galvanized steel may be used when it is accessible for inspection and points of bearing are equipped with special shoes to prevent damage to the galvanizing.

If wrappings and coatings are used on nongalvanized steel, the coating should protect the steel from corrosion during shipment, storage, construction, and after the steel is in place. It should permit movement of steel during stressing with minimum friction. The method of protection should be specified or approved by the engineer.

Anchorage and end fittings should be given protective treatment consistent with that given the prestressing steel. They should preferably be recessed in the member and covered with mortar.

404.3.3—Placement of steel and enclosure

Ducts or enclosures for prestressing steel are formed in the concrete using tubing, metallic casings, or other materials. They should be positioned and secured to maintain the prestressing steel within the allowable placement tolerances.

For bonded construction, ducts or duct-forming devices should be free from grease, paint, or other foreign matter. Ducts should be protected against entrance of foreign matter prior to grouting.

Anchorage hardware to be cast in the member should be firmly fastened to forms in the proper location.

404.3.4—Measurement of the prestressing force

Values of total elongation, corrected for assumed friction loss and anchorage set, and corresponding jack pressures at various increments of prestress should be supplied by the engineer. When a difference of over 5 per cent exists between steel stress determined from the corrected elongation and from corresponding gage reading, stressing operation should cease. If the cause of the discrepancy is neither faulty measurement nor equipment, the engineer should be consulted.

404.3.4.1—Factors influencing friction

As prestressing force is applied, friction between prestressing steel and curved enclosure reduces steel stress at points away from the jack. The amount of friction loss is a function of degree of curvature, type and length of prestressing steel, duct material, presence of friction reducing agents, accuracy of placing the duct, and degree of disturbance during concrete placement.

It is the responsibility of the contractor to be aware of these factors. He should use materials specified and insure that the quality of workmanship results in accurate duct positioning with minimum displacement during construction.

404.3.5—Prestressing in stages

When the prestressing force is to be applied in more than one stage, excessive concrete stresses should be avoided during intermediate stages. The engineer will designate location and magnitude of the forces to be used for each stage and allowable external loads that may be placed on the member. The contractor should be aware of the significance of overloading the member.

404.3.6—Anchorage set

For friction type anchorages the manufacturer or supplier should state the amount of slip normally expected in seating the anchorage device.

404.3.7—Effect of temperature

Changes in temperature should have little effect on prestressing reinforcement unless there is a significant temperature differential between concrete and seel.

405—GROUTING

405.1—General

When grouting is specified for post-tensioned members it should completely fill all enclosure voids.

405.2—Mixing

Grout should be mixed in a mechanical mixer. Immediately after mixing, it should be passed through a strainer into pumping equipment which provides for recirculation. Grout should be pumped into the duct as soon as possible after mixing but may be pumped as long as it retains the proper consistency.

405.3—Arrangement of Grout Pipes

Ducts must be provided with entrance and discharge ports, each of which can be closed. Extension pipes may be used when necessary.

For long members, grout may be introduced at one end until it discharges from an intermediate point. The point of application may then be moved successively forward. Grout may be introduced at an intermediate point if discharge ports are provided at duct ends. The sequence of grouting should be planned to insure complete filling. Devices for bleeding air may be required at high points of the duct profile.

405.4—Test for Passage of Grout

Free passage of grout from entrance to discharge port must be assured. Tests may be made by pumping water, air, or other fluids through the duct.

405.5—Application of Grout

Grout should be applied continuously until it flows steadily from the discharge port indicating removal of trapped air and water. The discharge port should then be closed and grouting pressure maintained for the length of time necessary to insure complete filling of the void. The entrance should then be closed and the pumping nozzle removed.

405.6—Protection against Freezing

Adequate precautions must be taken to prevent freezing fresh grout.

406—HANDLING AND ERECTION

Where precast members are specified, methods of handling and/or the sequence of erection should be indicated. When these are not indicated on the plans, the contractor should submit for approval the location of pick-up points, minimum concrete strength when handled, method of transporting, and sequence of erection.

8-3. PCI Specifications. The Prestressed Concrete Institute is an association of producers of prestressed concrete products, producers of materials and equipment allied to the prestressed concrete industry, and members of the architectural and engineering profession. It was founded in 1954 as a national organization to establish standards of production, quality control, and uniformity in prestressed concrete products and for exchange of ideas for the betterment of the industry.

PCI functions include an annual convention attended by engineers and producers from all parts of the United States and some foreign countries, publication of the *PCI Journal* containing discussion of prestressed concrete developments, cosponsorship of "short courses" or lecture series on prestressed concrete for engineers and producers, development of standard sections, etc., and preparation of specifications.

Appendix B includes the PCI Specification for Pretensioned Prestressed Concrete and the PCI Specification for Post-tensioned Prestressed Concrete.

When the PCI Specification for Pretensioned Prestressed Concrete was first published in November, 1954, it was the most comprehensive document available to the new but rapidly growing pretensioned industry, and it did much to standardize quality and methods.

Both of the PCI specifications printed in Appendix B are good specifications. On one or two points they are less conservative than the ACI-ASCE Recommendations, and they are less complete. They can be used as a guide to design by an engineer who is familiar with prestressed concrete and the various factors which need to be checked.

8-4. ASTM Specifications. The American Society for Testing Materials develops specifications for the various types of tendons as their use grows sufficiently to justify it. When an ASTM specification for a type of tendon is available, the tendon should be fabricated and handled in conformance with the ASTM specification rather than any other procedure.

The first two ASTM specifications for tendons for prestressed concrete are printed in Appendix F.

8-5. Bureau of Public Roads. Early in 1954 the Bureau of Public Roads published Criteria for Prestressed Concrete Bridges. Their purpose is best described by the first paragraph of the preface to the Criteria which says

The Criteria for prestressed concrete bridges presented in this pamphlet have been developed in the hope that they may be useful until such time as more complete specifications, covering the subject in far greater detail, may be presented to the civil engineering profession by American specification and code writing bodies.

The Criteria, the first American specification, gave the new industry a standard from which to work at a time when it was needed to encourage further development. A copy is presented in Appendix C.

The ACI-ASCE Recommendations now available are more complete and up to date on latest developments and are recommended in preference to the BPR Criteria.

8-6. Certificates. Customers often request that the fabricator of tendons furnish certificates stating that the tendons have been sampled and tested in a prescribed manner and have met certain requirements. Such certificates can be furnished from data developed in the standard manufacturing process, and a satisfactory tendon will be assured if the proper tests are required.

All reputable fabricators of tendons make frequent tests on their product both during fabrication and after completion. The tests used have been carefully chosen by metallurgists to assure a satisfactory product with foolproof and economical tests.   The regular tests do not include a check of every quality the tendon must have, but they have been so chosen that the tendon could not meet them without having all the required properties.   The tests required by ASTM specifications have been chosen to coincide with standard production tests and still ensure a satisfactory product.   All fabricators should be able to sample and test their products in accordance with ASTM requirements as a part of furnishing the material.

When tendons are not ordered to an ASTM specification, careful consideration should be given to the tests required.   Fabricators of tendons have specifications for their products which are available to engineers writing specifications.

Methods of identifying materials tested and shipped should be consistent.   Wires and bars are usually identified by heat numbers.   Strands are identified by reel numbers.   Strands cannot be identified by heat numbers because each wire in a strand could be from a different heat and no records are kept of which wire goes into which strand.   The wire which goes into the strand is in itself a finished product which has met its own test requirements, and only satisfactory wire has been accepted.

Fabricators have typical load-elongation curves for each size and type of tendon they produce.   These curves are the average of a number of tests and give accurate results when used for establishing specified loads.

Typical curves and certification to standard tests are available at no extra cost.   When curves for the specific material shipped are required, the cost of making them is charged to the customer.   Such curves are no more accurate than typical curves.

8-7. Testing Tendons.   In addition to the certificates supplied by the fabricator, some customers such as highway departments take sample lengths of tendons from the stock at the job site for test in their own laboratories.

Equipment and procedures for testing prestressed concrete tendons and especially seven-wire strands are not standard in the average testing laboratory.[1]   When a laboratory is to test a type of tendon for the first time, it should ask the fabricator for details on the best procedure. The laboratory should also obtain preliminary samples and make trial tests to ensure accurate results when samples from an actual job are tested.

BIBLIOGRAPHY

1. Godfrey, H. J.: The Physical Properties and Methods of Testing Wire and Strand, *J. Prestressed Concrete Inst.*, December, 1956, pp. 38–47.

CHAPTER 9

DESIGN OF A PRESTRESSED CONCRETE BRIDGE

9-1. General Conditions. The object of this chapter is to present a complete analysis of a typical prestressed concrete bridge. It deals with one of the most popular types, namely, precast pretensioned I section girders supporting a poured-in-place slab.

The bridge is designed to the following conditions:

Live load = AASHO − H20 − S16 − 44 (from 1953 edition of AASHO)
Provision for future wearing surface = 20 psf
Span = 75 ft 0 in. center to center of bearings
Width = 28-ft 0-in. roadway

Analysis of the reinforcing steel requirements for the poured-in-place slab is not included, since it is the same as for a similar slab supported on reinforced concrete stringers.

Details of bearing plates, rockers, expansion joints, etc., are not included, since they will be determined by requirements of customers, which vary from one locality to another.

9-2. Specification. The following data should be included in a specification for a bridge of this type to ensure the use of proper materials and methods of construction:

The work under this item consists of furnishing and installing the prestressed concrete girders and poured-in-place deck.

Except as hereinafter provided the following portions of ACI-ASCE Tentative Recommendations for Prestressed Concrete shall govern materials and procedures used:

Section 302
Sections 401 through 404.2.4 inclusive
Section 406

Uncoated seven-wire stress-relieved strands shall be fabricated, handled, sampled, and tested in accordance with ASTM Designation A 416-57T. The strand itself shall not be in contact with the ground during storage.

Dimensions as shown on drawings.

143

Tensioning elements and prestressing force as shown on drawings.

Minimum strength of prestressed girders when prestressing force is transferred from anchorages shall be 4,000 psi. Minimum ultimate strength of girders at 28 days shall be 5,000 psi.

Minimum ultimate strength of poured-in-place deck slab at 28 days shall be 4,000 psi.

Any alterations to details shown on drawings to suit the casting bed of the contractor must be in accordance with the complete ACI-ASCE Recommendations. Drawings showing alterations shall be submitted to the engineer and his written approval received before casting begins.

Each strand shall be tensioned individually and anchored at a load of 1,000 lb as measured by a calibrated dynamometer. The entire group shall then be tensioned in one operation to the specified initial prestressing force. This force shall be determined by elongation of the strand in accordance with Sec. 404.2.2 of the ACI-ASCE Recommendations. The elongation required to raise the tension from 1,000 lb per strand to the required load shall be read from a load-elongation curve. The load-elongation curve shall be the typical curve supplied by the strand fabricator for the size of strand being used. Loss of elongation due to seating of wedges in temporary grips shall be measured and added to the motion of the jacking crosshead. All strands elongated in one group shall have the same load-elongation curve, i.e., shall be made by the same strand fabricator.

The contractor shall submit to the engineer his planned procedure for placing and tensioning the deflected strands and also for releasing the hold-downs and the tension in the strands. The engineer's written approval of these procedures shall be received by the contractor before casting begins.

Use of admixtures and/or steam or radiant-heat curing in accordance with ACI-ASCE Recommendations is permissible.

If the contractor prefers, he may tension each strand individually to full load. The required elongation shall be determined from a typical load-elongation curve, and elongation and jack pressure shall check within the limits set forth in Sec. 404.2.2. Planned procedure shall be submitted to the engineer for written approval.

9-3. Design Calculations. The ACI-ASCE Recommendations for Prestressed Concrete are the basis for this design. Section 212 deals with the additional factors peculiar to composite structures. The analysis follows the steps outlined in Chap. 3. The reader should thoroughly understand the calculations in Chap. 4 before studying the following analysis.

Since the Recommendations do not limit the size of strand used we shall refer to Sec. 3(A)(3) of PCI Specification for Pretensioned Prestressed Concrete in Appendix B. Seven-sixteenths is the maximum size listed because there were no bond test data available on larger sizes at the time the specification was published. As test data on larger sizes become available, they will be included in revised editions of the specifications. Until then, we shall use nothing larger than $7/16$.

An AASHO-PCI standard type III beam will be used with pretensioned bonded tendons. Figure 9-1 shows a cross section of the bridge, and Fig. 9-2 shows dimensions of one beam and that portion of the slab which works with it when it is an interior stringer. Calculations are for an interior stringer. Design references are to ACI-ASCE Recommendations in Art. 8-2. Notations and symbols are those listed in Notations.

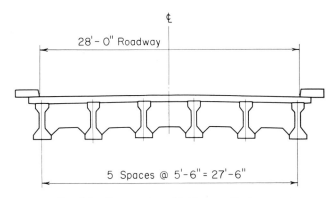

FIG. 9-1. Cross section of bridge at a diaphragm.

Step 1. Compute properties of the concrete cross section in Fig. 9-2. Properties for AASHO-PCI type III beam as listed in Art. 13-1 are:

$A_c = 560$ sq in.
$y_b = 20.27$ in.
$I_c = 125,390$ in.^{4}

From these and Fig. 9-2 we can compute:

$$y_t = 45 - 20.27 = 24.73 \text{ in.}$$
$$Z_t = 125,390 \div 24.73 = 5,070 \text{ in.}^3$$
$$Z_b = 125,390 \div 20.27 = 6,186 \text{ in.}^3$$

Weight using regular-weight concrete $= 560 \times {}^{150}/_{144} = 583$ lb per ft

The above properties are for the beam alone. We also need the properties of the composite section. Section 212.4.1 requires that the difference in modulus of elasticity between beam and slab be considered in computing section properties of the composite section.

From Sec. 203.2

$$E_c = 1,800,000 + 500f'_c$$

For the slab

$$E_c = 1,800,000 + (500 \times 4,000) = 3,800,000$$

For the beam

$$E_c = 1,800,000 + (500 \times 5,000) = 4,300,000$$

$$\text{Ratio} = 3,800,000 \div 4,300,000 = 0.88$$

Since the E_c of the slab is less than the E_c of the beam, its contribution to the stiffness, EI, of the composite section is less than if it were the same E_c as the beam. In computing the section properties of the composite section, allowance for the difference in E_c is made by multiplying the area of the slab by 0.88.

Find the section properties of the composite section taking moments about top of slab.

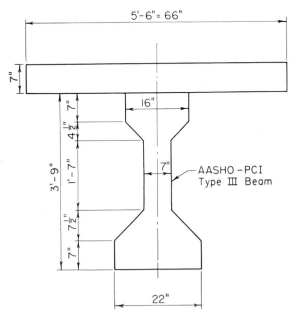

FIG. 9-2. Details of one beam and that portion of the roadway slab which acts with it as a composite section.

Section	Area	y	Ay	Ay^2	I_o
66 × 7 × 0.88	406	3.5	1,421	4,974	1,660
Beam	560	31.73	17,769	563,810	125,390
	966		19,190	568,784	127,050
				127,050	
				695,834	

$$y_t = 19,190 \div 966 = 19.86 \text{ in.}$$
$$y_b = 52 - 19.86 = 32.14 \text{ in.}$$
$$I_c = 695,834 - 966\,(19.86^2) = 314,825$$
$$Z_t = 314,825 \div 19.86 = 15,852$$
$$Z_b = 314,825 \div 32.14 = 9,795$$
$$\text{Weight of slab} = 66 \times 7 \times {}^{150}\!/_{144} = 480 \text{ lb per ft}$$

Step 2. Compute the stresses in the beam at the center of span due to its own dead weight.

$$M_G = \frac{583\,(75^2) \times 12}{8} = 4,915,000 \text{ in.-lb}$$
$$f'_G = 4,915,000 \div 5,070 = +969 \text{ psi}$$
$$f^b_G = 4,915,000 \div 6,186 = -794 \text{ psi}$$

Step 3. Compute the stresses in the beam at the center of span due to applied loads.

The beam alone must support the dead weight of the slab and diaphragms. It does not act as a composite section with the slab until the slab has cured.

$$\text{Weight of slab} = w_{ss} = 480 \text{ lb per ft}$$
$$M_{ss} = \frac{480\,(75^2) \times 12}{8} = 4,055,000 \text{ in.-lb}$$

The AASHO-PCI standards in Art. 13-1 show diaphragms at the one-third points of the span. The portion carried by one beam will be approximately 8 in. wide by 2 ft 6 in. by 5 ft 6 in. or a concentrated weight of $\tfrac{2}{3} \times 2.5 \times 5.5 \times 150 = 1,375$ lb. The moment M_{SD} caused by this load at the one-third point will be

$$M_{SD} = 1,375 \times 25 \text{ ft} \times 12 = 412,500 \text{ in.-lb}$$

The total moment carried by the beam only due to superimposed load is

$$M_S = M_{SS} + M_{SD}$$
$$= 4,055,000 + 412,500 = 4,467,500 \text{ in.-lb}$$
$$f'_S = 4,467,500 \div 5,070 = +881 \text{ psi}$$
$$f^b_S = 4,467,500 \div 6,186 = -722 \text{ psi}$$

The wearing surface and the live load are carried by the composite section. Analysis is based on Sec. 203.1.a which says "Strains vary linearly over the depth of the member throughout the entire load range." Figure 9-3*b* illustrates the elastic deformations developed when load is applied to the composite section.

Figure 9-3*c* shows the stresses developed in the composite section. When the applied bending moment is divided by the section modulus of the top fiber of the composite section, the resulting stress is that shown as f^{ts} in Fig. 9-3*c*. Because of the difference in E_c between the slab and the beam, the actual unit stress f^s in the top fiber of the slab is less than f^{ts} or

$$f^s = 0.88 f^{ts}$$

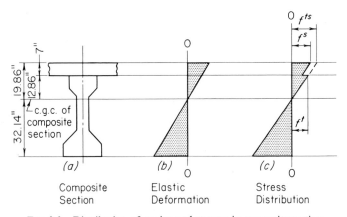

FIG. 9-3. Distribution of strains and stresses in composite section.

The stress in the top fiber of the beam is less than f^{ts} because it is closer to the c.g.c. than the top of the slab.

$$f^t = \frac{12.86}{19.86} f^{ts} = 0.65 f^{ts}$$

Wearing surface weight $w_{ws} = 20 \times 5.5 = 110$ lb per lin ft

$$M_{ws} = \frac{110\,(75^2) \times 12}{8} = 928{,}000 \text{ in.-lb}$$

$$f^{ts}_{ws} = 928{,}000 \div 15{,}852 = +59 \text{ psi}$$
$$f^b_{ws} = 928{,}000 \div 9{,}795 = -95 \text{ psi}$$
$$f^t_{ws} = +59 \times 0.65 = +38 \text{ psi}$$

From AASHO tables the live-load bending moment per lane is 1,075,100 ft-lb.

Impact $= 50/(75 + 125) = 25\%$
Wheel load per stringer $= 5.5 \div 5 = 1.1$
Wheel load $=$ one-half lane load

Net live-load moment M_L per stringer is

$M_L = 1,075,100 \times 1.25 \times 1.1 \times \frac{1}{2} \times 12 = 8,869,575$ in.-lb
$f^{ts}{}_L = 8,869,575 \div 15,852 = +560$ psi
$f^t{}_L = +560 \times 0.65 = +364$ psi
$f^b{}_L = 8,869,575 \div 9,795 = -905$ psi

Step 4. Determine the magnitude and location of the prestressing force at the center of span.

This computation is based on conditions after all stress losses.

From Sec. 207.3.2.a.1.a, maximum allowable compression $= 0.40f'_c = 0.40 \times 5,000 = 2,000$ psi.

From Sec. 207.3.2.b.1.a, the maximum permissible tensile stress f_{tp} in the bottom fiber is zero.

We now have enough information to write the equation for stress in the bottom fiber in terms of F and e.

$$\frac{F}{A_C} + \frac{Fe}{Z_b} = -f^b{}_G - f^b{}_s - f^b{}_L + f_{tp} \qquad (3\text{-}1)$$

Substituting known values,

$$\frac{F}{560} + \frac{Fe}{6,186} = +794 + 722 + 95 + 905 + 0$$

$$\frac{F}{560} + \frac{Fe}{6,186} = +2,516 \qquad (9\text{-}1)$$

Under final conditions the maximum permissible tensile stress in the top fiber is zero. This, however, is not the governing factor because under final conditions the top fiber of the girder has a compressive stress caused by the dead-weight bending moment of the poured-in-place slab.

The governing factor is the stress in the top fiber under prestress plus the dead weight of the girder only. The most critical combination of prestress and girder weight exists when the strands are first released from their anchorages, at which time the tension in the strands is maximum, F_o, and the strength of the concrete is minimum, f'_{ci}. From Sec. 207.3.1.b.1, the allowable tension at this point is

$$f_{tp} = 3\sqrt{f'_{ci}} = 3\sqrt{4,000} = -190 \text{ psi}$$

From Eq. (9-1) the prestressing force will create a stress of $+2,516$ psi in the bottom fiber at the center of span. Since the maximum allowable stress is 2,000 psi, some of the strands will slope up toward the end of the beam. Critical points for tension in the top fiber will be at the hold-down points, where stresses due to prestress are the same as at the center of span but where dead-load moment is less than at the center of span. Assume that hold-down points are 10 ft 0 in. each side of the center and find the stress in the top fiber due to the dead weight of the girder. Call the hold-down point "point x." See Fig. 9-8.

$$M_{Gx} = \frac{583 \times 27.5}{2}(75 - 27.5)\,12 = 4,570,000 \text{ in.-lb}$$

$$f'_{Gx} = 4,570,000 \div 5,070 = +901 \text{ psi}$$
$$f'_G - f'_{Gx} = 969 - 901 = +68 \text{ psi}$$

In order to stay within the allowable tensile stress at point x the tensile stress at center of span must be 68 psi less than the allowable or

$$f_{tp} = -190 + 68 = -122 \text{ psi}$$

Thus the allowable tensile stress in the top fiber under initial prestress plus the dead weight of the girder is 122 psi. The design procedure outlined in Chap. 3 uses Eq. (3-2).

$$\frac{F}{A_c} - \frac{Fe}{Z_t} = -f'_G + f_{tp} \qquad (3\text{-}2)$$

For the condition immediately after release of strands this is written

$$\frac{F_o}{A_c} - \frac{F_o e}{Z_t} = -f'_G + f_{tp} \qquad (9\text{-}2)$$

For tensioning elements we shall probably use ⁷⁄₁₆-in.-diameter strands at the initial tension of 18,900 lb recommended in Table A-2. This is a unit stress of $18,900 \div 0.1089 = 173,600$ psi. Section 208.3.2 indicates a stress loss of 35,000 psi, which gives a final stress of $173,600 - 35,000 = 138,600$. Section 204.3 states that the effective prestressing force F_o in a pretensioned member immediately after transfer of load is less than the initial prestress F_I. In computing initial prestress plus dead-load stresses we can therefore use F_o. The value of F_o is determined by subtracting the immediate losses from F_I. The value determined for F_o will not be exact because it is based in part on factors which can vary from one pour to the next. In our computations we shall work toward minimum losses so that the actual F_o will be less than our computed value and the actual critical stresses will be less than those we compute.

See Sec. 208.2 for sources of stress loss.

Section 208.2.1, Friction. There should be no loss due to friction in pretensioned strands.

Section 208.2.2, Elastic Shortening of Concrete. Since the tendons in a pretensioned member are bonded to the concrete when their load is applied to the concrete, they will shorten as the concrete compresses and the amount of shortening will vary along the member as the net compressive stress in the concrete varies. Our first concern is the stress at the center of span.

Elastic shortening of concrete is partly a function of F_o, and F_o is partly a function of the elastic shortening. An equation to give a direct value for F_o would be involved and hardly justified by the lack of accuracy of some of the other available data. We know from experience that the immediate stress losses in a typical pretensioned member total 20,000 to 24,000 psi. We shall assume 20,000 psi for our calculations and revise them if final calculations do not confirm this value.

We have shown that

$$f_{F_1} = 173,600 \text{ psi}$$
$$\text{Immediate losses} = \underline{20,000 \text{ psi}}$$
$$f_{F_o} = 153,600 \text{ psi}$$

We have shown that

$$f_F = 138,600 \text{ psi}$$

Therefore

$$f_{F_o} = \frac{153,600}{138,600} f_F = 1.108 f_F$$

From Eq. (9-1), $f^b{}_F$ will be set at $+2,516$ psi. Then

$$f^b{}_{F_o} = 2,516 \times 1.108 = +2,788 \text{ psi}$$

From Step 2

$$f^b{}_G = -794 \text{ psi}$$
$$f^b{}_{F_o+G} = +2,788 - 794 = +1,994 \text{ psi}$$

From Sec. 203.2

$$E_s = 27,000,000$$

and $\qquad E_c = 1,800,000 + 500\,(4,000) = 3,800,000$

Thus the stress loss in the seven-wire strand resulting from a concrete compressive stress of 1,994 psi is $(27,000,000/3,800,000)\,(1,994) = 14,200$ psi.

Section 208.2.3, Shrinkage of Concrete. A conservative value for shrinkage at transfer of load is 0.0001 in. per in. This is equivalent to a stress loss in the strand of $0.0001 \times 27,000,000 = 2,700$ psi.

Section 208.2.4, Creep of Concrete. Since creep is a function of time and we are considering the moment at which the load is first transferred, the stress loss due to creep will be zero.

Section 208.2.5, Relaxation of Steel Stress. Tests on seven-wire strand tensioned to 70 per cent of ultimate show that the initial rate of stress loss is high. At a normal transfer time, 18 to 20 hr after tensioning, it is about 3 per cent of the initial tension. For this case therefore it would be 3% × 173,600 = 5,200 psi.

In summary the immediate total stress loss is

$$14,200 + 2,700 + 5,200 = 22,100 \text{ psi}$$

We shall use 20,000 psi to remain on the conservative side. This gives

$$173,600 - 20,000 = 153,600$$

and
$$F_o = \frac{153,600}{138,600} (F) = 1.108F$$

Substituting this value in Eq. (9-2),

$$\frac{1.108F}{A_c} - \frac{1.108Fe}{Z_t} = -f'_G + f_{tp} \tag{9-3}$$

Substituting known values in Eq. (9-3),

$$\frac{1.108F}{560} - \frac{1.108Fe}{5,070} = -969 - 122$$

$$\frac{1.108F}{A_c} - \frac{1.108Fe}{5,070} = -1,091 \tag{9-4}$$

Multiplying (9-4) by

$$\frac{Z_t}{1.108Z_b} = \frac{5,070}{1.108 \times 6,186} = 0.74$$

we get

$$\frac{0.82F}{560} - \frac{Fe}{6,186} = -807 \tag{9-5}$$

Adding (9-1) to (9-5),

$$\frac{1.82F}{560} = +1,709$$

$$F = 526,000 \text{ lb}$$

Substituting this value of *F* in (9-1)

$$\frac{526,000}{560} + \frac{526,000e}{6,186} = +2,516$$

$$940 + 85e = 2,516$$

$$e = 18.54$$

$$20.27 - 18.54 = 1.73 \text{ in. from bottom of beam to c.g.s.}$$

Step 5. Select the tensioning elements to be used and work out the details of their location in the member.

Try $\frac{7}{16}$-in.-diameter strands at a final tension of 138,600 psi as computed in Step 4. This is a tension of $138,600 \times 0.1089 = 15,120$ lb per strand.

$$526,000 \div 15,120 = 34.8$$

In Step 4 we found that the c.g.s. of the 526,000-lb force should be 1.73 in. from the bottom. It is impossible to place 35 strands in a satisfactory pattern with the c.g.s. that close to the bottom. For a first trial we shall try 38 strands with $F = 574,560$ lb.

Substitute in (9-1) to find e:

$$\frac{574,560}{560} + \frac{574,560e}{6,186} = +2,516$$

$$1,026 + 92.9e = 2,516$$

$$e = 16.04 \text{ in.}$$

$$20.27 - 16.04 = 4.23 \text{ in. bottom of beam to c.g.s.}$$

From Sec. 216.2.1 the minimum spacing center to center of strands is four times the strand diameter, or in this case $4 \times \frac{7}{16} = 1\frac{3}{4}$ in. center to center of strands. This gives a clear space between strands of $1\frac{3}{4} - \frac{7}{16} = 1\frac{5}{16}$ in. From Sec. 216.2.1 the maximum aggregate for this spacing is $1\frac{5}{16} \div 1.33 = 0.99$ in., or nominally 1 in. aggregate.

For easier pouring and for standardization many casting yards prefer to use a spacing of 2 in. center to center in both directions whenever possible. We shall establish the strand pattern shown in Fig. 9-4 and compute its center of gravity

$$
\begin{array}{rcr}
30 \times 4 = & 120 \\
4 \times 8 = & 32 \\
4 \times 11 = & \underline{44} \\
\overline{38} & & \overline{196}
\end{array}
$$

$$196 \div 38 = 5.17 \text{ in. bottom to c.g.s.}$$

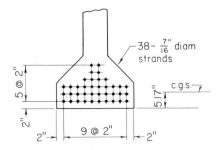

Fig. 9-4. Trial strand pattern at center of span.

This is almost an inch too high.

Section 216.1 requires a minimum cover of 1½ in. for surfaces exposed to weather. This means the minimum distance from the bottom to the center of the bottom row of strands is 1½ in. + ⁷⁄₃₂ in. or nominally 1¾ in. If we maintain the same pattern but place the bottom row up 1¾ in. and use vertical spacing of five rows at 1¾ in. the center of gravity will be

$$
\begin{array}{rl}
30 \times 3½ = & 105 \\
4 \times 7 = & 28 \\
\underline{4} \times 9⅝ = & \underline{38.5} \\
38 & 171.5
\end{array}
$$

$$171.5 \div 38 = 4.50 \text{ in. bottom to c.g.s.}$$

This is still too high.

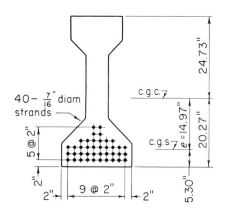

FIG. 9-5.   Final strand pattern at center of span.

By reducing the horizontal spacing to 1¾ in. center to center we could get an additional row of strands which combined with 1¾ in. vertical spacing would bring the c.g.s. down to the desired elevation. Such a pattern, however, puts three rows of strands in the web in those areas where the strands are sloping up. This makes it difficult to pour the bottom flange satisfactorily because the concrete must pass through the web with only 1⁵⁄₁₆ in. clear space between the rows of strand and only 1½ in. clear between the strands and the sides of the web.

We shall return to the much more desirable spacing of 2 in. center to center and add two strands as shown in Fig. 9-5. Compute the c.g.s.

$$30 \times 4 = 120$$
$$6 \times 8 = 48$$
$$\underline{4 \times 11} = \underline{44}$$
$$40 \qquad 212$$

$$212 \div 40 = 5.30 \text{ in. bottom to c.g.s.}$$
$$e = 20.27 - 5.30 = 14.97 \text{ in.}$$
$$F = 15,120 \times 40 = 604,800 \text{ lb}$$

Find the stress in the bottom fiber under the new F:

$$f^b{}_F = \frac{604,800}{560} + \frac{604,800 \times 14.97}{6,186}$$
$$= 1,080 + 1,464 = +2,544 \text{ psi}$$

The stress in the top fiber due to F using Eq. (3-5) is

$$f^t{}_F = \frac{604,800}{560} - \frac{604,800 \times 14.97}{5,070}$$
$$= 1,080 - 1,785 = -705 \text{ psi}$$

From Step 4, $F_o = 1.108F$. Therefore stresses due to F_o are 1.108 times stresses due to F. Thus $f^t{}_{F_o} = 1.108 \times (-705) = -781$ psi.

The stress in the top fiber under the critical condition of F_o plus the dead weight of the beam is

$$-781 + 969 = +188$$

The original equations were set up to give a stress of -122 psi, but the details made it necessary to use a higher prestressing force and smaller eccentricity than that indicated by the equations. This change in magnitude and location of the prestressing force is responsible for the resulting $+188$ psi.

Net stress in the top fiber of the beam under all applied loads is

$$f^t{}_F + f^t{}_G + f^t{}_S + f^t{}_{WS} + f^t{}_L = -705 + 969 + 881 + 38 + 364$$
$$= +1,547 \text{ psi}$$

From the foregoing calculations we see that the stress in the top fiber at the center of span will vary from $+188$ psi under F_o plus the dead weight of the girder to $+1,547$ psi under all applied loads. These stresses are within the specified limits of -122 to $+2,000$ psi.

Net stress in the bottom fiber under prestress plus the weight of the beam only is

$$f^b{}_F + f^b{}_G = +2,544 - 794 = +1,750 \text{ psi}$$

Net stress in the bottom fiber under all applied loads is

$$f^b_F + f^b_G + f^b_S + f^b_{WS} + f^b_L = +2{,}544 - 794 - 722 - 95 - 905$$
$$= +28 \text{ psi}$$

From this we see that stress in the bottom fiber will vary from $+1{,}750$ to $+28$ psi, which is within the limits of $+2{,}000$ to zero.

Check net stress in the top of the poured-in-place slab under all applied loads.

$$f^{ts}_{WS} + f^{ts}_L = +59 + 560 = +619 \text{ psi}$$

This would be the unit stress if the beam and slab had the same E_c. In Step 1 it was shown that the E_c of the slab was 0.88 of the E_c of the beam. Therefore the net stress in the top of the slab is

$$0.88 \times 619 = +545 \text{ psi}$$

At this point we should review the economy of the section chosen. Maximum compressive stresses in the top and bottom fibers of the beam are less than the allowable, and there is no tensile stress in the top even under the conditions when it is allowable. The maximum stress in the poured-in-place slab is $+545$ psi.

We cannot take advantage of the tensile stress permitted in the top fiber. To do this we would use a smaller prestressing force with a greater eccentricity, which we found impossible when working out the strand pattern. The eccentricity could be increased by using one or more post-tensioned tendons, but the higher cost of these tendons would probably offset any other advantage.

Changing the cross section of the beam is not feasible. The section being used is an AASHO-PCI standard, and the next smaller standard section is too small. The unused stress in the bottom fiber is not sufficient to take the additional load that would be created if the spacing center to center of beams were increased enough to eliminate one beam.

If the casting yards in the area can make the beams economically from 6,000-psi concrete, it might pay to investigate the economy of five beams at 6-ft 10½-in. centers in place of the six beams at 5-ft 6-in. centers shown in Fig. 9-1. This would almost certainly involve the use of 1¾-in. center-to-center spacing in both directions for the strands.

A good place to effect an economy in this design may be in the poured-in-place slab, which has a maximum stress of only $+545$ psi. Within the limits of its requirements for carrying the loads to the beams, the slab can be made thinner or of lower strength concrete or both. For use in a composite section, the final strength of the concrete slab should not be less than 3,000 psi.

If lower strength concrete is used in the slab, the section modulus of the composite section will be slightly reduced, which will cause higher stresses in the beam, and it may be necessary to use additional strands in each beam. Reducing the slab thickness will reduce the section modulus of the composite section, but it will also reduce the dead weight so that additional strands may not be necessary. In this case, however, the thinner slab will require more reinforcing steel to distribute the wheel loads to the beams.

In summary there are three changes in the design which might provide a more economical structure. Each change, however, involves additional costs of some sort which at least partially offset the savings. Approximate calculations incorporating the possible changes should be made, and the cost compared with the cost as already designed. If a change proves economical, it should be made and all the calculations in Steps 1 to 5 repeated for the new section.

For the purpose of this example, we shall assume that the section shown in Fig. 9-2 proved most economical, and we shall proceed with it.

Step 6. Establish the concrete strength f'_{ci} at the time of prestressing and check stresses under the initial prestress condition.

In Art. 9-2 it has already been stated

$$f'_{ci} = +4,000 \text{ psi}$$

From Sec. 207.3.1

Allowable compression $= 0.60 f'_{ci} = 0.60 \times 4,000 = +2,400$ psi
Allowable tension $= 3\sqrt{f'_{ci}} = 3\sqrt{4,000} = -190$ psi

From Step 4,
$$F_o = 1.108F$$
$$= 1.108 \times 604,800 = 670,000$$

From Step 5,
$$f^t{}_{F_o} = -781$$
and $$f^t{}_{F_o} + f^t{}_G = -781 + 969 = +188$$

The stress in the top fiber under initial prestress plus all applied loads is

$$f^t{}_{F_o} + f^t{}_G + f^t{}_s + f^t{}_{ws} + f^t{}_L = -781 + 969 + 881 + 38 + 364$$
$$= +1,471$$

$$f^b{}_{F_o} = \frac{F_o}{A_c} + \frac{F_o e}{Z_b}$$
$$= \frac{670,000}{560} + \frac{670,000 \times 14.97}{6,186}$$
$$= 1,195 + 1,621 = +2,816$$

The stress in the bottom fiber under F_o plus the girder only is

$$f^b{}_{F_o} + f^b{}_G = +2,816 - 794 = +2,022$$

The stress in the bottom fiber under F_o plus all applied loads is

$$f^b{}_{F_o} + f^b{}_G + f^b{}_S + f^b{}_{WS} + f^b{}_L = +2,816 - 794 - 722 - 95 - 905$$
$$= +300$$

From the foregoing calculations, all stresses at the center of span under F_o are within the allowable limits of -190 to $+2,400$ psi.

Step 7. Establish the path of the tendons and check any critical points along the member under initial and final conditions.

From previous calculations

$$f^t{}_{F_o} = -781 \text{ psi} \qquad f^b{}_{F_o} = +2,816 \text{ psi}$$
$$f^t{}_F = -705 \text{ psi} \qquad f^b{}_F = +2,544 \text{ psi}$$

Since these stresses, which are all in excess of the allowable, would exist at the ends of the beam if the strands were left in a straight line, it will be necessary to bend some of the strands up. We shall compute e at the ends of the span to satisfy the requirement that $f^b{}_{F_o}$ shall not exceed $+2,400$ psi.

$$f^b{}_{F_o} = +2,400 = \frac{670,000}{560} + \frac{670,000e}{6,186}$$
$$+2,400 = +1,196 + 108.3e$$
$$e = 11.12 \text{ in.}$$
$$f^b{}_F = 2,400 \div 1.108 = +2,166$$

Since this exceeds the allowable of 2,000 psi for final conditions, the final condition will govern.

$$f^b{}_F = 2,000 = \frac{604,800}{560} + \frac{604,800e}{6,186}$$
$$2,000 = 1,080 + 97.8e$$
$$e = 9.40 \text{ in.}$$
$$f^b{}_{F_o} = 2,000 \times 1.108 = +2,216$$
$$f^t{}_F = \frac{604,800}{560} - \frac{604,800 \times 9.40}{5,070}$$
$$= 1,080 - 1,120 = -40$$

If we follow the author's suggestion given in large type at the end of Sec. 207.3.2 of the Tentative Recommendations, a tensile stress of $0.04 \times 5,000 = 200$ psi is permissible. In this case, however, we can choose the location of the c.g.s., so we shall make it at least high enough to eliminate tensile stress. Then

$$f^t{}_F = 0 = \frac{604,800}{560} - \frac{604,800e}{5,070}$$
$$1,080 = 119.3e$$
$$e = 9.05 \text{ in.}$$

For this value of e

$$f^t_{F_0} = 0 \times 1.108 = 0$$
$$f^b_F = \frac{604,800}{560} + \frac{604,800 \times 9.05}{6,186}$$
$$= 1,080 + 885 = +1,965$$
$$f^b_{F_0} = 1.108 \times 1,965 = +2,177$$

As these stresses are all within the allowable, e at the ends of the beam can be 9.05 in. or less.

$$20.27 - 9.05 = 11.22 \text{ in. from bottom to c.g.s.}$$

The strand pattern in Fig. 9-5 is arranged so that 12 center strands can be sloped up in the web. The required moment of the strand group about the bottom at the ends is $40 \times 11.22 = 449$. The moment of the 28 strands which will be left in a straight line is

$$
\begin{aligned}
24 \times 4 &= 96 \\
4 \times 8 &= \underline{32} \\
&\ 128
\end{aligned}
$$

$$449 - 128 = 321$$

Thus the moment of the 12 raised strands must be 321, and the distance from the bottom to the center of gravity of the 12 strands is $321 \div 12 = 26.75$ in. This would be the lowest possible elevation of the raised strands to give stresses within the allowable.

Since higher elevations are permissible and in many cases desirable, we shall arbitrarily raise the 12 strands above the minimum to the position shown in Fig. 9-6 to illustrate the procedure. Find the c.g.s. for the pattern of strands in Fig. 9-6.

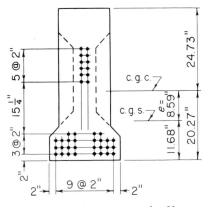

FIG. 9-6. Strand pattern at ends of beam.

$$24 \times 4 = 96$$
$$4 \times 8 = 32$$
$$\frac{12 \times 28\tfrac{1}{4} = 339}{40 \qquad 467}$$

$$467 \div 40 = 11.68$$
$$e = 20.27 - 11.68 = 8.59 \text{ in.}$$

Stresses at ends for $e = 8.59$ in. are

$$f'_F = \frac{604{,}800}{560} - \frac{604{,}800 \times 8.59}{5{,}070}$$

$$= 1{,}080 - 1{,}025 = +55$$

$$f'_{F_0} = +55 \times 1.108 = +61$$

$$f^b_F = \frac{604{,}800}{560} + \frac{604{,}800 \times 8.59}{6{,}186}$$

$$= 1{,}080 + 840 = +1{,}920$$

$$f^b_{F_0} = +1{,}920 \times 1.108 = +2{,}127$$

The strand pattern is now established at the center of span, Fig. 9-5, and at the ends of the beam, Fig. 9-6. The next step is to establish the path of the strands along the member. In this particular case this means to establish the location of the hold-down points. The critical condition is usually the stress in the bottom fiber under full load. Stresses for this condition are plotted in Fig. 9-7, which is constructed as follows:

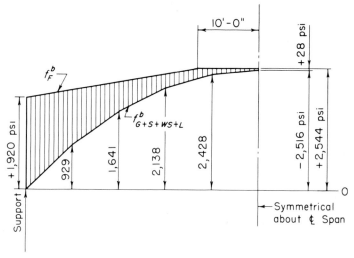

FIG. 9-7. Diagram of stresses in bottom fiber under final prestress plus all applied loads. Shaded area represents net compressive stress.

Stresses due to the prestressing force have already been computed at the center of span and at the ends. These are plotted.

The stress in the bottom fiber under all applied loads has already been computed at the center of span. It is zero at the ends. These are plotted.

Stresses under all applied loads are computed at various points along the span and then plotted (see Table 9-1 for values).

A horizontal line is drawn from the prestressing stress at the center of span to a point where a sloping straight line can be drawn to the prestressing stress at the end without cutting into the stress due to applied loads. The hold-downs will be located at the point where the line changes from horizontal to sloping.

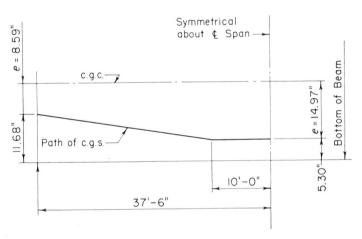

FIG. 9-8. Path of center of gravity of tendons.

The moments shown in Table 9-1 due to live loads at points other than center of span were computed by the simplified formula outlined in Appendix D. As shown in Step 3 the impact factor for this bridge is 25 per cent and each beam carries 0.55 of a lane load.

In Fig. 9-7 the hold-down points are set at 10 ft 0 in. each side of the center of span. We now have sufficient information to plot the path of the center of gravity of the strands in Fig. 9-8.

We must now check to make sure that stresses are within the allowable at all points along the beam under all conditions of loading and either initial or final prestress. A study of Table 9-1 indicates that maximum stresses will exist either under the dead load of the girder only or under

Table 9-1. Moments* and Stresses from Applied Loads

X†	Precast section						Composite section							
	M_G	f'_G	f^b_G	M_S	f'_S	f^b_S	M_{WS}	f'_{WS}	f^b_{WS}	M_L	f'_L	f^b_L	$f'_{G+S+WS+L}$	$f^b_{G+S+WS+L}$
7.5	147,500	+349	−286	132,000	+312	−256	27,800	+14	−34	288,000	+142	−353	+817	−929
15.0	262,500	+620	−508	237,000	+561	−460	49,500	+24	−61	500,000	+246	−612	+1,451	−1,641
22.5	344,500	+814	−667	314,000	+744	−610	65,000	+32	−80	638,000	+314	−781	+1,904	−2,138
30.0	393,800	+930	−762	358,000	+848	−695	74,400	+36	−91	718,000	+354	−880	+2,168	−2,428
37.5	410,000	+969	−794	372,000	+881	−722	77,400	+38	−95	739,000	+364	−905	+2,252	−2,516

* Moments are in foot-pounds.

† X is the distance from support to point being considered.

162

all applied loads. There is no need to check the net stresses under the weight of the slab and wearing surface. The critical conditions then are:

I. Final prestress plus
   A. All applied loads
      1. Top fiber—Fig. 9-10
      2. Bottom fiber—Fig. 9-7
   B. Dead load of beam only
      1. Top fiber
      2. Bottom fiber
II. Initial prestress (after immediate losses) plus
   A. All applied loads
      1. Top fiber
      2. Bottom fiber
   B. Dead load of beam only
      1. Top fiber— Fig. 9-11
      2. Bottom fiber— Fig. 9-9

Stress diagrams are plotted for conditions IA1, IA2, IIB1, and IIB2. The conditions not plotted are covered by the diagrams plotted as follows:

IB1 is less critical than IIB1 because the critical stress in these cases is tension and the tension due to F_o is greater than that due to F.

IB2 is less critical than IIB2 because the critical stress in these cases is compression and the compression due to F_o is greater than that due to F.

IIA1 is less critical than IA1 because the critical stress in these cases is compression and the compression due to F_o is less than that due to F.

IIA2 is less critical than IA2 because the critical stress in these cases is tension and the compression due to F is less than that due to F_o.

A study of the stress diagrams in Figs. 9-7 and 9-9 to 9-11 shows that all stresses are within the allowable.

Step 8. Check ultimate strength to make sure it meets the requirements of the specification. Check percentage of prestressing steel.

From Sec. 209.2.1.(b) evaluate the formula

$$\frac{1.4dpf_{su}}{f'_c}$$

In computing ultimate strength use the properties of the composite section. From Figs. 9-2 and 9-5

$$d = 52 \text{ in.} - 5.30 = 46.70 \text{ in.}$$

From Fig. 9-5 and Table A-2

$$A_s = 40 \times 0.1089 = 4.36 \text{ sq in.}$$
$$p = \frac{A_s}{bd} = \frac{4.36}{(66 \times 0.88)\,46.70} = 0.00161$$

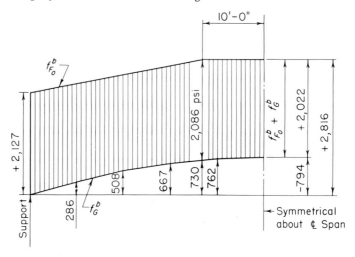

FIG. 9-9. Diagram of stresses in bottom fiber under initial prestress plus dead weight of beam only. Shaded area represents net compressive stress.

The ultimate bending moment is resisted by a couple composed of compression in the top fibers of the concrete section and tension in the tendons. In this example the top fibers involved are in the poured-in-place slab. In Step 1 it was shown that the E_C of the slab was 0.88 of the E_C of the beam. Since the width of 66 in. used in computing p is all

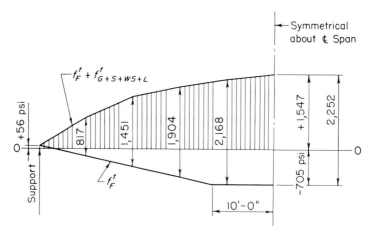

FIG. 9-10. Diagram of stresses in top fiber under final prestress plus all applied loads. Shaded area represents net compressive stress.

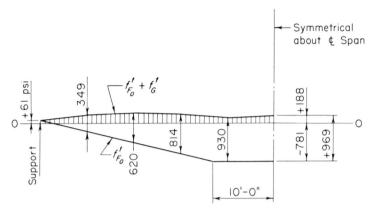

FIG. 9-11. Diagram of stresses in top fiber under initial prestress plus dead weight of beam only. Shaded area represents net compressive stress.

the lower strength concrete, it must be multiplied by the factor of 0.88 in computing p.

$$f'_c = 5,000 \text{ psi}$$

From Table A-2

$$f'_s = 27,000 \div 0.1089 = 248,000 \text{ psi}$$

From Sec. 209.2.2.2.a

$$f_{su} = f'_s \left(1 - 0.5 \frac{p f'_s}{f'_c} \right)$$

or

$$f_{su} = 248,000 \left(1 - 0.5 \frac{0.00161 \times 248,000}{5,000} \right)$$

$$= 248,000 \, (1 - 0.040) = 238,000 \text{ psi}$$

Substituting numerical values in the formula,

$$\frac{1.4 \times 46.70 \times 0.00161 \times 238,000}{5,000} = 5.00$$

Since the flange thickness of the composite section is 7 in., which is greater than 5.00 in., the following formula for rectangular sections in Sec. 209.2.1.(a) applies:

$$M_u = A_s f_{su} d \left(1 - \frac{k_2}{k_1 k_3} \frac{p f_{su}}{f'_c} \right) \tag{a}$$

Given in Sec. 209.2.1.(a)

$$\frac{k_2}{k_1 k_3} = 0.6$$

Substituting

$$M_u = 4.36 \times 238,000 \times 46.70 \left(1 - \frac{0.6 \times 0.00161 \times 238,000}{5,000}\right)$$

$$= 46,200,000 \div 12 = 3,850,000 \text{ ft-lb}$$

This is the ultimate moment the member can carry.
From Sec. 205.3.2 the minimum required ultimate is

$$1.5D + 2.5L$$

From Table 9-1 this is

$$1.5\,(410,000 + 372,000 + 77,400) + 2.5\,(739,000) = 3,136,600 \text{ ft-lb}$$

Since this is less than M_u, the member has sufficient ultimate strength.
Check the percentage of prestressing steel in accordance with Sec. 209.2.3.

$$\frac{pf_{su}}{f'_c} = \frac{0.00161 \times 238,000}{5,000} = 0.0766$$

Since this is less than 0.30, the member is not overreinforced.
Step 9. Design of shear steel.
From Sec. 210.2.1 web reinforcement is not needed when

$$\frac{pf'_s}{f'_c} \lessgtr 0.3\frac{f_{se}b'}{f'_s b}$$

Substituting numerical values from calculations in preceding steps,

$$\frac{0.00161 \times 248,000}{5,000} \lessgtr 0.3 \frac{140,000 \times 7}{248,000 \times 66}$$

$$0.0798 \lessgtr 0.018$$

Since this is not true, web reinforcement is required.
The critical section for shear in this member is described by the second paragraph of Sec. 210.2.5. Dead weight is

Beam only:	583 lb per ft
Poured-in-place slab:	480 lb per ft
Wearing surface:	110 lb per ft
Total:	1,173 lb per ft

Dead-load shear at the one-quarter point is

$$1,173 \times \frac{75}{4} = 22,000$$

$$\underline{1,375} \text{ weight of diaphragm}$$
$$\overline{23,375 \text{ lb}}$$

The live-load shear at the quarter point is 45,100 lb as computed in Fig. 9-12. From Step 3 one beam carries 0.55 lane load, so the live-load shear is $45,100 \times 0.55 = 24,800$ lb. The impact factor for loading in Fig. 9-12 is

$$I = \frac{50}{56.25 + 125} = 27.5\%$$

or total $V_L = 1.275 \times 24,800 = 31,600$ lb. (For bridges where the distance center to center of beams is less than 5 ft 0 in., each beam is designed to carry a shear equal to half the lane load shear plus impact. See the discussion in Step 9, Chap. 4.)

Ultimate shear factors are the same as ultimate moment factors, so

$$V_u = (1.5 \times 23,375) + (2.5 \times 31,600) = 114,000 \text{ lb}$$

From Fig. 9-8 the slope of the c.g.s. of the strands is

$$\frac{11.68 - 5.30}{[(37'\text{-}6'') - (10'\text{-}0'')] \times 12} = 0.0193$$

The shear carried by the strands is

$$0.0193 \times 604,800 = 11,700 \text{ lb}$$
$$\text{Effective } V_u = 114,000 - 11,700 = 102,300 \text{ lb}$$

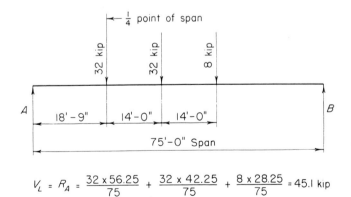

$$V_L = R_A = \frac{32 \times 56.25}{75} + \frac{32 \times 42.25}{75} + \frac{8 \times 28.25}{75} = 45.1 \text{ kip}$$

FIG. 9-12. Truck loading to produce maximum live load shear at one-quarter point of span.

Apply the formula from Sec. 210.2.2:

$$A_v = \frac{(V_u - V_c)s}{2f'_v jd}$$

In this example $V_c = 180b'jd$.

Since the tendons slope, d at the quarter point is less than d at mid-span. Refer to Fig. 9-8. The tendons slope $11.68 - 5.30 = 6.38$ in. in 27.5 ft. Since the quarter point is 18.75 ft from the end, the drop of the tendons to this point is

$$\frac{18.75}{27.5}(6.38) = 4.35 \text{ in.}$$

$$\begin{aligned}
8.59 &= e \text{ at end from Fig. 9-8} \\
24.73 &= \text{c.g.c. to top fiber from Fig. 9-5} \\
\underline{7.00} &= \text{poured-in-place slab} \\
d = 44.67 &
\end{aligned}$$

Then

$$p = \frac{4.36}{(66 \times 0.88)\,44.67} = 0.00168$$

$$f_{su} = 248,000\left(1 - \frac{0.5 \times 0.00168 \times 248,000}{5,000}\right) = 238,000$$

j can be computed from the following portion of formula (a) in Sec. 209.2.1:

$$j = 1 - \frac{k_2 p f_{su}}{k_1 k_3 f'_c}$$

Substituting numerical values,

$$j = 1 - 0.6\,\frac{0.00168 \times 238,000}{5,000} = 0.952$$

Then $V_c = 180 \times 7 \times 0.952 \times 44.67 = 53,600$ lb

From Sec. 210.2.4 the maximum spacing of stirrups is three-fourths of the depth of the member. Since this is a composite section, the provisions of Sec. 212.3.4 should also be considered. From this the maximum spacing of ties between the precast and poured-in-place sections is 24 in. For the first trial we shall use $s = 24$ in. and intermediate-grade reinforcing steel bars which have a yield strength of $f'_v = 40,000$ psi. Substituting numerical values in the equation for A_V,

$$A_V = \frac{(102,300 - 53,600)\,24}{2 \times 40,000 \times 0.952 \times 44.67} = 0.344 \text{ sq in.}$$

From Sec. 210.2.3 the minimum amount of web reinforcement is

$$A_V = 0.0025b's$$

Substituting numerical values,

$$A_V = 0.0025 \times 7 \times 24 = 0.420 \text{ sq in.}$$

This requirement governs, and the same stirrups will be used the full length of the beam. Since the unit strength of the stirrups is not a factor in this requirement, we shall check the use of structural-grade bars having a yield strength of $f'_y = 33,000$ psi.

$$\frac{40,000}{33,000}(0.344) = 0.417 \text{ sq in.}$$

This is less than 0.420, so we can furnish 0.420 sq in. of structural-grade bars every 24 in.

The area of two #4 bars is

$$2 \times 0.196 = 0.392 \text{ sq in.}$$

$$\frac{0.392}{0.420}(24) = 22.4 \text{ in.}$$

Use two #4 bars at a maximum spacing of 22⅜ in. center to center for the full length of the beam.

In a composite structure it is also necessary to check the shear between the precast section and the poured-in-place section. From Sec. 212.3.2 use the formula

$$v = \frac{V_u Q}{I_c t'}$$

in which t' is the width of the contact surface between the two sections. From Sec. 104.2, "Q = statical moment of cross section area, above or below the level being investigated for shear, about the centroid." Refer to Figs. 9-2 and 9-3 for dimensions used in computing Q.

$$Q = 7 \times 66 \times 0.88 \,(19.86 - 3.5) = 6,650$$

The shear due to the dead weight of the beam, slab, and diaphragms is carried by the precast beam. The shear carried by the composite section is only that due to the wearing surface and the live load, which is

$$
\begin{aligned}
\text{Wearing surface} &= & 110 \text{ lb per ft} \times 7\tfrac{3}{4} \times 1.5 &= & 3,100 \text{ lb} \\
\text{Live load} &= & 31,600 \text{ lb} \times 2.5 &= & 79,000 \text{ lb} \\
& & \text{Applicable } V_u &= & 82,100 \text{ lb}
\end{aligned}
$$

(The 1.5 and 2.5 are ultimate load factors.) Substituting the numerical values in the formula,

$$v = \frac{82,100 \times 6,650}{314,825 \times 16} = 109 \text{ psi}$$

Since this is less than 150 psi, the second item of Sec. 212.3.3 is applicable. It requires the minimum steel tie requirements of Sec. 212.3.4, and it also requires that the contact surface of the precast element be artificially roughened.

From Sec. 212.3.4 the minimum requirement is two #3 bars at 12-in. centers or $2 \times 0.11 = 0.22$ sq in. in 12 in. For stirrups we are using two #4 bars which have an area of 0.392 sq in. The required spacing for these bars as ties is

$$\frac{0.392}{0.22} \times 12 = 21.4 \text{ in.}$$

Use two #4 bars at 21⅜-in. centers for stirrups and ties. If the tie requirement were appreciably greater than the stirrup requirement, it might be more economical to use stirrups as required and intermediate dowels to complete the requirement for ties.

Step 10. Compute camber.

As stated at the beginning of Step 10 in Chap. 4, precise computation of camber in a prestressed concrete member is difficult because E_c, determined by the formula given in Sec. 203.2, can be in error by 25 per cent. Other factors, some of them difficult to evaluate, also influence the accurate computation of camber. The following factors affect camber:

1. The actual prestressing force applied to the concrete member is less than the initial prestressing force by the stress losses in the steel due to
   a. Relaxation of stress in the strands while attached to the anchors in the casting bed
   b. Shrinkage of the concrete during curing
   c. Elastic shortening of the concrete when prestressed
2. Changes in conditions which occur as time passes
   a. Prestressing force decreases approaching F
   b. E_c increases as concrete strength increases
   c. E_c is less under a constant load than under a short-time load because of creep (Sec. 203.3)
3. Effect of erection procedure (applied here to the composite structure being designed in this chapter)
   a. After the concrete member is prestressed, camber increases due to creep in the concrete. The rate of increase drops as tension in the strands drops, concrete strength increases, and rate of creep drops. The total increase is a function of the length of time that elapses between the prestressing operation and placement of the poured-in-place slab.
   b. When the slab and diaphragms are poured, their dead weight, which is carried by the beam, causes a deflection that reduces the camber in the beam.
   c. During its entire period of service the beam is under constant stress due to the prestressing force plus the dead-weight moment

of beam, slab, and diaphragms. The camber tends to change as mentioned in Sec. 203.3. There is no stress in the slab under this condition, but the cured slab forms a composite section with the beam, and this stiffer section acts to reduce the change in camber due to creep.

When computing camber the engineer should consider the degree of accuracy with which he knows the various properties of the structure and set up his analysis accordingly. For this structure we shall assume that the camber at the time the roadway slab is poured is equal to the instantaneous camber that would be caused by the application of the full initial prestressing force. In doing this we are assuming that the reduction in initial prestressing force due to relaxation, shrinkage, and elastic shortening is offset by the growth in camber due to creep in the concrete from the time of prestressing to the time the slab is poured.

At the time of prestressing $f'_c = 4,000$ psi. From Sec. 203.2,

$$E_c = 1,800,000 + 500f'_c = 1,800,000 + (500 \times 4,000) = 3,800,000$$

Deflection Δ_G due to the dead load of the beam is computed by the standard formula

$$\Delta_G = \frac{5wl^4}{384EI}$$

$$= \frac{5 \times 583\,(75^4)\,12^3}{384 \times 3,800,000 \times 125,390} = -.87 \text{ in.}$$

Deflection due to the eccentricity of the prestressing force is computed by the moment-area method as described in detail in Step 10 of Chap. 4. At the ends of the girder

$$M_e = 8.59 \times 670,000 = 5,750,000 \text{ in.-lb}$$

At the center of span

$$M_e = 14.97 \times 670,000 = 10,030,000 \text{ in.-lb}$$

The moment diagram for the bending moment due to prestress is plotted in Fig. 9-13. Taking moments about the support

$$\Delta_I = \frac{5,750,000\,(37.5 \times 12)(18.75 \times 12)}{EI} = \frac{582,000\,(10^6)}{EI}$$

$$\Delta_{II} = \frac{4,280,000\,(27.5 \times 12)\,\tfrac{1}{2}\,(\tfrac{2}{3} \times 27.5 \times 12)}{EI} = \frac{155,000\,(10^6)}{EI}$$

$$\Delta_{III} = \frac{4,280,000\,(10 \times 12)\,(32.5 \times 12)}{EI} = \frac{200,000\,(10^6)}{EI}$$

$$\Delta_{F_0} = \Delta_I + \Delta_{II} + \Delta_{III} = \frac{937,000\,(10^6)}{EI}$$

$$\Delta_{F_0} = \frac{937,000\,(10^6)}{3,800,000 \times 125,390} = +1.97 \text{ in.}$$

Net camber $= +1.97 - 0.87 = +1.10$ in.

When the slab and diaphragms are poured, the strength of the concrete in the beam will be 5,000 psi and

$$E_c = 1,800,000 + (500 \times 5,000) = 4,300,000$$

We shall assume that the slab and diaphragm are poured in such a manner that their entire weight is carried by the beam before the slab

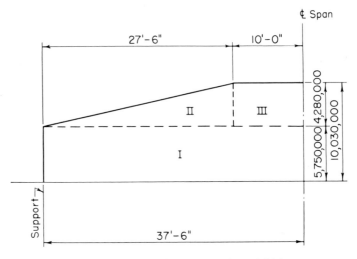

¢ Span

27'-6"   10'-0"

II   III

I

-4,280,000
5,750,000   10,030,000

Support

37'-6"

FIG. 9-13.   Diagram of bending moment due to initial prestress.

concrete sets sufficiently to create a composite section.   Deflection due to slab weight is

$$\Delta_{ss} = \frac{5 \times 480\,(75^4)\,12^3}{384 \times 4,300,000 \times 125,390} = -0.63 \text{ in.}$$

Deflection at the center of span due to the diaphragms is

$$\Delta_{SD} = \frac{1,375\,(25 \times 12)[3\,(75 \times 12)^2 - 4\,(25 \times 12)^2]}{24 \times 4,300,000 \times 125,390} = -0.07 \text{ in.}$$

Total deflection from the slab and diaphragms is

$$-0.63 + (-0.07) = -0.70 \text{ in.}$$

After the slab is poured, the net camber in the beam is $1.10 - 0.70 = +0.40$ in. Since all the stresses in the beam at this time will be sustained permanently, the camber will gradually increase owing to creep in the concrete. If the beam were acting independently, camber could be expected to increase 100 to 300 per cent per Sec. 203.3. Actually the beam and slab now form a composite structure in which the stress in the slab is zero. The tendency of the beam to increase its camber is resisted by the composite section, so that the resultant increase is less than would be expected if the beam were acting alone. We shall assume that the camber growth beyond this point would be 150 per cent if the beam were acting independently. The resistance of the composite section will reduce this in the ratio of the moments of inertia of the two sections. Thus the camber growth will be

$$1.50\,(0.40)\frac{125{,}390}{314{,}825} = 0.25$$

Total final camber $= 0.25 + 0.40 = 0.65$ in.

Compute live-load deflection under the truck loading shown in Fig. 9-14a. Considering transverse load distribution and impact factor, the portion of a 32-kip axle load carried by one beam and slab unit is

$$32 \times 0.55 \times 1.25 = 22 \text{ kips}$$

and of an 8-kip axle load is

$$8 \times 0.55 \times 1.25 = 5.5 \text{ kips}$$

We shall compute the deflection by the method of loading the beam with the M/EI diagram. Deflection is equal to the moment caused by this load.

Compute the bending-moment diagram, referring to Fig. 9-14a.

$$R_1 = \frac{22 \times 51.5}{75.0} + \frac{22 \times 37.5}{75.0} + \frac{5.5 \times 23.5}{75.0} = 27.8 \text{ kips}$$

$R_2 = 22 + 22 + 5.5 - 27.8 = 21.7$ kips
$M_A = 23.5 \times 27.8 = 653$ ft kips
$M_B = (37.5 \times 27.8) - (14.0 \times 22.0) = 734$ ft-kips
$M_C = 23.5 \times 21.7 = 510$ ft-kips

Plot the bending-moment diagram (Fig. 9-14b).

Compute the moment at the center of span under the moment diagram applied to the beam in Fig. 9-14b. Take moments about R'_1.

I. $23.5 \times 653 \times 0.5 = \quad 7{,}672 \times 15.7 \ = \quad 120{,}500$
II. $14.0 \times 653 \qquad\quad = \quad 9{,}140 \times 30.5 \ = \quad 278{,}500$
III. $14.0 \times \quad 81 \times 0.5 = \quad\quad 567 \times 32.83 = \quad 18{,}600$

$$
\begin{aligned}
\text{IV. } 14.0 \times 510 &= 7{,}140 \times 44.5 = 317{,}600 \\
\text{V. } 14.0 \times 224 \times 0.5 &= 1{,}568 \times 42.17 = 66{,}100 \\
\text{VI. } 23.5 \times 510 \times 0.5 &= \underline{5{,}990} \times 59.3 = \underline{355{,}000} \\
&\quad\ \ 32{,}077 \qquad\qquad\quad 1{,}156{,}300
\end{aligned}
$$

$$R'_2 = 1{,}156{,}300 \div 75 = 15{,}430 \text{ ft}^2\text{-kips}$$
$$R'_1 = 32{,}077 - 15{,}430 = 16{,}647 \text{ ft}^2\text{-kips}$$

Compute the moment at the center of span for Fig. 9-14*b*. Take moments of loads and reactions to the left of the center of span.

$$
\begin{aligned}
R'_1 &= 37.5 \times 16{,}647 = +624{,}000 \\
\text{I} &= 21.8 \times 7{,}672 = -167{,}000 \\
\text{II} &= 7.0 \times 9{,}140 = -64{,}000 \\
\text{III} &= 4.7 \times 567 = -\ \ \underline{2{,}700} \\
M &= +390{,}300 \text{ ft}^3\text{-kips}
\end{aligned}
$$

$$\text{Deflection} = \frac{M}{EI}$$

or
$$\frac{390{,}300 \times 1{,}000\,(12^3)}{4{,}300{,}000 \times 314{,}825} = 0.50 \text{ in.}$$

Final camber under live load $= 0.65 - 0.50 = 0.15$ in.

9-4. End-block Details. In Tentative Recommendations for Prestressed Concrete, Sec. 214, which covers end blocks, is written in general terms only and does not include any specific formulas for calculation of concrete stresses or required reinforcing steel. At the present stage in the development of prestressed concrete there are not enough test data on end blocks to form the basis of an empirical criterion. Although theoretical methods of analysis have been offered, none of them has been proved precise enough for inclusion in the Tentative Recommendations. As a result the statement in Sec. 214.3 "End blocks are usually proportioned by experience" applies not only to the selection of end-block dimensions but also to the selection of end-block reinforcing steel.

Since the member being designed in this chapter is 45 in. high, it is in the bottom of the range of deep beams. From Sec. 214.3 the length of the end block should be about three-quarters of the beam depth, or 34 to 36 in. The AASHO-PCI standard drawings show a length of 51 in. We shall use the most conservative recommendation in Sec. 214.3 and make the end block equal to the depth, or 45 in. long. If a casting yard has end-block forms that are 51 in. long in conformance with the AASHO-PCI drawings, they should, of course, be permitted to use 51 in.

Standard practice for reinforcing steel in the end blocks of pretensioned I beams is to use two #5 bars at 4-in. centers for the full length of the end block plus two #5 bars at about 5-in. centers for the full height of the block. Details are shown in Fig. 9-15.

The use of end blocks complicates the forming of pretensioned members and therefore adds appreciably to their cost. Although typical standards and specifications all call for end blocks, a few progressive designers of prestressed concrete have successfully designed I-beam bridge members with a constant cross section for the full length of the

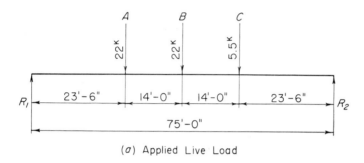

(*a*) Applied Live Load

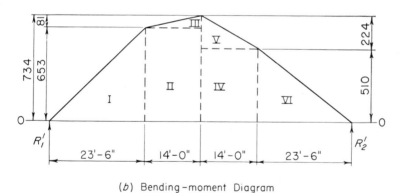

(*b*) Bending-moment Diagram

Fig. 9-14. Loading condition for deflection at center of span due to live load.

member. In place of the end block they have used closely spaced stirrups in the web.

Attempts to eliminate the end block in relatively heavy beams and girders without substituting enough stirrups result in severe cracking of the web at the end of the member. In a member of the type shown in this chapter the group of strands which is anchored in the web creates a high compressive stress in the web immediately around the strands.

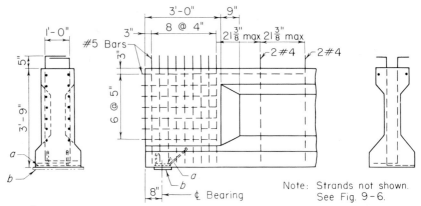

$a = \frac{1}{2}''$ steel plate with welded bars.
Cast with girder.

b = flat or rocker plate to suit span.
Weld to a after removing girder
from form.

FIG. 9-15. Typical details of end block of pretensioned I-beam bridge member.

This stress causes elastic compression of the concrete around the strands. Since the concrete above and below the strand group at the end of the beam is not subjected to compression, there is a tendency for movement of the compressed concrete with respect to the uncompressed concrete, which causes cracks. If adequate stirrups are provided, the cracks are prevented. Such stirrups are needed only for a length equivalent to that

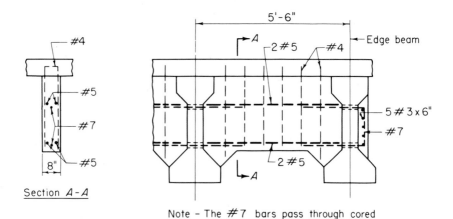

Section *A-A*

Note – The #7 bars pass through cored
holes in the precast beams

FIG. 9-16. Details of diaphragm in I beam and slab bridge.

of an end block, as the stress is spread uniformly over the cross section of the member in this distance.

9-5. Diaphragms. When prestressed concrete I-beam bridges of this type were first used and there were few data on their behavior, prestressed diaphragms at relatively close spacing were standard design. Experience has shown that these designs were extremely conservative. For this structure we shall use reinforced concrete diaphragms as shown in Fig. 9-16 at the spacing shown on the AASHO-PCI standard drawings. Reinforced diaphragms are less expensive than post-tensioned diaphragms because they eliminate the threading of long tendons through holes in the precast members as well as the need of jacking and grouting equipment.

CHAPTER 10

DESIGN OF A DOUBLE-T ROOF IN LIGHTWEIGHT CONCRETE

The majority of prestressed concrete members for buildings are made in standard shapes to suit the standard forms of the casting yards in the vicinity of the structure. Each producer has tables showing the details of his standard sections and their load-carrying capacity for various spans. Knowing the applied load and the span, the architect can select the required section from the tables.

The following analysis determines the maximum span of a typical double-T section under specific conditions. Such an analysis would be used in setting up a table for standard sections. The conditions of design are:

1. Design in accordance with provisions of Tentative Recommendations for Prestressed Concrete in Art. 8-2.

2. Tendons to be seven-wire strands in a straight line. (Deflected strands almost always give better efficiency and more camber control, but straight strands are often used for simplicity of casting-bed operation. It is therefore desirable to present one analysis using straight strands. For design of members using deflected strands see Chaps. 4 and 9.)

3. Lightweight concrete at 110 lb per cu ft, $f'_c = 5,000$ psi; $f'_{ci} = 4,000$ psi.

4. Roofing weight $= 10$ psf.

5. Live load $= 30$ psf.

6. We shall assume that actual tests on concrete made with the lightweight aggregate being used show that its E_c is approximately 75 per cent of that for standard concrete and that the stress loss in the strands is 7,500 psi greater than in standard concrete.

The reader should thoroughly understand the calculations in Chap. 4 before attempting to understand the following analysis.

Step 1. Compute properties of concrete section.

See Fig. 10-1 for dimensions.

Take moments about the bottom of the section.

Section	Area, A	y	Ay	Ay^2	I_0
I $= 72 \times 2$	$= 144$	15	2,160	32,400	48
II $= 6\frac{1}{2} \times 2 \times 2$	$= 26$	13	338	4,400	8
III $= 2 \times 2 \times \frac{1}{2} \times 4$	$= 8$	13.33	107	1,430	2
IV $= 5 \times 12 \times 2$	$= 120$	6	720	4,320	1,440
V $= 1\frac{1}{2} \times 12 \times \frac{1}{2} \times 2 =$	$\underline{18}$	8	$\underline{144}$	$\underline{1,152}$	$\underline{144}$
	316		3,469	43,702	1,642
				1,642	
				45,344	

$$y^b = 3,469 \div 316 = 10.98$$
$$y^t = 16 - 10.98 = 5.02$$
$$I = 45,344 - 316(10.98^2) = 7,250$$
$$Z_b = 7,250 \div 10.98 = 660$$
$$Z_t = 7,250 \div 5.02 = 1,445$$

Weight at 110 lb per cu ft

$$w_G = \frac{110 \times 316}{144} = 240 \text{ lb per ft}$$

In this problem our procedure will deviate somewhat from that established in Chap. 3, since our aim is to determine the maximum span the member can support and this span is unknown at this stage of the computations. Our next step is to establish the details of the maximum permissible prestressing force for the member.

Since the strands are tensioned in a straight line rather than deflected, the maximum amount of prestress is limited by the stresses it produces at the end of the span where there is no counteracting dead-load moment.

Maximum allowable compressive stress in the bottom fiber is (Sec. 207.3)

$$0.45 \times 5,000 = 2,250 \text{ psi under final prestress}$$
$$0.60 \times 4,000 = 2,400 \text{ psi under initial prestress}$$

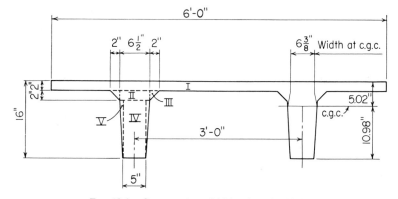

Fig. 10-1. Cross section of 16-in.-deep double T.

Maximum allowable tensile stress in the top fiber is

$$3\sqrt{4,000} = 190 \text{ psi under initial prestress}$$
$$0.04 \times 5,000 = 200 \text{ psi under final prestress}$$

(See note under Sec. 207.3.2, Art. 8-2.)

Assume that the tendons will be 7⁄16-in.-diameter strands at an initial tension of 18,900 lb per strand. This is a stress of $18,900 \div 0.1089 = 173,600$ psi. From Sec. 208.3.2 stress loss in standard concrete is 35,000 psi. Additional loss because of the lightweight aggregate being used is 7,500 for a total of 42,500 psi. Final stress is $173,600 - 42,500 = 131,100$ psi.

Find immediate stress losses between F_I and F_o following the procedure used in Step 4 of Chap. 9 based on Sec. 208.2.

Section 208.2.1, Friction. No stress loss.

Section 208.2.2, Elastic Shortening of Concrete. For this lightweight concrete a reasonable estimate of immediate losses is 25,000 psi. Then

$$f_{F_I} = 173,600 \text{ psi}$$
$$\text{Immediate losses} = \underline{25,000} \text{ psi}$$
$$f_{F_o} = 148,600 \text{ psi}$$

Therefore

$$f_{F_o} = \frac{148,600}{131,100} f_F = 1.134 f_F$$

In this problem our object is to compute the maximum capacity of the member, so we shall choose the magnitude and location of the prestressing force which will develop the maximum negative moment without exceeding allowable stresses. In pretensioned members these factors are usually governed by the stresses due to F_o. We can check this by assuming that the stresses due to F_o are the maximum allowable, or

$$f^t{}_{F_o} = -190 \qquad \text{and} \qquad f^b{}_{F_o} = +2,400$$

Then

$$f^t{}_F = -190 \div 1.134 = -167$$
$$f^b{}_F = +2,400 \div 1.134 = +2,120$$

Both of these are less than the maximum allowed, so F_o is the governing factor.

From Chap. 1 using F_o in place of F,

$$\frac{F_o}{A_c} - \frac{F_o e}{Z_t} = f^t{}_{F_o} \qquad\qquad (1\text{-}1a)$$

Substituting numerical values,

$$\frac{F_o}{316} - \frac{F_o e}{1,445} = -190 \qquad\qquad (10\text{-}1)$$

From Chap. 1 using F_o in place of F,

$$\frac{F_o}{A_c} + \frac{Fe}{Z_b} = f^b{}_{F_o} \qquad (1\text{-}1b)$$

Substituting numerical values,

$$\frac{F_o}{316} + \frac{F_o e}{660} = +2,400 \qquad (10\text{-}2)$$

Multiply (10-2) by $660/1,445 = 0.457$ to get

$$\frac{0.457F_o}{316} + \frac{F_o e}{1,445} = +1,097 \qquad (10\text{-}3)$$

Add
$$\frac{F_o}{316} - \frac{F_o e}{1,445} = -190 \qquad (10\text{-}1)$$

$$\overline{\frac{1.457F_o}{316}} \qquad = +907$$

$$F_o = 196,600$$
$$F = 196,600 \div 1.134 = 173,500 \text{ lb}$$

From Table A-2 the area of one $\frac{7}{16}$-in. strand is 0.1089 sq in. We have shown that the final stress in this lightweight concrete will be 131,100 psi so the final load per strand will be

$$131,100 \times 0.1089 = 14,275 \text{ lb}$$
$$173,500 \div 14,275 = 12.15$$

We shall use the nearest even number of strands, which is 12. Then

$$F = 12 \times 14,275 = 171,300 \text{ lb}$$
and
$$F_o = 171,300 \times 1.134 = 194,200 \text{ lb}$$

Since the force from 12 strands is slightly less than that computed for maximum prestress, the tensile stress in the top fiber will limit the eccentricity we can use. (If the calculations had required 11.6 strands, we would have used 12 strands but tensioned them only enough to give the required load instead of using their full allowable stress.) Substitute the numerical value of F_o in Eq. (1-1a) and solve for e.

$$\frac{194,200}{316} - \frac{194,200e}{1,445} = -190$$
$$614 - 134.2e = -190$$
$$e = 5.98 \text{ in.}$$
$$10.98 - 5.98 = 5.00 \text{ in. from bottom to c.g.s.}$$

Use the strand pattern shown in Fig. 10-2. Compute the bottom fiber stress using Eq. (1-1*b*).

$$f^b_{F_o} = \frac{194{,}200}{316} + \frac{194{,}200 \times 5.98}{660} = +2{,}376 \text{ psi}$$

Stresses under final prestress are

$$f^t_F = -190 \div 1.134 = -167 \text{ psi}$$
$$f^b_F = +2{,}376 \div 1.134 = +2{,}090 \text{ psi}$$

From Sec. 207.3.2.b.1.b the allowable tension in a member of this type is

$$6\sqrt{f'_c} \text{ or } 6\sqrt{5{,}000} = -425 \text{ psi}$$

In going from its compressive stress of $+2{,}090$ psi under no load to its maximum allowable tensile stress of -425 psi, the bottom fiber undergoes a stress change of $2{,}090 - (-425) = 2{,}515$ psi. This means that it

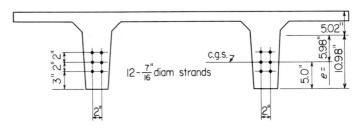

FIG. 10-2.   Trial strand pattern.

can carry a total moment of $2{,}515 \times 660 = 1{,}660{,}000$ in.-lb or $138{,}000$ ft-lb.

Total applied load is 10 psf for roofing plus 30 psf live load = 40 psf $\times$ 6-ft width = 240 lb per lin ft. Weight of double T = 240 lb per lin ft. Total load = $240 + 240 = 480$ lb per lin ft. Substitute this load and the allowable moment in the standard formula for beams subjected to uniform loading.

$$M = \frac{wl^2}{8} \quad \text{or} \quad l^2 = \frac{8M}{w}$$

$$l^2 = \frac{8 \times 138{,}000}{480} = 2{,}300 \qquad l = 48 \text{ ft}$$

Since this particular lightweight concrete has a relatively low E_c, camber may be a problem, so we shall check it before we go into other calculations.

Step 10. Compute camber.

Section 203.2 gives $E_c = 1,800,000 + 500f'_c$.

At the time of prestress release $E_c = 1,800,000 + (500 \times 4,000) = 3,800,000$. This is for standard concrete, and our tests showed that the value for our concrete was about 75 per cent of this, or $E_c = 75\% \times 3,800,000 = 2,850,000$.

Deflection: Δ_G due to dead load is

$$\Delta_G = \frac{5wl^4}{384EI} = \frac{5\,(240)\,48^4\,(12^3)}{384\,(2,850,000)\,7,250} = -1.39 \text{ in.}$$

See the discussion concerning camber calculations at the beginning of Step 10, Chap. 9. In our present problem we shall assume that the

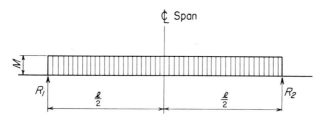

Take moment about R_I of that portion of moment diagram between R_I and $\mathcal{C}$ span.

$$M\left(\frac{\ell}{2}\right)\left(\frac{\ell}{4}\right) = \frac{M\ell^2}{8}$$

Deflection Δ at $\mathcal{C}$ span is $\Delta = \frac{M\ell^2}{8EI}$

FIG. 10-3. Deflection of beam due to constant moment for full length of beam computed by moment-area method.

camber at the time of erection is that which would be caused instantaneously by the force F_I.

$$F_I = 18,900 \times 12 = 227,000 \text{ lb}$$

Since the strands are straight, they create a constant negative moment for the full length of the member. This moment is $227,000 \times 5.98 = 1,360,000$ in.-lb. From Fig. 10-3 the camber ΔF_I at the center of span due to F_I is

$$\Delta F_I = \frac{1,360,000\,(48 \times 12)^2}{8 \times 2,850,000 \times 7,250} = +2.73 \text{ in.}$$

Net camber $= 2.73 - 1.39 = +1.34$ in.

As discussed under Step 10 in Chap. 9 this is the approximate net camber when the members are erected if the time lapse between casting and erection is not too large.

Deflection due to roofing at 60 lb per lin ft is

$$\Delta_s = \frac{5\,(60)\,48^4\,(12^3)}{384\,(2,850,000)\,7,250} = -0.35 \text{ in.}$$

Net camber under dead load at time of erection $= 1.34 - 0.35 = +0.99$ in.

If camber growth is 150 per cent, then final camber under dead load will be $0.99 + 150\%\,(0.99) = +2.48$ in.

This might be considered a rather high camber for a 48-ft span.

The design and details of a prestressed concrete member of this type can be altered by one or more of five methods to decrease the camber. They are:

1. Use a deeper double T which will have a higher moment of inertia and will be operating at lower unit stress. An 18-in.-deep member would weigh about 8 per cent more than the 16-in. member.

2. Use standard concrete (150 lb per cu ft). This will increase the dead weight about 36 per cent (20 psf), which adds considerably to the load on the supporting beams and columns. Stress loss will be less, but this advantage is offset by the additional dead weight of the member itself, which increases the total bending moment.

3. Use deflected strands. Computations for camber of members with deflected strands are carried out in Step 10 of Chaps. 4 and 9.

4. Use "partial prestress." Partial prestress is discussed more fully in a later chapter. For this particular section it would probably involve the same number of strands as shown in Fig. 10-2 but used at a lower initial tension. As a result the section would have the same ultimate strength as the fully prestressed section but it would develop higher tensile stresses under full live load.

5. Use a larger prestressing force. The magnitude of the camber is a function of the difference between the unit stress in the top fiber of the section and the unit stress in the bottom fiber. If the difference in stress is large, the camber is large. In the double-T section being considered, the stresses in the top fiber are always low. The difference between top and bottom fiber stress can be decreased by setting the magnitude and location of the prestressing force to put some compressive stress in the top fiber. Since we want to keep maximum stress in the bottom fiber, this means a larger prestressing force with a smaller e.

In this particular analysis our object is to establish the maximum capacity of the double T in Fig. 10-1 when made of lightweight aggregate with straight strands in accordance with the Tentative Recommendations. Those conditions eliminate all but Method 5, which we shall try.

We shall determine the prestressing force that gives the maximum allowable compressive stress in the top fiber of the concrete and compute the camber. If this camber is too small, we can interpolate between the two conditions of prestress to get the desired camber.

The limiting condition for maximum prestress in the top fiber occurs under final prestress plus full live load. The dead- and live-load stresses are a function of the span chosen. The maximum span is dependent upon the compressive stress in the bottom fiber. From previous calculations the maximum $f^b{}_{F_0} = 2,400$ psi and $f^b{}_F = 2,400 \div 1.134 = 2,120$ psi. The resulting stress change in the bottom fiber is $2,120 - (-425) = 2,545$ psi, which gives a bending moment of $(2,545 \times 660) \div 12 = 140,000$ ft-lb. Total load is 480 lb per ft.

$$1^2 = \frac{8 \times 140,000}{480} = 2,333 \qquad 1 = 48.2 \text{ ft}$$

Use 48.0 ft. Compressive stress in the top fiber under full live-load moment $f'{}_{G+S+L}$ is

$$f'{}_{G+S+L} = \frac{140,000 \times 12}{1,445} = +1,161 \text{ psi}$$

From previous calculations the maximum allowable compressive stress is 2,250 psi. Thus the maximum compressive stress in the top fiber due to final prestress is $2,250 - 1,161 = +1,089$ psi. Using $f'{}_F = +1,089$ and $f^b{}_F = +2,120$ psi, substitute in Eqs. (1-1a) and (1-1b) and solve for F and e.

$$\frac{F}{316} - \frac{Fe}{1,445} = +1,089 \qquad (10\text{-}4)$$

$$\frac{F}{316} + \frac{Fe}{660} = +2,120 \qquad (10\text{-}5)$$

Multiply (10-5) by $660/1,445 = 0.457$ to get

$$\frac{0.457F}{316} + \frac{Fe}{1,445} = +970$$

Add
$$\frac{F}{316} - \frac{Fe}{1,445} = +1,089 \qquad (10\text{-}4)$$

$$\frac{1.457F}{316} = 2,059$$

$$F = 446,000 \text{ lb}$$

Substituting in (10-4),

$$\frac{446,000}{316} - \frac{446,000e}{1,445} = +1,089$$

$$1,410 - 309e = +1,089$$

$$e = 1.04 \text{ in.}$$

The ratio that F_I has to F will be the same as the ratio that the stress due to F_I has to the stress due to F, or

$$F_I = \frac{446,000 \times 173,600}{131,100} = 590,000$$

$$M_{F_I} = F_I e = 590,000 \times 1.04 = 613,000 \text{ in.-lb}$$

$$\Delta_{F_I} = \frac{613,000 (48 \times 12)^2}{8 (2,850,000) 7,250} = +1.23 \text{ in.}$$

$$\Delta_G = \frac{5 (240) 48^4 (12^3)}{384 (2,850,000) 7,250} = -1.39 \text{ in.}$$

Under its own dead weight the section would have a negative camber of $1.23 - 1.39 = -.16$ in. Therefore the required prestress is somewhere between the first and second of the foregoing calculations. Its magnitude will depend upon the desired camber.

We shall arbitrarily try 14 strands $\frac{7}{16}$ in. in diameter. Then

$$F_o = 14 \times 131,100 \times 0.1089 \times 1.134 = 227,000 \text{ lb}$$

Since we want to keep the maximum allowable prestress in the bottom fiber, we shall set $f^b{}_{F_o} = 2,400$ psi and solve Eq. (1-1b) for e.

$$\frac{227,000}{316} + \frac{227,000e}{660} = 2,400$$

$$718 + 344e = 2,400$$

$$e = 4.89 \text{ in.}$$

$$10.98 - 4.89 = 6.09 \text{ in. from bottom to c.g.s.}$$

Use the strand pattern shown in Fig. 10-4. Find its c.g.s.

$$
\begin{array}{rl}
4 \times \ 2\frac{3}{4} = & 11 \\
8 \times \ 6\frac{3}{4} = & 54 \\
\underline{2 \times 10\frac{3}{4}} = & \underline{21.5} \\
14 \qquad & 86.5
\end{array}
$$

$$86.5 \div 14 = 6.17 \text{ in. bottom to c.g.s.}$$

$$e = 10.98 - 6.17 = 4.81$$

Using the strand pattern in Fig. 10-4 as a final design, establish the maximum span of the member and check stresses, camber, and deflection.

$$F = F_o \div 1.134 = 227,000 \div 1.134 = 200,000 \text{ lb}$$

$$f^t{}_F = \frac{200,000}{316} - \frac{200,000 \times 4.81}{1,445} = -33$$

$$f^b{}_F = \frac{200,000}{316} + \frac{200,000 \times 4.81}{660} = +2,090$$

Total stress change in the bottom under dead plus live load will be from $+2,090$ to $-425 = 2,515$ psi. This is, entirely by coincidence, identical with the value computed using 10 strands with a larger e. From the previous computations this stress change is good for a span of 48 ft and

$$\Delta_G = -1.39 \text{ in.} \qquad \Delta_S = -0.35 \text{ in.}$$

Check camber:

$$F_I = 14 \times 18,900 = 265,000 \text{ lb}$$
$$M_{F_I} = 265,000 \times 4.81 = 1,275,000 \text{ in.-lb}$$
$$\Delta_{F_I} = \frac{1,275,000\,(48 \times 12)^2}{8\,(2,850,000)\,7,250} = +2.56 \text{ in.}$$
$$\Delta_{F_I} - \Delta_G = 2.56 - 1.39 = +1.17 \text{ in.}$$

Net camber under dead load and weight of roofing is $1.17 - .35 = +.82$ in. If camber growth is 150 per cent, then the final camber under dead load will be

$$0.82 + 150\%\,(0.82) = +2.05 \text{ in.}$$

When full live load is applied, concrete strength will be 5,000 psi and

$$E_c = 1,800,000 + 500\,(5,000) = 4,300,000 \times 75\% = 3,225,000$$
$$\Delta_L = \frac{5\,(180)\,(48^4)\,(12^3)}{384\,(3,225,000)\,7,250} = -0.92 \text{ in.}$$

Under full live load the net camber will be $2.05 - 0.92 = +1.13$ in. This is a reasonable value, so we shall complete the design on this basis. The designer must remember that the camber calculations are only as accurate as the data on which they are based such as the value of E_c at various stages, the time lapse before application of roofing, etc.

Check other critical stresses.

$$f'_{F_o} = -33 \times 1.134 = -37$$
$$f^b_{F_o} = +2,090 \times 1.134 = +2,370$$

These are within the allowable limits. Since with straight strands the stresses from prestress are constant for the full length of the member, the only other critical stresses are those at mid-span under full load.

$$M_{G+S+L} = \frac{480\,(48^2)\,12}{8} = 1,658,000 \text{ in.-lb}$$
$$f'_{G+S+L} = 1,658,000 \div 1,445 = +1,148$$
$$f^b_{G+S+L} = 1,658,000 \div 660 = -2,512$$
$$f'_{F+G+S+L} = -33 + 1,148 = +1,115$$
$$f^b_{F+G+S+L} = +2,090 - 2,512 = -422$$

Since these stresses are within the allowable limits and the camber was satisfactory, we can use the strand pattern shown in Fig. 10-4 for a 48-ft span.

It should be noted that either the original design with greater camber or a partial prestress design is more economical where acceptable. The method we have chosen uses two extra strands for the purpose of reducing camber. Since the section is 6 ft wide, we are using ⅓ ft of strand per square foot of roof. If 1 ft of ⁷⁄₁₆-in. strand increases the selling price of the concrete member by 9 cents, then this method increases the selling price by 3 cents per square foot over the original design.

At this point it is suggested that the reader make computations of his own using, separately, Methods 1, 2, and 3 for decreasing camber as suggested near the beginning of this step. To give a true comparison each method should be designed to the roofing and live load used here and to a 48-ft span. In comparing the results remember these factors:

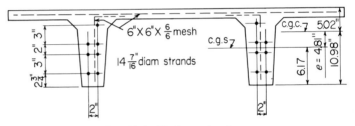

FIG. 10-4. Final strand pattern.

Method 1. The deeper section uses more concrete and has more dead weight. It also makes the structure slightly higher and requires a higher wall to seal it off at the sides of the structure.

Method 2. The supporting structure must carry the additional dead weight. This may not be important if the double T's rest on a masonry wall, but it is important if they are supported by a girder.

Method 3. This method increases neither material cost nor dead weight. If the casting bed is equipped for efficiently deflecting strands, the additional cost will be small and this method will be more economical than 1, 2, or 5.

We can now complete our analysis on the basis of the procedure set up in Chap. 3. Steps 1 to 7 inclusive and Step 10 have been covered by the foregoing calculations.

Step 8. Check ultimate strength to make sure it meets the requirements in the specification. Check the percentage of prestressing steel.

From Sec. 209.2.1(b) evaluate the formula

$$\frac{1.4 d p f_{su}}{f'_c}$$

From Fig. 10-4

$$d = 16 - 6.17 = 9.83 \text{ in.}$$

From Fig. 10-4 and Table A-2

$$A_s = 14 \times 0.1089 = 1.525 \text{ sq in.}$$

$$p = \frac{A_s}{bd} = \frac{1.525}{72 \times 9.83} = 0.00215$$

From Table A-2

$$f'_s = 27,000 \div 0.1089 = 248,000 \text{ psi}$$

From Sec. 209.2.2.a

$$f_{su} = f'_s \left(1 - 0.5 \frac{p f'_s}{f'_c}\right)$$

$$= 248,000 \left(1 - 0.5 \frac{0.00215 \times 248,000}{5,000}\right)$$

$$= 248,000 \, (1 - 0.053) = 235,000 \text{ psi}$$

$$f'_c = 5,000 \text{ psi}$$

Substituting in the formula,

$$\frac{1.4 \times 9.83 \times 0.00215 \times 235,000}{5,000} = 1.39 \text{ in.}$$

Since this is less than the flange thickness of 2 in., the formula for rectangular sections in Sec. 209.2.1(a) is applicable. This formula is

$$M_u = A_s f_{su} d \left(1 - \frac{k_2}{k_1 k_3} \frac{p f_{su}}{f'_c}\right) \tag{a}$$

The statement in Sec. 209.2.1(a) that $k_2/k_1 k_3 = 0.6$ is also correct for a lightweight concrete of the comparatively high strength being used here. Substituting numerical values in (a),

$$M_u = 1.525 \times 235,000 \times 9.83 \left(1 - \frac{0.6 \times 0.00215 \times 235,000}{5,000}\right)$$

$$= 3,312,000 \text{ in.-lb} = 276,000 \text{ ft-lb}$$

From Sec. 205.3.1 the minimum ultimate required is

$$1.2D + 2.4L$$

or

$$1.8 \, (D + L)$$

Where values for W are specified, the other expressions in Sec. 205.3.1 should also be evaluated and checked.

The dead weight of the member plus the roofing is $240 + 60 = 300$ lb per lin ft. Then

$$M_D = \frac{300\,(48^2)}{8} = 86{,}400 \text{ ft-lb}$$

$$M_L = \frac{180\,(48^2)}{8} = 51{,}800 \text{ ft-lb}$$

$$1.2\,(86{,}400) + 2.4\,(51{,}800) = 228{,}000 \text{ ft-lb}$$
$$1.8\,(86{,}400 + 51{,}800) = 249{,}00 \text{ ft-lb}$$

Since both of these are less than M_u, the member has sufficient ultimate strength.

Check the percentage of prestressing steel in accordance with Sec. 209.2.3.

$$\frac{pf_{su}}{f'_c} = \frac{0.00215 \times 235{,}000}{5{,}000} = 0.1011$$

Since this is less than 0.30, the member is not overreinforced.

Step 9. Design of shear steel.

From Sec. 210.2.1 web reinforcement is not needed when

$$\frac{pf'_s}{f'_c} \leqq 0.3 \frac{f_{se}b'}{f'_s b}$$

Since shearing unit stress is normally greatest at the c.g.c., we shall use the web thickness at that point giving $b' = 2 \times 6\tfrac{3}{8} = 12\tfrac{3}{4}$.

Substituting numerical values from calculations in preceding steps,

$$\frac{0.00215 \times 248{,}000}{5{,}000} \leqq 0.3 \frac{131{,}100 \times 12.75}{248{,}000 \times 72}$$

$$0.1066 \leqq 0.0281$$

Since this is not true, web reinforcement is required.

The web-reinforcement requirement for this member is that described by the last paragraph of Sec. 210.2.5. The maximum requirement occurs 16 in. from the support, at which point the loaded length producing shear is

$$24 \text{ ft } 0 \text{ in.} - 1 \text{ ft } 4 \text{ in.} = 22 \text{ ft } 8 \text{ in.} = 22.67 \text{ ft}$$
$$\text{Dead-load shear} = 300 \text{ lb} \times 22.67 = 6{,}800 \text{ lb}$$
$$\text{Live-load shear} = 180 \text{ lb} \times 22.67 = 4{,}080 \text{ lb}$$
$$V_u = 1.2\,(6{,}800) + 2.4\,(4{,}080) = 17{,}950 \text{ lb}$$
$$V_u = 1.8\,(6{,}800 + 4{,}080) = 19{,}600 \text{ lb}$$

The V_u to be used is 19,600 lb. Since the strands are in a straight line, they do not carry any shear.

Compute web reinforcement using the formula in Sec. 210.2.2. From Sec. 210.2.4 maximum spacing of stirrups is three-quarters of the depth of the member. Use $s = 12$ in. Use stirrups of structural-grade steel, which has $f'_y = 33,000$ psi. For this example

$$V_c = 180b'jd$$

j can be computed from the following portion of formula (*a*) in Sec. 209.2.1:

$$j = \left(1 - \frac{k_2}{k_1 k_3} \frac{pf_{su}}{f'_c} \right)$$

Substituting previously computed values,

$$j = 1 - \frac{0.60 \times 0.00215 \times 235,000}{5,000} = 0.939$$

$$V_c = 180 \times 12.75 \times 0.939 \times 9.83 = 21,200 \text{ lb}$$

Substituting in the formula,

$$A_v = \frac{1}{2} \frac{(19,600 - 21,200) \, 12}{33,000 \times 0.939 \times 9.83} = \text{a negative number}$$

which means that the concrete section will carry more than the existing shear at ultimate load. Under this condition the minimum requirement of Sec. 210.2.3 will govern. It says

$$A_v = 0.0025b's = 0.0025 \times 12.75 \times 12 = 0.382 \text{ sq in.}$$

It also says "This requirement may be excessive for members with unusually thick webs and the amount of web reinforcement may be reduced if tests demonstrate that the member can develop its required flexural capacity." This last statement applies to most double-T sections. It is common practice to use a 6 by 6 in. by 6/6 mesh in each leg of a double T for its full length. This provides $A_v = 4 \times 0.029 = 0.116$ sq in. where $s = 12$ in.

CHAPTER 11

DESIGN OF A POST-TENSIONED GIRDER

11-1. Choosing a Post-tensioned Member. The decision to use a post-tensioned member instead of a pretensioned one is influenced by so many different conditions that there are no rules which can be applied to determine the economical dividing line between the two. When the member is too large to be shipped from a casting yard to the job site, it is obvious that it must be cast at the job site and post-tensioned tendons will be required. When the size of the member is within shipping limitations, the following factors should be included in comparing the cost of the two methods:

1. Capacity of local casting beds. On long-span members the use of deflected tendons to offset dead weight is important. If facilities for deflecting enough strands for this purpose are not available, either a post-tensioned design or a pretensioned–post-tensioned combination is indicated.

2. Cross section of member. The cross section of a post-tensioned member is more efficient than that of a pretensioned member for the same loading if the web of the pretensioned member must be thickened appreciably to accommodate the deflected strands.

Post-tensioned members are used in bridges and buildings and for many special applications such as pile caps for piers. The girder designed in this chapter is a 100-ft-span roof girder such as might be used over a school gym.

11-2. Design Conditions. Design in accordance with tentative Recommendations for Prestressed Concrete in Art. 8-2 except tendons to be in accordance with Sec. 3-A, B, and C of Prestressed Concrete Institute Specifications for Post-Tensioned Prestressed Concrete, Appendix B. As ASTM specifications become available for one or more types of post-tensioned tendon, they should be used in place of the PCI requirements. (Use ASTM A421-58T, Appendix F, for wire properties if parallel wire cables are used.) The PCI specification for tendons is used because Sec. 304 of the Tentative Recommendations is only a general description of the tendons rather than a numerical list of specific properties to which an engineer or inspector can work.

Span: 100 ft 0 in. center to center of bearings
Live load: 30 psf
Roofing: 10 psf
Double-T roof deck: 33 psf
Girder spacing: 30 ft center to center
Concrete: $f'_c = 5,000$ psi
Concrete: $f'_{ci} = $ to be determined by calculations
Standard concrete at 150 lb per cu ft
Tendons to be grouted after tensioning operation is complete

11-3 Design Calculations. Calculations will follow the steps outlined in Chap. 3. The reader should thoroughly understand Chap. 4 before attempting to follow this analysis.

Step 1. Compute the properties of the cross section in Fig. 11-1. Take moments about the bottom.

Section	Area, A	y	Ay	Ay²	I₀
I = 21 × 6	= 126	3	378	1,134	378
II = 8 × 52	= 416	32	13,300	426,000	93,750
III = 2 × 6.5 × 6 × ½ =	39	8	312	2,496	78
IV = 2 × 11 × 4 × ½ =	44	56.7	2,500	141,500	40
V = 30 × 8	= 240	62	14,900	923,000	1,280
	865		31,390	1,494,130	95,526
				95,526	
				1,589,656	

$$y_b = 31,390 \div 865 = 36.3$$
$$y_t = 66 - 36.3 = 29.7$$
$$I = 1,589,656 - 865(36.3^2) = 448,500$$
$$Z_t = 448,500 \div 29.7 = 15,100$$
$$Z_b = 448,500 \div 36.3 = 12,350$$
$$\text{Weight} = \frac{150 \times 865}{144} = 900 \text{ lb per ft}$$

Step 2. Compute stresses in the member due to its own dead weight.

$$M_G = \frac{900(100^2) \times 12}{8} = 13,500,000 \text{ in.-lb}$$

$$f^t_G = 13,500,000 \div 15,100 = +894 \text{ psi}$$
$$f^b_G = 13,500,000 \div 12,350 = -1,093 \text{ psi}$$

Step 3. Compute stresses in the member due to applied loads.

Double T = 33 psf
Roofing = 10 psf
           ‾‾‾‾‾‾
           43 psf

$$w_s = 43 \times 30 \text{ ft} = 1{,}290 \text{ lb per lin ft}$$

$$M_s = \frac{1{,}290\,(100^2) \times 12}{8} = 19{,}350{,}000 \text{ in.-lb}$$

$$f^t_s = 19{,}350{,}000 \div 15{,}100 = +1{,}281$$
$$f^b_s = 19{,}350{,}000 \div 12{,}350 = -1{,}567$$

Live load $= 30 \times 30 = 900$ lb per lin ft

$$M_L = \frac{900\,(100^2) \times 12}{8} = 13{,}500{,}000 \text{ in.-lb}$$

$$f^t_L = 13{,}500{,}000 \div 15{,}100 = +894 \text{ psi}$$
$$f^b_L = 13{,}500{,}000 \div 12{,}350 = -1{,}093 \text{ psi}$$

Step 4. Determine the magnitude and location of the prestressing force at the center of span.

This computation is based on final conditions, that is, after all stress losses have taken place.

From Sec. 207.3.2

Maximum compressive stress $= 0.45 \times 5{,}000 = 2{,}250$ psi
Maximum tensile stress in bottom $= 6\sqrt{5{,}000}$ * $= -425$ psi $= f_{tp}$
From Step 4 in Chap. 3

$$\frac{F}{A_c} + \frac{Fe}{Z_b} = -f^b_G - f^b_s - f^b_L + f_{tp} \qquad (3\text{-}1)$$

Substituting numerical values,

$$\frac{F}{865} + \frac{Fe}{12{,}350} = +1{,}093 + 1{,}567 + 1{,}093 - 425$$

$$\frac{F}{865} + \frac{Fe}{12{,}350} = +3{,}328 \qquad (11\text{-}1)$$

From Step 4, Chap. 3,

$$\frac{F}{A_c} - \frac{Fe}{Z_t} = -f^t_G + f_{tp} \qquad (3\text{-}2)$$

Since this member will constantly be under a large dead load, there will be no tensile stress in the top fiber under final conditions, so the tensile stress in the top fiber will be governed by the initial prestress condition. From Sec. 207.3.1.b.1 this is $3\sqrt{f'_{ci}}$. Not knowing f'_{ci} we

---

* This is not in strict accordance with the Tentative Recommendations. The author, accustomed to designing pretensioned structures, used an allowable tensile stress of $6\sqrt{f'_c}$. For post-tensioned bonded elements Sec. 207.3.2.b.1.c permits only $3\sqrt{f'_c}$. The discrepancy was not noted until the manuscript had been set in type. It does not change the design procedure but for an actual building the engineer should use $3\sqrt{f'_c}$ in accordance with Tentative Recommendations.

shall assume it to be 4,000 psi, which gives $3\sqrt{4,000} = -190$ psi. We shall also assume that the final prestress is 80 per cent of the initial prestress giving

f_{tp} (for the top fiber) $= -190 \times 80$ per cent $= -150$ psi

Substituting in (3-2),

$$\frac{F}{865} - \frac{Fe}{15,100} = -894 - 150$$
$$= -1,044 \qquad (11\text{-}2)$$

Multiply (11-1) by $12,350/15,100 = 0.82$ to get

$$\frac{0.82F}{865} + \frac{Fe}{15,100} = +2,730$$

$$\text{Add} \quad \frac{F}{865} - \frac{Fe}{15,100} = -1,044$$

$$\frac{1.82F}{865} \qquad\qquad = +1,686$$

$$F = 801,000 \text{ lb}$$

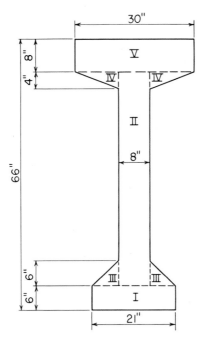

FIG. 11-1. Cross section of girder.

Substituting in Eq. (11-2)

$$\frac{801,000}{865} - \frac{801,000e}{15,100} = -1,044$$
$$926 - 53.0e = -1,044$$
$$e = 37.17 \text{ in.}$$

Since y_b is only 36.3 in., this value of e would put the tendons below the bottom of the girder.

Step 5. Select the tensioning elements to be used, and work out the details of their location in the member.

Since the value of e computed in Step 4 is too large for satisfactory details, we shall arbitrarily choose a smaller value. In a member of this type the c.g.s. for an F of about 1,00,000 lb will be 4 to 5 in. above the bottom if the tendons are to be kept in an open pattern. If tendons are to be bunched as permitted by Sec. 216.3, the distance can be reduced. We shall try 4.5 in. from the bottom to the c.g.s., which gives

$$e = 36.3 - 4.5 = 31.8 \text{ in.}$$

Substituting known values in Eq. (11-1),

$$\frac{F}{865} + \frac{31.8F}{12,350} = +3,328$$
$$12,350F + (865 \times 31.8) F = 3,328 \times 865 \times 12,350$$
$$F = 892,000 \text{ lb}$$
$$f^t{}_F = \frac{892,000}{865} - \frac{892,000 \times 31.8}{15,100} = -847 \text{ psi}$$
$$f^b{}_F = \frac{892,000}{865} + \frac{892,000 \times 31.8}{12,350} = +3,328 \text{ psi}$$

Stresses under full load:

$$f^t{}_{F+G+S+L} = -847 + 894 + 1,281 + 894 = +2,222 \text{ psi}$$
$$f^b{}_{F+G+S+L} = +3,328 - 1,093 - 1,567 - 1,093 = -425 \text{ psi}$$

Since these stresses are within the allowable, we can use the F and e computed to select the tendons and work out their pattern in the member.

In designing a pretensioned member it is standard procedure to select the size of seven-wire strand to be used and to work out a satisfactory pattern. This can be done because the properties of seven-wire strands have been standardized and they are available from a number of suppliers. Choosing the tendons for a post-tensioned member is another matter. There are several systems or methods of post-tensioning involving different types of tendons and anchor fittings, most of which are patented. The drawings and specifications must be so prepared that the proper magnitude and location of the prestressing force will be assured and also

that each post-tensioning system can be used to the best advantage.
One common procedure is to specify the prestressing force and its
location as shown in Fig. 11-2. (A would be given as a numerical value
after calculations for Step 7 were completed.) The disadvantage to the
method shown in Fig. 11-2 is that it is inflexible and therefore does not
permit the most efficient use of the various systems. As an example let
us assume that using the tendons of one system at full capacity, it takes
10.10 tendons to produce an F of 892,000 lb but that 10 tendons of this
system can be arranged so that their c.g.s. is less than 4½ in. from the
bottom, which gives a larger e than shown. The economical procedure
would be to use 10 tendons and lower them enough to give the required
compressive stress in the bottom fiber as long as this does not create
excessive tensile stress in the top fiber. Working from the information
given in Fig. 11-2 the bidder has no way of telling whether or not this
method would work.

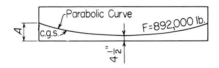

FIG. 11-2.   Computed magnitude and location of prestressing force.

In order to obtain maximum efficiency in the choice of tendons the
design drawings should give the properties of the concrete cross section
and the permissible range of stresses due to the prestressing force.

The minimum value of $f^b{}_F$ must be large enough to keep the stress in
the bottom fiber from exceeding -425 psi.

$$\text{Minimum } f^b{}_F = -f^b{}_G - f^b{}_S - f^b{}_L + f_{tp}$$
$$= 1{,}093 + 1{,}567 + 1{,}093 - 425 = +3{,}328$$

The maximum value of $f^b{}_F$ must keep the compressive stress under
prestress plus dead load from exceeding $+2{,}250$ psi.

$$\text{Maximum } f^b{}_F = 2{,}250 - f^b{}_G$$
$$= 2{,}250 + 1{,}093 = +3{,}343 \text{ psi}$$

The minimum tensile stress $f^t{}_F$ must be large enough so that the
compressive stress under full load does not exceed the allowable $+2{,}250$
psi.

$$\text{Minimum } f^t{}_F = 2{,}250 - f^t{}_G - f^t{}_S - f^t{}_L$$
$$= 2{,}250 - 894 - 1{,}281 - 894 = -819$$

The maximum tensile stress in the top fiber must not exceed the allowable -150 psi under prestress plus dead load.

$$\text{Maximum } f'_F = -150 - f'_G$$
$$= -150 - 894 = -1,044$$

In summary, at the center of span

$$f^b{}_F = +3,328 \text{ to } +3,343 \text{ psi}$$
$$f'{}_F = -819 \text{ to } -1,044 \text{ psi}$$

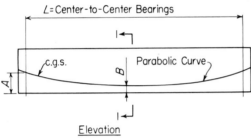

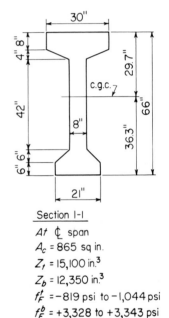

One combination of values which gives satisfactory stresses is

$A = 36.3''$, $B = 4\frac{1}{2}''$, $F = 892,000$ lb

The values of A, B and F may be altered as long as f'_F and f^b_F are kept within the limits shown hereon and the tendon spacing and cover coincide with "Tentative Recommendations for Prestressed Concrete".

Section I-I
At ₵ span
$A_c = 865$ sq in.
$Z_t = 15,100$ in.^{3}
$Z_b = 12,350$ in.^{3}
$f'_F = -819$ psi to $-1,044$ psi
$f^b_F = +3,328$ to $+3,343$ psi

FIG. 11-3. Method recommended for showing prestressing requirements when submitting post-tensioned members for competitive bids.

When the member is submitted to contractors for bids, these values as well as the properties of the cross section should be shown as illustrated in Fig. 11-3.

Another method of presentation is to list several different values for B (Fig. 11-3) and to list the corresponding F required for each value of B. With this method, all calculations are done by the designer and the bidder need only select the most economical combination of B and F which the details of his tendons can suit.

Any post-tensioning system whose properties meet the requirements of the specification can be used.   For the purpose of this example we shall use the Freyssinet system.   As a first trial we shall use the A and F shown in Fig. 11-3.

From Table 7-1 a 12/0.276 Freyssinet cable (a cable composed of 12 wires each 0.276-in. diameter and having a minimum ultimate strength of 236,000 psi) has a recommended final prestress of 93,000 lb.   The number of these cables required is

$$892,000 \div 93,000 = 9.6 \text{ cables}$$

We can use 10 cables or try to lower the c.g.s. enough to make 9 cables suffice.

We shall try lowering the c.g.s.   The F for nine cables is $9 \times 93,000 = 837,000$ lb.   From Fig. 11-3 the minimum value of $f^b{}_F = +3,328$.   Substitute known values in Eq. (1-1b) and solve for e.

$$\frac{837,000}{865} + \frac{837,000e}{12,350} = +3,328$$
$$968 + 67.8e = +3,328$$
$$e = 34.8 \text{ in.}$$
$$36.3 - 34.8 = 1.5 \text{ in. bottom to c.g.s.}$$

We cannot arrange nine cables in a pattern that meets the specification requirements for cover and spacing when the c.g.s. is only 1.5 in. from the bottom.

An alternate would be to use Freyssinet cables 18/0.196, which have a recommended final prestress of 77,000 lb according to Table 7-1.   The number of these cables required would be $892,000 \div 77,000 = 11.58$. The c.g.s. for 11 of these cables would be almost as low as for nine cables 12/0.276, so 12 cables would be required.   Since the "in-place" cost of 12 of these cables would be higher than that of 10 of the larger cables, we shall use 10 cables 12/0.276.   Since Fig. 11-3 gives the details for $F = 892,000$ lb, we shall use this value of

$$F = 892,000 \div 10 = 89,200 \text{ lb per cable}$$

See Fig. 11-4 for cable pattern.   Check the c.g.s.

$$
\begin{array}{l}
6 \times 2\frac{1}{2} = 15 \\
2 \times 5\frac{7}{8} = 11.75 \\
\underline{2 \times 9\frac{1}{4} = 18.50} \\
\hphantom{2 \times 9\frac{1}{4} = }10 \qquad\quad 45.25 \div 10 = 4.52
\end{array}
$$

Step 6. Establish the concrete strength f'_{ci} at the time of prestressing and check stresses under the initial prestress condition.

First we must compute the initial prestress F_I.

The area of the cable being used from Table 7-1 is 0.723 sq in.　The final stress is $89,200 \div 0.723 = 123,400$ psi.　From Sec. 208.3.2 the stress loss is 25,000 psi, so the initial stress is $123,400 + 25,000 = 148,400$ psi and the initial tension is $148,400 \times 0.723 = 107,300$ lb per cable.　Total $F_I = 107,300 \times 10 = 1,073,000$ lb.

Substituting in Eqs. (1-1*a*) and (1-1*b*), the stresses at center of span are

$$f^t{}_{F_I} = \frac{1,073,000}{865} - \frac{1,073,000 \times 31.8}{15,100} = -1,020$$

$$f^b{}_{F_I} = \frac{1,073,000}{865} + \frac{1,073,000 \times 31.8}{12,350} = +3,976$$

Adding dead-weight stresses,

$$f^t{}_{F_I+G} = -1,020 + 894 = -126$$
$$f^b{}_{F_I+G} = +3,976 - 1,093 = +2,883$$

From Sec. 207.3.1

$$\text{Maximum allowable tensile stress} = 3\sqrt{f'_{ci}}$$

$$\text{or } 126 = 3\sqrt{f'_{ci}} \qquad f'_{ci} = \left(\frac{126}{3}\right)^2$$

$$f'_{ci} = 1,760 \text{ minimum}$$
$$\text{Maximum allowable compressive stress} = 0.55f'_{ci}$$
$$\text{or } f'_{ci} = 2,883 \div 0.55 = 5,242$$

Therefore the required f'_{ci} is governed by the compressive stress and is slightly larger than the specified f'_c.　This is a condition which often occurs in the design of post-tensioned members for buildings when the Tentative Recommendations are followed because the allowable stress at design loads is $0.45f'_c$ while the allowable stress under initial conditions is only $0.55f'_{ci}$.　Since the values are so close in this example, we shall simply specify $f'_c = f'_{ci} = 5,300$ psi.　This means that the concrete must have a minimum ultimate strength of 5,300 psi at the time of post-

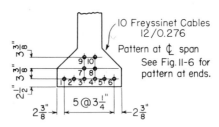

FIG. 11-4.　Pattern of tendons at center of span.

tensioning. In most cases of post-tensioned members such a requirement is not a serious drawback. The side forms can be removed for use
elsewhere after the concrete has set, and the member can stand until
completely cured. It is not holding up production as a pretensioned
member on a casting bed would be.

Step 7. Establish the path of the tendons and check any critical points
along the member under initial and final conditions.

Since all the loads on this member are uniform loads and the bending-
moment curve of a uniform load is a parabola, the logical curve for the
tendons is also a parabola. The lowest point of the parabola at the
center of span is already established. If we can establish the highest
points, at the ends of the member, and know the equation of the curve,
the entire curve will be established. Within certain limits the location
of the elevation of the ends of the curve is usually a matter of choice rather
than design. It must be high enough so that the stresses it creates at the
end of the member are within the allowable, and it must permit suitable
details for the tendon anchors. Unless some condition indicates otherwise, a most convenient location is the c.g.c. For this example we shall
locate the end of the curve on the c.g.c.

The parabolic bending-moment curve due to a uniform load is shown
in Fig. 11-5a, page 204. The parabolic curve of the cables is shown in
Fig. 11-5b. These curves have the same equation except that in the
bending-moment curve B and y are measured in foot-pounds while in
the cable curve B and y are measured in inches.

Now that the curve of the tendons is established, we can plot the
stresses at points along the span. Table 11-1 shows the critical condition
under initial prestress plus the dead load of the girder only. Since the
section modulus of the girder is constant for its full length, the stresses
due to dead load will vary in accordance with the equation in Fig. 11-5,
and we already know the stresses at the center of span.

We can use Eq. (1-1) to compute the stresses due to F:

$$f_{F_I} = \frac{F_I}{A_c} \pm \frac{Fe}{Z} \qquad (1\text{-}1)$$

Substituting in (1-1) for the stresses due to F_I at the ends of the span
(where $e = $ zero because the cables are on the c.g.c.), we get

$$f_{F_I} = \frac{F_I}{A_c} \pm \frac{F(\text{zero})}{Z} = \frac{F_I}{A_c}$$

which means that the stress is uniform over the full depth of the member
and equal to

$$\frac{F_I}{A_c} = \frac{1,073,000}{865} = +1,240 \text{ psi}$$

At the center of span the stress in the top fiber due to F_I is

$$f^t{}_{F_I} = \frac{F_I}{A_c} - \frac{F_I e}{Z_t} \tag{1-1a}$$

In this equation F_I/A_c is a constant value of $+1,240$ and is so listed in Table 11-1. $-F_I e/Z_t$ is made up of two constants F_I and Z_t and the variable e. In Fig. 11-5a, e is equal to y, and at the center of span $e = y = B$. Thus at the center of span

$$-\frac{F_I e}{Z_t} = \frac{1,073,000 \times 31.8}{15,100} = -2,260 = B$$

$$\frac{F_I e}{Z_b} = \frac{1,073,000 \times 31.8}{12,350} = +2,763 = B$$

The values of $-F_I e/Z_t$ at the tenth points of the span can be computed using the formula or table of coefficients in Fig. 11-5.

We now have sufficient data and shall complete Table 11-1.

The figures in column 10 of Table 11-1 show that the compressive stress at points along the span is always less than that at the center of span, which is therefore the governing stress and which has already been provided for by making $f'_{ci} = 5,300$ psi. All the top fiber stresses in column 6 are well within the allowable.

Table 11-2 shows the critical condition under final prestress plus all applied loads. Stresses at the tenth points of the span are based on the parabolic curves in Fig. 11-5 in the same manner as those in Table 11-1.

$$\frac{F}{A_c} = \frac{892,000}{865} = +1,031$$

At the center of span

$$-\frac{Fe}{Z_t} = \frac{892,000 \times 31.8}{15,100} = -1,878$$

$$+\frac{Fe}{Z_b} = \frac{892,000 \times 31.8}{12,350} = +2,297$$

Using these values we shall complete Table 11-2.

The figures in columns 6 and 10 of Table 11-2 show that the stresses are within the allowable for the full length of the member.

If the magnitude of the net stresses is not clear to the reader from Tables 11-1 and 11-2, he should plot stress diagrams similar to those in Chaps. 4 and 9 using the stresses listed in these tables as a basis for the diagrams.

The elevation of the c.g.s. at the tenth points of the span is developed using the equation in Fig. 11-5.

Table 11-1. Critical Conditions under Initial Prestress

X (1)	$\dfrac{F_i}{A_c}$ (2)	$-\dfrac{F_i e}{Z_t}$ (3)	$f^t_{F_i} = 2+3$ (4)*	f^t_G (5)	$f^t_{F_i+G}$ (6)	$\dfrac{F_i e}{Z_b}$ (7)	$f^b_{F_i} = 2+7$ (8)†	f^b_G (9)	$f^b_{F_i+G}$ (10)
0	+1,240	0	+1,240	0	+1,240	0	+1,240	0	+1,240
0.1L or 0.9L	+1,240	-814	+426	+322	+748	+985	+2,225	-393	+1,832
0.2L or 0.8L	+1,240	-1,446	-206	+572	+366	+1,751	+2,991	-700	+2,291
0.3L or 0.7L	+1,240	-1,898	-658	+750	+92	+2,298	+3,538	-918	+2,620
0.4L or 0.6L	+1,240	-2,170	-930	+858	-72	+2,626	+3,866	-1,050	+2,816
0.5L	+1,240	-2,260	-1,020	+894	-126	+2,736	+3,976	-1,093	+2,883

*$f^t_{F_i}$ = column 2 plus column 3.
†$f^b_{F_i}$ = column 2 plus column 7.

Table 11-2. Critical Conditions under Final Prestress

X (1)	$\dfrac{F}{A_c}$ (2)	$-\dfrac{Fe}{Z_t}$ (3)	$f^t_F = 2+3$ (4)*	f^t_{G+S+L} (5)	$f^t_{F+G+S+L}$ (6)	$\dfrac{Fe}{Z_b}$ (7)	$f^b_F = 2+7$ (8)†	f^b_{G+S+L} (9)	$f^b_{F+G+S+L}$ (10)
0	+1,031	0	+1,031	0	+1,031	0	+1,031	0	+1,031
0.1L or 0.9L	+1,031	-676	+355	+1,105	+1,460	+827	+1,858	-1,351	+507
0.2L or 0.8L	+1,031	-1,202	-171	+1,964	+1,793	+1,470	+2,501	-2,402	+99
0.3L or 0.7L	+1,031	-1,578	-547	+2,578	+2,031	+1,930	+2,961	-3,153	-192
0.4L or 0.6L	+1,031	-1,803	-772	+2,946	+2,174	+2,205	+3,236	-3,603	-367
0.5L	+1,031	-1,878	-847	+3,069	+2,222	+2,297	+3,328	-3,753	-425

*f^t_F = column 2 plus column 3.
†f^b_F = column 2 plus column 7.

203

Step 8. Check ultimate strength to make sure it meets the requirements of the specification. Check the percentage of prestressing steel.

Use the formula in Sec. 209.2.1(b) to determine the location of the neutral axis under the ultimate condition.

$$1.4 \frac{dp f_{su}}{f'_c}$$

$$d = 29.7 + 31.8 = 61.5$$
$$A_s = 0.723 \times 10 = 7.23 \text{ sq in.}$$
$$f'_c = 5,300$$
$$p = \frac{A_s}{bd} = \frac{7.23}{30 \times 61.5} = 0.00392$$

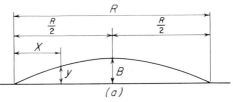

Curve of Bending Moment Due to Uniform Load

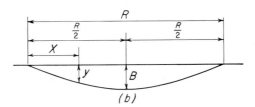

Curve of Parabolic Path of Tendons

Equation for curves *(a)* and *(b)*

$$y = 4B \, \frac{X}{R} \left(1 - \frac{X}{R}\right)$$

Values of y for X at Tenth Points of Span as Computed from Above Equation

X	y
0	0
0.1R or 0.9R	0.36B
0.2R or 0.8R	0.64B
0.3R or 0.7R	0.84B
0.4R or 0.6R	0.96B
0.5R	B

$L = R\,(1 + 2.67\,n^2)$

L = length along parabolic curve

$n = \dfrac{B}{R}$

For tangent to curve see Eq. 11-3
For unsymmetrical parabola
see Fig. 14-3

FIG. 11-5. Parabolic curves for uniform bending moment and path of tendons.

From Sec. 209.2.2.2(a)

$$f_{su} = f'_s \left(1 - 0.5 \frac{p f'_s}{f'_c} \right)$$

This formula is applicable because conditions 1 and 2 of Sec. 209.2.2 are met by this member.

$$f_{su} = 236,000 \left(1 - 0.5 \frac{0.00392 \times 236,000}{5,300} \right) = 215,000$$

Substituting these values in the equation,

$$1.4 \frac{61.5 \times 0.00392 \times 215,000}{5,300} = 13.70$$

Since the flange thickness is less than this, the following formula applies:

$$M_u = A_{sr} f_{su} d \left(1 - 0.6 \frac{A_{sr} f_{su}}{b' d f'_c} \right) + 0.85 f'_c (b - b') t (d - 0.5t) \qquad (b)$$

$b = 30$
$b' = 8$
t = average thickness of flange = area of flange $\div$ b
Area of flange = $(30 \times 8) + (2 \times 11 \times 4 \times \frac{1}{2}) = 284$
$t = 284 \div 30 = 9.47$
$f'_c = 5,300$

$$A_{sf} = \frac{0.85 f'_c (b - b') t}{f_{su}}$$

$$= \frac{0.85 (5,300)(30 - 8) 9.47}{215,000} = 4.37$$

$$A_{sr} = A_s - A_{sf}$$
$$= 7.23 - 4.37 = 2.86$$

Substituting in formula (b),

$$M_u = 2.86 \times 215,000 \times 61.5 \left(1 - 0.6 \frac{2.86 \times 215,000}{8 \times 61.5 \times 5,300} \right)$$

$$+ 0.85 \times 5,300 (30 - 8) 9.47 (61.5 - 0.5 \times 9.47)$$
$$= 32,450,000 + 53,250,000$$
$$= 85,700,000 \text{ in.-lb} = 7,140,000 \text{ ft-lb}$$

Determine maximum required ultimate strength from Sec. 205.3.1.

$$M_D = M_G + M_S = (13,500,000 + 19,350,000) \div 12 = 2,740,000 \text{ ft-lb}$$
$$M_L = 13,500,000 \div 12 = 1,125,000 \text{ ft-lb}$$
$$1.2D + 2.4L = 1.2 (2,740,000) + 2.4 (1,125,000) = 5,990,000 \text{ ft-lb}$$
$$1.8 (D + L) = 1.8 (2,740,000 + 1,125,000) = 6,960,000 \text{ ft-lb}$$

The member has the required ultimate strength.
Check the percentage of steel in accordance with Sec. 209.2.3.

$$\frac{A_{sr}f_{su}}{b'df'_c} = \frac{2.86 \times 215,00}{8 \times 61.5 \times 5,300} = .236$$

Since this is less than 0.30, the member is not overreinforced.

Step 9. Design of shear steel.
From Sec. 210.2.1 web reinforcement is not needed if

$$\frac{pf'_s}{f'_c} \lessgtr 0.3 \frac{f_{se}b'}{f'_s b}$$

Substituting numerical values,

$$\frac{0.00392 \times 236,000}{5,300} \lessgtr 0.3 \frac{123,400 \times 8}{236,000 \times 30}$$

$$0.175 \lessgtr 0.042$$

Since this is not true, web reinforcement is needed.
From the third paragraph of Sec. 210.2.5 maximum shear occurs 5 ft 6 in. from the support.
Determine ultimate shear in accordance with Sec. 205.3.1.

$$W_D = w_G + w_S = 900 + 1,290 = 2,190 \text{ lb per ft}$$
$$W_L = 900 \text{ lb per ft}$$
$$1.2D + 2.4L = 1.2\,(2,190) + 2.4\,(900) = 4,790 \text{ lb per ft}$$
$$1.8\,(D + L) = 1.8\,(2,190 + 900) = 5,560 \text{ lb per ft}$$

Total ultimate shear 5 ft 6 in. from the support is $5,560\,(50 - 5.5) = 247,000$ lb. Part of this shear is carried by the tendons.
Using the symbols shown in Fig. 11-5b, the tangent of the angle of the curve with the horizontal at a point X from the end of the curve is

$$\tan \phi = \frac{4B}{R}\left(1 - \frac{2X}{R}\right) \tag{11-3}$$

Substituting numerical values for the point on the curve of the tendons 5 ft 6 in. from the support,

$$B = 31.8 \div 12 = 2.65 \text{ ft}$$
$$\tan X = \frac{4 \times 2.65}{100}\left(1 - \frac{2 \times 5.5}{100}\right) = 0.0943$$

The shear carried by the cables at this point is equal to the vertical component of the final tension in the cables, which is

$$0.0943 \times 892,000 = 84,100 \text{ lb}$$
$$V_u = 247,000 - 84,100 = 162,900 \text{ lb}$$

Since the tendons are in a parabolic curve, d at this point will be less than at mid-span. Compute d using the formulas in Fig. 11-5 and the dimensions in Fig. 11-3. Using the symbols in Fig. 11-5,

$R = 100$ ft 0 in. $= 1,200$ in.
$B = 36.3 - 4.5 = 31.8$ in.
$X = 5$ ft 6 in. $= 66$ in.

Substituting in the formula,

$$y = 4(31.8)\,\frac{66}{1,200}\left(1 - \frac{66}{1,200}\right) = 6.6 \text{ in.}$$

Then

$$d = 6.6 + 29.7 = 36.3 \text{ in.}$$

$$p = \frac{7.23}{30 \times 36.3} = 0.00664$$

Since the bending moment at this point is small, failure will not occur by bending, so we are not concerned about the high percentage of steel. From Sec. 209.2.2.2

$$f_{su} = 236,000\left(1 - \frac{0.5 \times 0.00664 \times 236,000}{5,000}\right) = 199,000 \text{ psi}$$

Compute web reinforcing using the formula in Sec. 210.2.2.

$$A_V = \frac{1}{2}\,\frac{(V_u - V_c)\,s}{f'_y jd}$$

j is computed using the following portion of formula (a) in Sec. 209.2.1:

$$j = 1 - \frac{k_2 p f_{su}}{k_1 k_3 f'_c}$$

$$j = 1 - \frac{0.6 \times 0.00664 \times 199,000}{5,000} = 0.842$$

From Sec. 210.2.2

$$V_c = 180 \times 8 \times 0.842 \times 36.3 = 44,000 \text{ lb}$$

Using structural grade bars $f'_y = 33,000$
From Sec. 210.2.4 maximum stirrup spacing $= 0.75 \times 66 = 49.5$
Use $s = 49.5$

Substituting numerical values in the formula,

$$A_V = \frac{1}{2}\,\frac{(162,900 - 44,000)\,49.5}{33,000 \times 0.842 \times 36.3} = 2.92 \text{ sq in.}$$

From Sec. 210.2.3 the minimum web reinforcement is

$$A_V = 0.0025 b's = 0.0025 \times 8 \times 49.5 = 0.99$$

Try two #5 bars for that portion of the beam where minimum reinforcement is required.   The area of two #5 bars is $2 \times 0.307 = 0.614$
sq in.

$$s = \frac{0.614}{0.99} \,(49.5) = 30.7 \text{ in.}$$

Use two #5 bars at 30 in. on centers.

At the point 5 ft 6 in. from the support where A_v was computed as
2.92 sq in., we shall try $s = 26$ in.   Then the required stirrup area is

$$\frac{26}{49.5} \,(2.92) = 1.53 \text{ sq in.}$$

Use two #8 bars $= 2 \times 0.78 = 1.56$ sq in. at 26 in. centers.   Go
through a similar calculation for required web reinforcement at points
10 ft 0 in. from the support, 15 ft 0 in. from the support, etc., until a point
is reached where the minimum of two #5 bars at 30 in. centers is sufficient.   Use two #5 bars at 30-in. centers from this point to mid-span.
The stirrup pattern will be symmetrical about mid-span.   Note that Sec.
210.2.5 requires that the web reinforcement in the middle third of the
span be the same as that required at the third points.   If this is greater
than the minimum of $0.0025b's$, then the third-point requirement will
govern and the $0.0025b's$ will not apply to this design.

The foregoing calculations are based on Sec. 210.   While this method
is reasonable for prestressed concrete members at points where the tendons are near the bottom, the author feels that it is conservative at points
of low bending moment where the tendons are an appreciable distance
above the bottom.   All available test data show that the first sign of an
impending shear failure is a diagonal tension crack.   Thus it follows that
there will be no shear failure if the diagonal tension stress is below the
tensile strength of the concrete.   Diagonal tension stress can be computed
by Mohr's circle method.   This stress is usually greatest at the neutral
axis of the section.   It is suggested that the maximum allowable diagonal tension stress under ultimate load be $6\sqrt{f'_c}$.   Even if the diagonal tension proves low, the minimum web steel of $A_v = 0.0025b's$ should be used
unless the "unusually thick webs" provision of Sec. 210.2.3 is applicable.

Step 10. Compute camber.

In Step 7 we deliberately set the curve of the c.g.s. in a parabolic path
with e equal to zero at the ends of the member and 31.8 in. at the center
of span.   The bending moment due to F_i is $F_i e$.   Since e varies in a parabolic curve, the bending moment due to F_i will also vary in a parabolic
curve from zero at the ends of the member to $F_i e$ at the center of span.
Since a uniform load produces a parabolic bending-moment curve, it is

apparent that the tendons exert a uniform vertical load w_T against the member. Find w_T.

$$F_t e = 1,073,000 \times 31.8 = 34,100,000 \text{ in.-lb} = 2,841,000 \text{ ft-lb}$$

The formula for bending moment due to a uniform load is

$$M = \frac{wl^2}{8} \quad \text{or} \quad w = \frac{8M}{l^2}$$

Substituting,

$$w_T = \frac{8 \times 2,841,000}{100^2} = 2,271 \text{ lb per ft}$$

The vertical uplift of 2,271 lb per ft exerted by the tendons is offset by the 900-lb-per-ft dead weight of the member, so that the net uplift causing camber is $2,271 - 900 = 1,371$ lb per ft.

From Section 203.2.a

$$E_c = 1,800,000 + 500f'_c = 1,800,000 + 500\,(5,300) = 4,400,000$$

The standard formula for deflection (or camber) due to a uniform load is

$$\Delta = \frac{5wl^4}{384EI} = \frac{5 \times 1,371\,(100^4)\,12^3}{384 \times 4,400,000 \times 448,500} = 1.56 \text{ in.}$$

Since the concrete reached full strength before the tendons were tensioned, the member can be erected and subjected to the full dead load of the roof. If this is done, the growth in camber, Sec. 203.3, before the roof load is applied will be negligible.

Deflection due to roof load of $w_s = 1,290$ lb per ft will be

$$\Delta_s = \frac{5 \times 1,290\,(100^4)\,12^3}{384 \times 4,400,000 \times 448,500} = 1.47 \text{ in.}$$

The net camber under dead load of the member plus double T's and roofing is $1.56 - 1.47 = 0.09$ in. If camber growth per Sec. 203.3 is 150 per cent, the final camber will be

$$0.09 + 1.5\,(0.09) = 0.22 \text{ in.}$$

Deflection under a live load of 900 lb per lin ft will be

$$\Delta_L = \frac{5 \times 900\,(100^4)\,12^3}{384 \times 4,400,000 \times 448,500} = 1.00 \text{ in.}$$

11-4. End-block Details. In Step 7 we chose 10 Freyssinet cables 12/0.276 for the tendons in this example and arranged them in the pat-

tern shown in Fig. 11-4. As shown in Fig. 11-3 the c.g.s. is 36.3 in. above
the bottom at the center of bearing. Using this information and the
recommended spacing for Freyssinet cones from Art. 7-4, we can establish the pattern shown in Fig. 11-6.

Compare the details at the end of the member we are designing with
the factors mentioned in Sec. 214.3. The prestressing force is concentrated in as small a space as details will permit, which means that the
end block will have to distribute the force across the entire section.
There is no eccentricity, so the end block has no stresses from this factor.
Since this is a deep member and there are no conditions which require
a particularly heavy end block, we shall follow Sec. 214.3 and make the

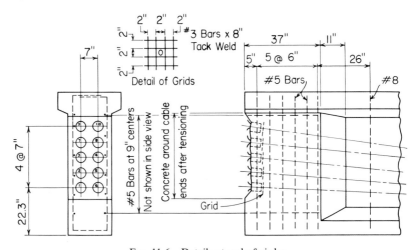

FIG. 11-6. Details at end of girder.

length of the end block about three-quarters of the beam depth, or 48 in.

As discussed in Art. 9-4 the reinforcing used in end blocks is based on
experience. Common practice for many designers of deep girders is to
use two #5 bars at 6-in. centers for the length of the end block and two
#5 bars at 9-in. centers for the height of the block. We have followed
this practice as shown in Fig. 11-6.

The details of the end block of a post-tensioned member include provision for distributing the load from the anchor fittings to the concrete.
Section 214.4 calls for a reinforcing grid beneath the anchorage. The
grid used with Freyssinet anchors is shown in Fig. 11-6. A similar grid
can be used with other types of anchor and should be based on the recommendations of the supplier of the anchor fitting. No grid is needed

when a bearing plate with welded steel tube attached like those shown in Fig. 7-18 is used in conjunction with a Roebling-type anchorage.

11-5. Friction in Tendons. When a tendon is post-tensioned, it elongates and therefore moves with respect to the tube or cored hole in which it is encased. The sliding of the tendon along the encasement creates friction, which reduces the tension in the tendon. The drop in tension due to friction increases with the distance from the jack and is a function of several factors as described in Sec. 208.2.1 of Tentative Recommendations for Prestressed Concrete.

Calculations in Step 6 of this chapter show that each Freyssinet cable in this girder should have an initial tension of 107,300 lb. This is the tension required at the center of span. We shall use the method outlined in Sec. 208.2.1 and compute the tension at the jack required to give 107,300 lb at the center of span. The applicable formula is

$$T_0 = T_X e^{(KL + \mu\alpha)}$$

We shall consider cable 9, since it and cable 10 have the greatest curvature and therefore the most friction. See Fig. 11-3 for the cable curvature and Figs. 11-4 and 11-6 for the location of cable 9. For cable 9 the factors in the equation have the following values:

$$T_X = 107,300$$
$$e = 2.718$$
$$L = 50 \text{ ft}$$
$$K = 0.0020$$
$$\mu = 0.30$$

The value of α is a function of the curvature of the cable. Since the cable is horizontal at the center of span, the angular change from the center of span to the end of the member is the angle of the cable at the end. This angle is computed by Eq. (11-3).

Elevation of cable above bottom at end of member = 50.30
Elevation of cable above bottom at center of span = 9.25

$$\text{Rise} = B = 41.05 \text{ in.}$$

$$X = 0$$
$$R = 100 \times 12 = 1,200$$

Substituting numerical values in Eq. (11-3),

$$\tan \phi = \frac{4 \times 41.05}{1,200} \left(1 - \frac{0}{1,200}\right) = 0.1368$$

The angle whose tangent is 0.1368 is 7° 47′ or 0.136 radian. Thus

$$\alpha = 0.136$$

Substituting numerical values,

$$T_0 = 107,300\,(2.718)^{(0.0020\times50+0.30\times0.136)}$$
$$= 107,300\,(2.718)^{0.141}$$
$$= 107,300\,(1.154) = 123,800 \text{ lb}$$
$$\text{Unit stress} = 123,800 \div 0.723 = 171,200 \text{ psi}$$
$$171,200 \div 236,000 = 72.5\% \text{ of ultimate}$$

Section 207.1.1 permits jack loads up to 80 per cent of ultimate as long as the load is relaxed before the anchor fittings are set so that the load in the tendon after anchoring does not exceed 70 per cent of ultimate. As the tension is partially relaxed at the jack, friction works in the opposite direction and there is no reduction in the tension at the center of span.

Similar computations should be made to determine the tension at the jacks for each of the other layers of cable. Since the other layers have less curvature, they will have less friction and therefore a lower tension at the jack.

11-6. Transformed Section. Throughout the calculations in this chapter we have used the properties computed for the section in Fig. 11-1 as a solid concrete member. Actually this member has 10 holes cored in it as shown in Fig. 11-4. Tendons are placed in these holes and tensioned, after which the holes are filled with grout. Obviously the actual stresses are not the same as those we have computed. We shall check the actual stresses at center of span.

Compute the properties of the section shown in Fig. 11-1 except with holes out for cables as shown in Fig. 11-4. The hole diameter is 1½ in., and the area is 1.77 sq in. Take moments about the bottom. Begin with totals from calculations in Step 1.

	A	y	Ay	Ay^2	I_o
	865		31,390	1,494,130	95,526
$-6 \times 1.77 =$	-10.6	2½	-26	-66	
$-4 \times 1.77 =$	-7.1	7%₁₆	-54	-408	
	847.3		31,310	1,493,656	95,526
				95,526	
				1,589,182	

$$y_b = 31,310 \div 847.3 = 37.0$$
$$y_t = 66 - 37 = 29.0$$
$$I = 1,589,182 - 847.3\,(37^2) = 429,000$$
$$Z_t = 429,000 \div 29 = 14,800$$
$$Z_b = 429,000 \div 37 = 11,600$$

We shall assume that the tendons are to be tensioned and grouted before the double T's are erected. This means that the member will carry its own dead weight while the holes are out. Check dead-load stresses using the moment from Step 2.

$$f^t{}_G = 13,500,000 \div 14,800 = \quad +912 \text{ psi}$$
$$f^b{}_G = 13,500,000 \div 11,600 = -1,164 \text{ psi}$$

When the tendons have been grouted, they will work with the concrete section and their area should be added to its properties. Since the grout is not prestressed, its area will not be included.

$$E_c = 1,800,000 + 500\,(5,300) = 4,400,000$$
$$E_s = 29,000,000 \qquad \text{(From Art. 5-7)}$$
$$n = \frac{E_s}{E_c} = \frac{29,000,000}{4,400,000} = 6.6$$

The area of each cable $= 0.723$ sq in., and it is equivalent to a concrete area of $6.6 \times 0.723 = 4.77$ sq in. Compute the properties of sections with holes out and tendons added. Begin with totals for calculations of the section with holes out.

	A	y	Ay	Ay^2	I_o
	847.3		31,310	1,493,656	95,526
$6 \times 4.77 =$	28.6	$2\frac{1}{2}$	71	178	
$4 \times 4.77 =$	19.1	$7\frac{9}{16}$	145	1,095	
	895.0		31,526	1,494,929	95,526
				95,526	
				1,590,455	

$$y_b = 31,526 \div 895 = 35.2$$
$$y_t = 66 - 35.2 = 30.8$$
$$I = 1,590,455 - 895\,(35.2)^2 = 480,500$$
$$Z_t = 480,500 \div 30.8 = 15,600$$
$$Z_b = 480,500 \div 35.2 = 13,650$$

Check stresses from applied loads using moments from Step 3.

$$f^t{}_s = 19,350,000 \div 15,600 = +1,240$$
$$f^b{}_s = 19,350,000 \div 13,650 = -1,417$$
$$f^t{}_L = 13,500,000 \div 15,600 = +865$$
$$f^b{}_L = 13,500,000 \div 13,650 = -989$$

Adding these stresses we get

$$f^t{}_{G+S+L} = +912 + 1,240 + 865 = +3,017$$
$$f^b{}_{G+S+L} = -1,164 - 1,417 - 989 = -3,570$$

From Table 11-2 the values obtained for these stresses based on a solid concrete cross section were

$$f^t{}_{G+S+L} = +3,069 \quad \text{and} \quad f^b{}_{G+S+L} = -3,753$$

Check the stresses due to F in the section with holes out.

$$e = 37.0 - 4.52 = 32.48$$

$$f^t{}_F = \frac{892,000}{847.3} - \frac{892,000 \times 32.48}{14,800} = -905$$

$$f^b{}_F = \frac{892,000}{847.3} + \frac{892,000 \times 32.48}{11,600} = +3,550$$

Then

$$f^t{}_{F+G+S+L} = -905 + 3,017 = +2,112$$
$$f^b{}_{F+G+S+L} = +3,550 - 3,570 = -20$$

From Table 11-2 the values obtained for these stresses using a solid concrete cross section were

$$f^t{}_{F+G+S+L} = +2,222 \quad \text{and} \quad f^b{}_{F+G+S+L} = -425$$

The foregoing calculations show that, in this case as in most cases, design based on a solid concrete cross section results in lower actual stresses than those found by computation. It is common practice to base pre-stressed concrete computations on a solid cross section, but the effect of the holes should be given consideration in each design and should be checked if there is any doubt about their influence on actual stresses.

CHAPTER 12

PILES

12-1. Advantages of Prestressed Piles. Prestressed concrete piles have several properties which make them preferable to other types for many applications.

They withstand severe driving conditions without cracking or spalling. A nonprestressed concrete pile will crack as it recoils from a heavy hammer blow. When the hammer strikes, its force creates compression in the pile which causes an elastic shortening. As soon as the energy of the hammer is expended and there is no force to maintain the elastic shortening, the pile springs back to its original length. By the time it reaches its original length, it has gathered momentum, causing further elongation which in turn creates tensile stresses in the pile. Under a heavy hammer blow these tensile stresses cause cracks, and under repeated blows spalling develops. Prestressed concrete piles are fabricated with sufficient compressive stress to offset the tensile stresses caused by recoil. Experience indicates that an initial compressive stress of 800 psi is normally sufficient for this purpose.[1]* Where especially severe driving conditions exist, the magnitude of the prestress should be increased. Final determination of the amount required is a matter of trial and experience with the existing driving conditions.

Prestressed concrete piles are easy to lift and transport. Their compressive stress enables them to resist large bending moments, so that they can be lifted with simple one- or two-point picks where reinforced concrete piles of the same dimensions require complicated rigging for multi-point picks.

Prestressed concrete piles are durable because they are crackless. They are seldom cracked by driving or handling, and even if they should be, the compressive stress will keep the cracks tightly closed once the pile is in place.

A prestressed concrete pile has a much higher moment of inertia than a reinforced pile of the same dimensions. In a prestressed pile the entire cross-sectional area of the concrete contributes to the moment of inertia,

---

* Superscript numbers indicate references listed in the Bibliography at the end of the chapter.

while in a reinforced pile the concrete in the tensile side has no function and only the reinforcing contributes to the moment of inertia. This additional moment of inertia is important in piles whose capacity is determined by their slenderness ratio.

12-2. Details of an 18-in.-square Pretensioned Pile. Figure 12-1 shows details of a typical pretensioned square pile. It has the following properties:

$A_c = 18 \times 18 = 324$ sq in.
$I = 18^4/12 = 8750$ in.^{4}
$Z = 18^3/6 = 972$ in.^{3}
Initial prestressing force $F_I = 20 \times 14,000 = 280,000$ lb
Initial prestress $f_{F_I} = 280,000 \div 324 = 864$ psi
Final prestressing force $F = 20 \times 11,200 = 224,000$ lb
Final prestress $f_F = 224,000 \div 324 = 692$ psi
Weight $= 324 \times {}^{150}\!/_{144} = 338$ lb per ft
Minimum f'_c at time of driving $= 5,000$ psi

Compute the maximum length that can be handled without cracking. Use a moment equal to that caused by the dead weight of the pile plus 50 per cent impact. Since handling is a temporary condition, we allow a temporary tensile stress near the modulus of rupture. For 5,000-psi concrete we shall allow 600-psi tensile stress. Actually the tensile stress will probably be less than this because the pile is usually handled and driven before all creep, shrinkage, etc., are complete so that the unit compressive stress in the pile is higher than the final prestress on which the computations are based.

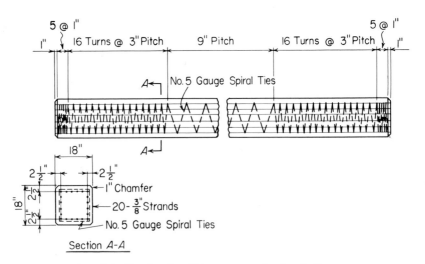

Section *A-A*

FIG. 12-1. Details of an 18-in.-square pretensioned pile.

Under the foregoing conditions the total allowable stress change due to bending moment is $692 + 600 = 1,292$ psi. This represents a moment of $(1,292 \times 972) \div 12 = 104,500$ ft-lb. Including 50 per cent impact the effective weight of the pile is

$$338 \times 1.50 = 507 \text{ lb per ft}$$

Using the data in Fig. 12-2, compute the maximum length for a two-point pick.

$$M_A = 0.022wL^2$$

Substituting numerical values,

$$104,500 = 0.022 \times 507L^2$$
$$L^2 = 9,400 \qquad L = 97 \text{ ft}$$

Using the data in Fig. 12-3, compute the maximum length for a one-point pick.

$$M_A = 0.045wL^2$$

Substituting numerical values,

$$104,500 = 0.045 \times 507L^2$$
$$L^2 = 4,600 \qquad L = 68 \text{ ft}$$

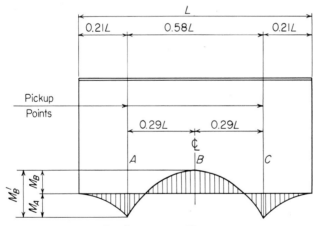

Bending-moment Diagram

$$M_A = \frac{w(0.21L)^2}{2} = 0.022\,wL^2$$

$$M_B' = \frac{w(0.58L)^2}{8} = 0.042\,wL^2$$

$$M_B = 0.042\,wL^2 - 0.022\,wL^2 = 0.020\,wL^2$$

Fig. 12-2. Bending moments for lifting a pile with a two-point pick.

12-3. Capacity of a Prestressed Concrete Pile. Neither Tentative Recommendations for Prestressed Concrete nor any other currently recognized specification for prestressed concrete includes criteria for determining the capacity of prestressed concrete compression members.   The
chief reason for this is lack of test data.   The formulas for allowable stresses
in compression members which are presented in specifications for steel
and reinforced concrete are largely empirical, being based on numerous
tests of members with various slenderness ratios.   Empirical formulas
have been used because none of the theoretical methods of column analysis give results consistent with test results on actual columns.

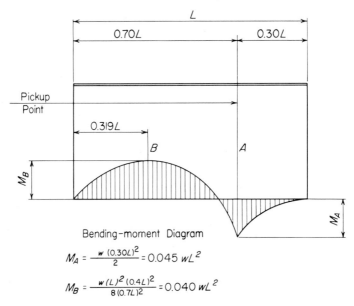

$$M_A = \frac{w\,(0.30L)^2}{2} = 0.045\ wL^2$$

$$M_B = \frac{w\,(L)^2\,(0.4L)^2}{8\,(0.7L)^2} = 0.040\ wL^2$$

Fig. 12-3. Bending moments for lifting a pile with a one-point pick.

Our object here will be to establish conservative values of allowable
stress which can be used until test data are available for establishing an
accurate empirical formula.   Since the chief use of prestressed concrete
compression members is as piles, we shall base our analysis on the
properties of typical piles with the following properties:

$f'_c = 5{,}000$ psi
$f_{F_I} = 800$ psi
$f_F = 640$ psi
Final stress in strands $= 140{,}000$ psi
$E_c = 2{,}000{,}000$ (for long-time loading)
$E_s = 27{,}000{,}000$

First we must establish the allowable stress in a relatively short, thick column where buckling is not the primary cause of failure. Short compression members fail in one of two ways, depending upon the properties of the material in the member. For materials which are brittle or nonductile, failure occurs by crushing or diagonal shear at approximately the ultimate compressive strength of the material. For ductile materials failure occurs by buckling when the compressive stress reaches the yield strength of the material. The yielding of the material is the primary cause of failure and leads to buckling. Arguments can be offered to show both that 5,000-psi concrete is a ductile material and that it is not. Since we are leaning toward the conservative side, we shall assume that it is ductile until actual test data are available. The stress-strain curve of 5,000-psi concrete does not have a definite yield point. Its slope does begin to increase more rapidly beyond 4,000 psi, so we shall take this as the yield point and the basis of computing the allowable stress.

In a prestressed concrete beam the compressive stress provided by the tendons is reduced by the application of the live load. The same thing is true, to a lesser degree, in a prestressed concrete compression member. As the live load is applied, it creates a compressive stress in the concrete which in turn causes an elastic shortening of the member. Since the tendons are an integral part of the member, they, too, shorten and undergo a loss of tensile stress proportional to their shortening. This decrease in tensile stress in the tendons decreases the compressive stress that the tendons have created in the concrete. The net result is that the compressive stress developed in the concrete by application of an external load is something less than the load divided by the area of the concrete section.

We shall determine the net increase in compressive stress due to the application of a live load. In this analysis we shall use the following symbols in addition to those which are standard:

P = total applied external load
P_c = portion of P carried by increase in concrete stress
P_s = portion of P carried as a result of decrease in stress in tendons
Δ = net shortening of member

From these definitions it is apparent that

$$P = P_c + P_s \tag{12-1}$$

Using the standard equation for elongation we can write for the concrete

$$\Delta = \frac{P_c L}{A_c E_c} \tag{12-2}$$

For the steel

$$\Delta = \frac{P_s L}{A_s E_s} \tag{12-3}$$

Since the right-hand sides of Eqs. (12-2) and (12-3) are both equal to Δ, they are equal to each other or

$$\frac{P_c L}{A_c E_c} = \frac{P_s L}{A_s E_s}$$

from which

$$P_s = P_c \frac{A_s E_s}{A_c E_c}$$

Substituting in Eq. (12-1),

$$P = P_c + P_c \frac{A_s E_s}{A_c E_c}$$

$$= P_c \left(1 + \frac{A_s E_s}{A_c E_c}\right)$$

or

$$P_c = \frac{P}{1 + (A_s E_s / A_c E_c)} \qquad (12\text{-}4)$$

As already listed in the properties of typical piles

$$E_c = 2{,}000{,}000$$

and

$$E_s = 27{,}000{,}000$$

Values for A_c and A_s will be dependent upon the size of pile chosen, but the ratio will still be $A_s / A_c = 640 / 140{,}000 = 0.00456$. Substituting numerical values in Eq. (12-4),

$$P_c = \frac{P}{1 + \dfrac{0.00456 \times 27{,}000{,}000}{2{,}000{,}000}} = 0.94P$$

Thus in a pile with the typical properties used here, the actual increase in compressive stress due to an applied load of P would be $0.94P/A_c$.

Our pile has a yield strength of 4,000 psi and a final prestress of 640 psi, or an available stress of $4{,}000 - 640 = 3{,}360$ psi. In terms of external load which can be applied to the pile, this is $3{,}360 \div 0.94 = 3{,}580$ psi. For short columns of this type a factor of safety of 4 is usual, which gives an allowable applied load of $3{,}580 \div 4 = 895$, say 900 psi. This means that in the range of short columns, up to the point where capacity is determined by buckling rather than the yield strength of the material, the allowable applied load is 900 psi.

The function of the test data in setting up the empirical formulas used for steel and reinforced concrete columns was to determine the slenderness ratio at which buckling becomes the controlling factor and to establish allowable stresses for slenderness ratios above this point. In the absence of test data we shall follow the general pattern of the empirical formulas, leaning toward the conservative side.

When compared with actual test data Euler's column formula has been found to be on the conservative side for values of L/r, slenderness ratio, of 120 and up. We can therefore use his formula for this range. Euler's basic formula is

$$P' = \frac{\pi^2 EI}{L^2}$$

Since $I = Ar^2$, this can be rewritten

$$P' = \frac{\pi^2 EAr^2}{L^2}$$

or $\qquad\qquad \dfrac{P'}{A} = \dfrac{\pi^2 E}{(L/r)^2}$ $\qquad\qquad$ (12-5)

Note that P'/A is the unit compressive stress in the member. In Euler's formula P' is the load at which the column will buckle. Since this is the ultimate strength of the column, a factor of safety must be applied in determining the allowable load. For other materials with L/r of 120 and up a factor of safety of 2 is common and will be used here. Substituting in Eq. (12-5) we can establish the following values:

$\dfrac{L}{r}$	$\dfrac{P'}{A}$	Allowable compressive stress using factor of safety = 2
120	1,376	688
130	1,170	585
140	1,010	505
150	880	440
160	774	387

Plot these values of allowable stress and L/r in Fig. 12-4. The factor of 0.94 has not been applied in determining allowable stresses by the Euler formula because failure in long columns is due to buckling and therefore is a function of the modulus of elasticity of the material rather than the stress at which it yields. As pointed out in Art. 1-5 the compressive stress created by the tendons should not be included when computing the load which will cause buckling.

We have now established the allowable stresses for the ranges of short columns and long columns, but not for intermediate lengths. The empirical formulas for allowable column stresses are all of the "straight-line" type. That is, on a chart like Fig. 12-4, the straight line begins at the point where buckling controls the column capacity and shows a straight line or uniform decrease in allowable stress which is proportional to the increase in L/r. Since the member we are considering is spiral-wrapped

222   *Piles*

and prestressed, it is stiffer and able to carry a higher load than a spiral-wrapped reinforced concrete column in the length range where buckling determines the capacity of the reinforced column. Under the ACI

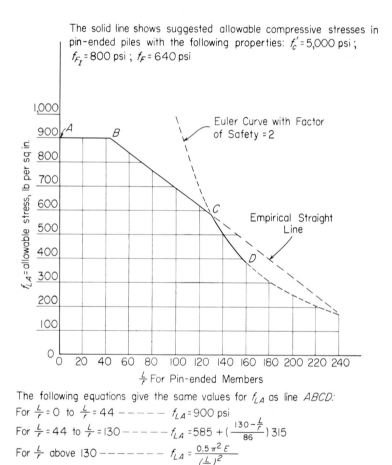

The solid line shows suggested allowable compressive stresses in pin-ended piles with the following properties: $f_c' = 5,000$ psi ; $f_{F_I} = 800$ psi ; $f_F = 640$ psi

Euler Curve with Factor of Safety = 2

Empirical Straight Line

f_{LA} = allowable stress, lb per sq in.

$\frac{L}{r}$ For Pin-ended Members

The following equations give the same values for f_{LA} as line *ABCD*:

For $\frac{L}{r} = 0$ to $\frac{L}{r} = 44$ ----- $f_{LA} = 900$ psi

For $\frac{L}{r} = 44$ to $\frac{L}{r} = 130$ ----- $f_{LA} = 585 + (\frac{130 - \frac{L}{r}}{86}) 315$

For $\frac{L}{r}$ above 130 ------- $f_{LA} = \frac{0.5 \pi^2 E}{(\frac{L}{r})^2}$

FIG. 12-4. Suggested allowable applied compressive stresses in a pile having the properties listed.

Building Code the capacity of spiral-wrapped reinforced concrete columns is a function of their slenderness ratio when L/d is greater than 10, i.e., L/r is greater than 34.5. The formula given in the ACI Code is $P/A = 0.225f'_c(1.3 - 0.03L/d)$. We shall apply this formula to see what length of reinforced concrete column would be safe when $P/A = 900$ psi. The stress available, f'_c, is $5,000 - 640 = 4,360$ psi. Then

$$900 = 0.225 \times 4,360 \left(1.3 - \frac{0.03L}{d} \right)$$

$$1.3 - \frac{0.03L}{d} = 0.917$$

$$\frac{0.03L}{d} = 0.383$$

$$\frac{L}{d} = 12.75$$

For a square solid section $r = 0.289d$; thus $L/r = 12.75 \div 0.289 = 44$. Our curve in Fig. 12-4 should be on the conservative side if it begins to slope down from 900 psi at $L/r = 44$. The curve in Fig. 12-4 is made up of the following parts:

A to *B* Short column range governed by the yield strength of the material.

B to *C* Arbitrary straight line with pattern similar to those in the empirical standards that are based on test results. Point *C* has been located at $L/r = 130$ rather than 120 to bring the straight line into the same relation with the bottom of the Euler curve that exists in the empirical formulas based on tests of other material.

C to *D* Long column range based on Euler formula with factor of safety of 2.

The curve in Fig. 12-4 applies to piles with a minimum amount of prestress. Many piles will have higher prestress because of handling, hard driving conditions, or other details. We shall check allowable stresses for a pile having $f'_c = 5,000$ psi, $f_{F_1} = 1,000$ psi, and $f_F = 800$ psi. Following the pattern of calculations used to establish the curve in Fig. 12-4 we find that line *AB* at 900 psi has a factor of safety of 3.82. This is well within reason. Line *CD* will not change, since it is dependent upon E_c rather than the strength of the material. Since *AB* and *CD* are the same, it follows that *BC* will be the same. This means that the curve on Fig. 12-4 can be applied to piles with f_{F_1} from 800 to 1,000 psi.

The length *L* used in Eqs. (12-2), (12-3), and (12-5) and in Fig. 12-4 is the unsupported length of the member if it is pin-ended (free to rotate at each end) and restrained from horizontal movement at each end. An equivalent value of *L* should be used where other end conditions exist.

When the member is fixed at one end (prevented from rotating), pinned at the other, and prevented from horizontal movement, the L used in the formula should be 70 per cent of the unsupported length of the member.

When the member is fixed at both ends and prevented from horizontal motion, the L used in the formula should be 50 per cent of the unsupported length of the member.

When the member is fixed and prevented from horizontal motion at one end but pinned and free to move horizontally at the other, the L used in the formula should be the unsupported length of the member.

12-4. Combined Bending and Direct Load. For members subjected to a combination of bending plus direct compression the condition governing maximum allowable loads is usually the compressive stress in the concrete. The limiting condition is expressed by Eq. (12-6).

$$\frac{f_L}{f_{LA}} + \frac{f_M}{f_{MA}} \lessgtr 1 \tag{12-6}$$

in which

f_L = compressive stress due to direct load
f_M = compressive stress due to bending moment
f_{LA} = allowable compressive stress under direct load (see Fig. 12-4)
f_{MA} = allowable compressive stress due to bending moment

When the bending moment is high and the direct load is low, the stress on the tensile side of the member may be the critical factor. In this case the ultimate strength of the member in bending should be computed and should show a factor of safety of at least 2.

12-5. Numerical Examples. The load-carrying capacity of a pile is more often determined by the capacity of the soil to support load than by the structural strength of the pile. In the following examples we shall compute the capacity of the pile based on its structural strength. For those cases where this is greater than the soil capacity, the soil capacity would be the governing factor.

Each of the following examples is based on the 18-in.-square pile shown in Fig. 12-1. Its properties and prestress are itemized at the beginning of Art. 12-2.

Example 1. Find the maximum allowable compressive load that can be applied to the pile when its unsupported length is 35 ft and it is pinned at both ends and prevented from horizontal motion.

$$r = 18 \times 0.289 = 5.2$$
$$\frac{L}{r} = \frac{35 \times 12}{5.2} = 80.7$$

From Fig. 12-4 the allowable stress for $L/r = 80.7$ is 765 psi. The allowable load on the column is $765 \times 324 = 248,000$ lb.

Example 2. Find the maximum allowable compressive load that can be applied to the pile when its unsupported length is 30 ft and it is fixed at one end and pinned but prevented from horizontal motion at the other end.

From Art. 12-3 a length factor of 70 per cent is used with this combination of end conditions. Thus

$$\frac{L}{r} = \frac{30 \times 12 \times 0.70}{5.2} = 48.5$$

From Fig. 12-4 the allowable stress is 885 psi and the total allowable load on the column is $885 \times 324 = 287,000$ lb.

Example 3. Find the maximum allowable compressive load that can be applied to the pile when its unsupported length is 30 ft and it is fixed at one end and pinned but prevented from horizontal motion at the other and subjected to a bending moment of 800,000 in.-lb.

This problem is covered by Eq. (12-6) established in Art. 12-4. The unit stress due to the bending moment is $f_M = 800,000 \div 972 = 822$ psi. The allowable compression in a bridge member subjected to bending is given in Sec. 207.3.2.a of Tentative Recommendations for Prestressed Concrete as $0.40f'_c$. In this case f'_c should be taken as the available stress after prestress, or $5,000 - 640 = 4,360$ psi. Then $f'_{MA} = 4,360 \times 0.40 = 1,745$ psi. Substituting numerical values in Eq. (12-6),

$$\frac{f_L}{f_{LA}} + \frac{822}{1,745} = 1$$

$$\frac{f_L}{f_{LA}} = 1 - 0.471 = 0.529$$

$$\frac{L}{r} = \frac{30 \times 12 \times .70}{5.2} = 48.5$$

From Fig. 12-4

$$f_{LA} = 885 \text{ psi}$$

$$\frac{f_L}{885} = 0.529$$

$$f_L = 468 \text{ psi}$$

Total allowable compressive load on the column is $468 \times 324 = 151,500$ lb.

Example 4. Check the pile to see if it will carry a direct load of 160,000 lb plus a moment of 640,000 in.-lb when it is fixed at both ends and has an unsupported length of 60 ft.

For this combination of end conditions a length factor of 50 per cent is applicable.

$$\frac{L}{r} = \frac{60 \times 12 \times 0.50}{5.2} = 69$$

From Fig. 12-4, $f_{LA} = 810$ psi

From Example 3 for this same pile

$$f_{MA} = 1,745 \text{ psi}$$
$$f_L = 160,000 \div 324 = 494$$
$$f_M = 640,000 \div 972 = 658$$

Substituting in Eq. (12-6),

$$\frac{494}{810} + \frac{658}{1,745} = 0.610 + 0.377 = 0.987$$

Since this is less than 1, the pile can safely carry these loads.

Example 5. Compute the allowable bending moment in the pile as determined by the tensile side of the pile. This is based on ultimate strength. Use the formula in Sec. 209.2.1.(a) of Tentative Recommendations for Prestressed Concrete.

$$M_u = A_s f_{su} d \left(1 - \frac{k_2}{k_1 k_3} \frac{p f_{su}}{f'_c} \right) \tag{a}$$

Consider the strands on the tension side of the center line of cross section of the pile as acting in tension. From Fig. 12-5

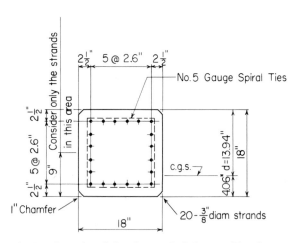

Center of gravity of the 10 strands being considered

$$\begin{array}{ll}
6 \times 2.5'' = 15.0 \\
4 \times 6.4'' = 25.6 \\
\hline
10 \qquad\quad 40.6 \div 10 = 4.06''
\end{array}$$

Fig. 12-5. Determination of center of gravity of strands acting in tension at ultimate bending moment. See Example 5 in text.

$$d = 13.94$$
$$A_s = 10 \times 0.0799 = 0.799$$
$$f'_s = 20,000 \div 0.0799 = 250,000$$
$$f'_c = 5,000$$
$$p = 0.799 \div 324 = 0.00247$$
$$\frac{k_2}{k_1 k_3} = 0.6$$

$$f_{su} = f'_s \left(1 - 0.5 \; \frac{p f'_s}{f'_c}\right)$$

$$f_{su} = 250,000 \left(1 - 0.5 \; \frac{0.00247 \times 250,000}{5,000}\right)$$

$$f_{su} = 234,500$$

Substituting in (*a*),

$$M_u = 0.799 \times 234,500 \times 13.94 \left(1 - .6 \; \frac{0.00247 \times 234,500}{5,000}\right)$$

$$= 2,430,000 \text{ in.-lb}$$

With a factor of safety of 2 this means a maximum allowable moment of 1,215,000 in.-lb.

From Example 3 the allowable $f_{MA} = 1,745$. The moment due to this would be $1,745 \times 972 = 1,700,000$ in.-lb. If the maximum moment of 1,215,000 in.-lb is used,

$$\frac{f_M}{f_{MA}} = \frac{1,215,000}{1,700,000} = 0.714$$

This leaves only $1 - 0.714 = 0.286 f_{LA}$ available for direct load. Since load combinations of this type are seldom found in practice, the allowable combination of bending and direct loads is usually determined by Eq. (12-6).

12-6. Typical Details of Pretensioned Piles. The majority of pretensioned bearing piles are of either square or octagonal cross section. The small-diameter piles are solid, and the larger diameter piles have cored holes. Figures 12-6 and 12-7 show properties of the popular sizes of square and octagonal piles.

Driving tips can be blunt, as shown in Fig. 12-1, or tapered to suit the existing driving conditions. For a soft rock layer found beneath the surface in parts of Florida the state road department's standard pile drawings show a 12-ft-long wide-flange beam tip. Six feet of the beam are cast in the end of the pile, and 6 feet project beyond the end.

The seven-wire strands are allowed to project from the top of the pile where they can be used to tie the pile more securely to the pile cap or where a build-up to raise the elevation of the top of the pile may be needed.

Past experience must be considered when designing piles with cored holes. Small-diameter piles with cored holes frequently crack and fail when subjected to hard driving conditions. Although specific proof is lacking, it is believed that the reason for this is that the core cannot be kept exactly central in the pile until the concrete has set. Under hard driving, the eccentricity of the core creates stress concentrations severe enough to cause failure. Experience indicates that 24-in. piles with 12-in.-

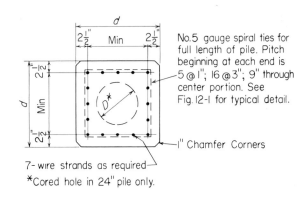

No.5 gauge spiral ties for full length of pile. Pitch beginning at each end is 5 @ 1"; 16 @ 3"; 9" through center portion. See Fig. 12-1 for typical detail.

1" Chamfer Corners

7-wire strands as required

*Cored hole in 24" pile only.

d	Hole diam, in.	Min No. of strands*	A_c, sq in.	Z, in.³	r, in.
12	Solid	12–5⁄16	144	288	3.47
14	Solid	12–3⁄8	196	457	4.05
18	Solid	20–3⁄8	324	972	5.20
20	Solid	20–7⁄16	400	1,333	5.78
24	12	24–7⁄16	463	2,220	7.60

*For severe driving conditions or handling long lengths of pile it may be necessary to increase the number of strands.

FIG. 12-6. Typical details of square pretensioned piles.

diameter cored holes can be driven satisfactorily. Some designers also specify 20-in.-square piles with 12-in.-diameter holes and 20-in.-octagonal piles with 11-in.-diameter holes.

When a hole is cored in a pile, it usually extends the full length of the pile so that the pile is open at each end. A pile should not be cast with a cored hole for most of its length and then an abrupt change to a solid section for a short distance at the end. Under driving conditions the abrupt change of section creates stress concentrations which cause failure in the region of the change in section.   If a cored hole must be used in conjunction with a solid end, the change in section should be made gradually, using a cone-shaped core to taper the hole from full diameter to a point.   The length of the cone should be about twice the diameter of the hole.

Since prestressed concrete piles are often subjected to much harder driving than reinforced concrete piles, something must be done to pre-

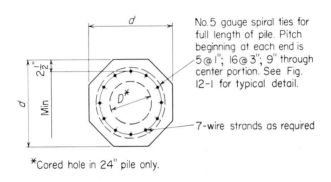

No. 5 gauge spiral ties for full length of pile. Pitch beginning at each end is 5 @ 1"; 16 @ 3"; 9" through center portion. See Fig. 12-1 for typical detail.

— 7-wire strands as required

*Cored hole in 24" pile only.

d	Hole diam, in.	Min No. of strands*	A_c, sq in.	Z, in.³	r, in.
12	Solid	7–⅜	119	189	3.08
14	Solid	10–⅜	162	300	3.60
18	Solid	16–⅜	268	640	4.63
20	Solid	22–⅜	331	876	5.14
24	12	18–⁷⁄₁₆	364	1,430	6.86

*For severe driving conditions or handling long lengths of pile it may be necessary to increase the number of strands.

Fig. 12-7.   Typical details of octagonal pretensioned piles.

vent serious damage to the top of the pile by the hammer blows.   The most common type of cushion between the top of the pile and the hammer is about 6 in. of a soft wood.   This can be made of several layers of scrap lumber.   These cushions must be replaced before they become so compressed that they do not supply the desired cushioning effect.   Sometimes two or even more cushions are needed in driving one long pile.   In addition some pile drivers use a piece of 2-in. hemp wound in a tight spiral and laid on the concrete beneath the wooden cushion.

12-7. Pretensioned Sheet Piles. Although pretensioned sheet piles are durable and have the required structural strength, they have not proved so economically competitive as pretensioned bearing piles. In order to provide room for the tongue and groove, thicknesses are from 8 in. up.

Pretensioned piles have proved economical as a combination sheet and bearing pile. In this case square piles are used with a tongue on one face and a groove on the other.

12-8. Circular Bearing Piles. Large-diameter circular piles of the post-tensioned type prove especially economical on projects where conditions are favorable to their use. In the United States the majority of these piles are produced by Raymond International Incorporated. Details are shown in Fig. 12-8. These piles are best described by the following quotation from Raymond's catalogue:

Description of the Pile—The Raymond Cylinder Pile is a hollow, cylindrical, precast, prestressed concrete pile, made of a series of sections placed end-to-end and held together by cables of high strength steel wire. The pile sections are manufactured by various processes, similar to the manner in which concrete pipe is commonly made.

Each section is reinforced with a small amount of longitudinal and spiral steel to facilitate handling. Longitudinal holes for the prestressing wires are cored in the walls of the sections.

The sections are placed end-to-end with cable holes in alignment. A plastic joint compound completely seals the section joints. The strength of the hardened plastic both in tension and in compression is greater than that of the concrete itself.

The number of cables can be varied, depending on the size of the pile and use. The cables usually consist of 12 No. 6 gage high tensile wires.

After all the cables in the pile have been tensioned by means of jacks, the ends of the cables are anchored temporarily with metal locking cones. Cement grout is pumped into the cable holes under pressure. After the grout has hardened the locking cones are removed.

Concrete—A dense, high quality, impervious concrete of 5,000 psi to 10,000 psi is attained according to the type of precasting method used. Several specially developed precasting methods have been successfully employed to meet construction requirements most economically.

Structural Strength—Of particular significance to the designer is the great structural strength developed by the Raymond Cylinder Pile which permits combined axial loads and bending moments of considerable magnitude.

High Capacity—In most cases, the Raymond Cylinder Pile is driven open end. The large area in contact with the soil provides greater resistance and, therefore, economy. Where underlying soil conditions permit, design loads of 200 or more tons per pile are feasible.

Long Life—This pile of prestressed concrete has many inherent qualities that insure a long life with no maintenance costs. It is non-combustible, and is highly resistant to corrosion and to damage by marine life and water action.

Adaptability—The Raymond Cylinder Pile is generally manufactured in standard

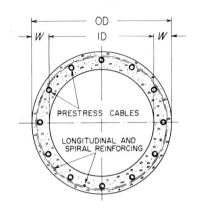

Standard sizes

OD	W , in.	Number of prestressing cables
36	4 and 4 ½	8-12 or 16
54	4 ½ and 5	12-16 or 24

While present output is standardized to the two sizes given in the above table, other sizes and wall thicknesses, as listed in the table below, can be furnished, provided the project is of sufficient size to warrant the purchase of the special equipment required.

Properties for Design

OD	ID	Wall Thickness	Area, in.^{2}	I, in^4	Z, in^3	r, in.	Circumference	Volume Per Foot, ft^3	Weight Per Foot, lb	Concrete Design Stress Per Cable, lb/sq in.
*24	16	4	251	13,060	1,089	7.2	75	1.74	262	166.0
	15	4½	276	13,810	1,150	7.1	75	1.92	288	150.5
	14	5	298	14,380	1,198	6.9	75	2.07	310	139.5
30	22	4	327	28,200	1,880	9.3	94	2.27	341	127.2
	21	4½	361	30,170	2,010	9.1	94	2.50	376	115.0
	20	5	393	31,800	2,120	9.0	94	2.73	410	106.0
*36	28	4	402	52,200	2,900	11.4	113	2.79	419	103.5
	27	4½	445	56,400	3,130	11.3	113	3.09	463	93.6
	26	5	487	60,000	3,330	11.1	113	3.38	507	85.5
42	34	4	477	87,000	4,140	13.5	132	3.32	497	87.3
	33	4½	530	94,800	4,520	13.4	132	3.68	551	78.6
	32	5	581	102,000	4,850	13.2	132	4.04	605	71.7
	30	6	679	113,300	5,390	12.9	132	4.72	708	61.3
48	40	4	553	134,900	5,620	15.6	151	3.84	576	75.3
	39	4½	615	146,700	6,100	15.4	151	4.27	641	67.7
	38	5	675	158,100	6,600	15.3	151	4.69	703	61.7
	36	6	792	178,000	7,400	15.0	151	5.50	826	52.6
*54	46	4	628	197,400	7,320	17.7	170	4.36	655	66.4
	45	4½	700	216,000	8,000	17.6	170	4.86	728	59.5
	44	5	770	233,000	8,630	17.4	170	5.35	802	54.2
	42	6	904	264,000	9,770	17.1	170	6.28	941	46.1

✱ Standard sizes

FIG. 12-8. Details of Raymond Concrete Pile Co. circular post-tensioned piles.

diameters of 36 and 54 inches. The cylinder wall thickness can be varied. The number of prestressing cables ranges from eight to sixteen or even more for special requirements. The pile can be cut off at any place in its length without injury or impairment to its structural strength. The driving of the pile is accomplished by established methods and heavy-duty pile driving equipment. Piles 192 feet long have been driven. Lengths in excess of this can be furnished.

BIBLIOGRAPHY

1. Dean, W. E.: Prestressed Concrete—Difficulties Overcome in Florida Bridge Practice, *Civil Eng.,* June, 1957, pp. 60–63. See p. 61.
2. Remington, William F., and George F. Nicholson: Prestressed Piles Look Good in Tests, *Western Construct.,* August, 1956, p. 58.
3. Pretensioned Piles Are 132 Feet Long, *Eng. News-Record,* July 19, 1956, pp. 33–36.
4. Lin, T. Y.: A Prestressed Column under Eccentric Loading, *J. Prestressed Concrete Inst.,* December, 1957.

CHAPTER 13

TYPICAL MEMBERS AND STRUCTURES

13-1. AASHO-PCI Bridge Beams. One of the most economical types of prestressed concrete bridges is that composed of precast pretensioned I beams and poured-in-place concrete deck slab which function as a composite structure.[1-5]* In 1957 a joint committee composed of members from the American Association of State Highway Officials and the Prestressed Concrete Institute established a series of Standard Prestressed Concrete Beams for Highway Bridge Spans 30 Feet to 100 Feet designed for use with a poured-in-place slab.[24] Chapter 9 covers the design of a typical bridge using these beams. Details of the bridge and its beams are shown in Figs. 9-1, 9-2, 9-5, 9-6, 9-15, and 9-16.

Details and properties of the AASHO-PCI standard beams are shown in Fig. 13-1. The following notes appear on the drawing with the standard beam:

General Notes for AASHO-PCI Standard Beams

SPECIFICATIONS: "AASHO Standard Specifications for Highway Bridges" 1953, and "Criteria for Prestressed Concrete Bridges, U.S. Bureau of Public Roads" 1954, together with any subsequent revisions of either with particular reference to revisions based on "Recommended Practice for Prestressed Concrete, ACI-ASCE Joint Committee 323."

LIVE LOAD: All Highway Live Loads as specified in AASHO Standard Specifications for Highway Bridges.

PURPOSE: The purpose of the beams shown on this sheet shall be to establish a limited number of simple, practical sections leading to uniformity and simplicity of practice, forming, and production methods, and which are applicable to all conditions of highway bridge loading and to all spans within the approximate limits shown. The purpose is specifically not to disrupt or supplant established prestressed concrete beam practice utilizing present plants and forms. Beams of similar cross sections but with minor dimensional differences, manufactured with presently established plant facilities and which comply with structural and geometric requirements for any particular project may be substituted upon submission by the Producer of data necessary to show compliance with job requirements and approval by the Engineer.

---

* Superscript numbers indicate references listed in the Bibliography at the end of the chapter.

SPAN LIMITS: Span limits shown for each beam are approximate only and are not mandatory at either limit. Lateral spacing of beams shall be varied in keeping with the requirements of span and loading. The span limits shown contemplate the use of concrete weighing 150 pounds per cubic foot, cast-in-place deck slabs 6″

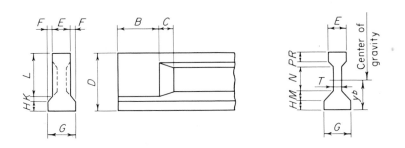

Beam type	I	II	III	IV
Recommended spans, ft	30–45	40–60	55–80	70–100
Area, sq in.	276	369	560	789
Moment of inertia, in.[4]	22,750	50,980	125,390	260,730
y^b, in.	12.59	15.83	20.27	24.73
Dimensions, in.				
B	24	24	42	54
C	6	6	9	12
D	28	36	45	54
E	12	12	16	20
F	2	3	3	3
G	16	18	22	26
H	5	6	7	8
K	2	3	3	3
L	21	27	35	43
M	5	6	7½	9
N	11	15	19	23
P	3	3	4½	6
R	4	6	7	8
T	6	6	7	8
Diaphragm locations	Center of span		Third points of span	

Fig. 13-1. Standard prestressed concrete beams for highway-bridge spans 30 to 100 ft. Published 1957 by Joint Committee of American Association of State Highway Officials and Prestressed Concrete Institute. These beams are designed for use in beam and slab bridges of the type designed in Chap. 9. See text for general notes.

to 8″ thick composed of concrete with f'_c not less than 3,000 psi and having elastic properties approximately equal to that of the beam concrete. All dead load is assumed to be carried by the beam alone with live load carried by the beam and slab composite section.

At the upper limit of length shown for each beam, using concrete in the beams of the minimum strengths recommended below, the full allowable working stresses listed in the "Criteria," a sufficient portion of the prestressed tendons draped to compensate for dead load of the beam at midspan and to maintain allowable working stresses at ends, and H20-S16-44 loading, the approximate lateral spacing for Beams I and II is 4'-8" requiring 7 beams per span with 28-ft. roadway; for Beams III and IV approximate lateral spacing is 5'-6" requiring 6 beams per span with 28-ft roadway. Under the same conditions and loading, for the lower span limit shown for each beam the allowable lateral spacing, with all straight prestressing tendons, is 8 to 9 feet requiring 4 beams per span with 28-ft roadway. Allowable lateral spacing will be subject to some variation depending on slab thickness, diaphragms, allowance for wearing surface and other job variables.

By using light weight concrete, or reduced lateral spacing, or live loadings lighter than H20-S16-44, span limits may be increased.

CONCRETE: Recommended minimum strengths for concrete in beams are $f'_c = 5,000$ psi; at transfer of stressing force, $f'_{ci} = 4,000$ psi. Concrete of greater or less compressive strength, but not less than $f'_c = 4,000$ psi, may be used in which case allowable working stresses and resulting utility of the beams will be based upon the actual concrete specifications for the particular project.

PRESTRESSING REINFORCEMENT: Prestressing reinforcement shall generally be designed for particular projects or for prevailing bridge practices and available manufacturing facilities.

The beams are applicable for use with any acceptable type of prestressing in current practice; namely, pretensioning with straight or deflected strands, post-tensioning or a combination of pretensioning and post-tensioning. Placing of a portion of the stressing force on a draped or deflected profile will result in economy of beam section for all sizes and spans but not, necessarily, economy of manufacture or overall job cost. Use of draped reinforcement will generally be required for the longer spans in each beam series.

Materials for prestressing reinforcement may be any of the materials specified in the "Bureau Criteria" or recommended by "ACI-ASCE Joint Committee 323" or subsequent developments by manufacturers which have generally been accepted in common prestressed practice.

END BLOCKS: The use of end blocks is recommended for all beams and all types of prestressing. The lengths of end block shown for types III and IV contemplate the heavy concentrations of stress at ends of beams normally associated with the longer span lengths. The lengths of end block shown for each beam type are recommended minima. If desired by the producer, lengths of the end blocks may be increased to accommodate local plant facilities or particular job requirements. Sufficient mild steel reinforcement should be provided in end blocks to resist the tensile forces due to the concentrated prestressing loads.

DIAPHRAGMS: Diaphragms of precast or cast-in-place construction using prestressed or non-stressed reinforcement are recommended at span ends, at midspan to lengths of not more than 60 feet and at span third points for lengths above 60 feet.

FORMS: For standard plant manufacturing, the use of steel forms on concrete floored casting beds is recommended.

CHAMFERS AND CORNERS: All exposed corners shall be chamfered ¾″ or rounded to ¾″ radius. Angles of intersection between webs and flanges shall be rounded to not less than ¼″ radius.

FINISH OF TOPS: Tops of all beams shall be left rough. At approximately the time of initial set, all laitance shall be removed with a coarse wire brush.

HANDLING: In the handling of beams, they must be maintained in an upright position at all times and must be picked up only by means of approved devices anchored within the end blocks. Disregard of this requirement may result in collapse of the member.

MILD STEEL REINFORCING, SHOES, BEARINGS AND MISCELLANE-OUS DETAILS: All details not shown or specified hereon shall be designed for particular job requirements and shall be in accordance with applicable job specifications.

13-2. Rectangular Pretensioned Bridge Deck Sections. The first pretensioned prestressed concrete highway bridge in the United States was composed of rectangular sections prestressed with small seven-wire strands and erected side by side to form a slab- or deck-type bridge. Use of prestressed bridges of this general type is second only to the I-beam and slab type already illustrated.[6]

The most popular width for these sections is 36 in.* Cardboard tubes placed in the form before the concrete is poured create holes in the member which reduce the dead weight without appreciably reducing the section modulus. The round cardboard tubes are a readily available standard product. The rectangular tubes are made to the required dimensions by fabricators of corrugated-paper products.

On the bridge piers the rectangular sections are placed side by side and pulled together by tightening nuts on transverse bars. Shear keys between the sections are dry-packed with a sand and cement mortar. Some of the bridges are designed for use with an asphalt wearing surface. Others are designed for a poured-in-place concrete topping which forms a composite structure with the precast section. Typical details are shown in Figs. 13-2 to 13-7. The following design notes are published by American-Marietta Company in connection with the details shown in these figures:

AMDEK Design Notes

Minimum 28 day cylinder strength of concrete—5,000 psi.
Minimum cylinder strength at time of prestressing—4,000 psi.
Prestressing steel—⅜-in. diameter seven-wire stress-relieved strand.
Minimum tensile strength—250,000 psi.
Initial tension of strand—175,000 psi.
Maximum stress in concrete at time of prestressing—2,400 psi.

---

* AASHO-PCI Standard Rectangular Deck Sections 36 and 48 in. wide will be established during 1959.

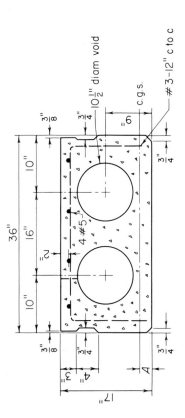

17-in. DEPTH—H20—S16—44 (OR MILITARY)

Clear span, ft	C. to c. bearing, ft	Max allowable superimposed moment, ft-lb	Max allowable superimposed shear, lb	A, in.	B, in.	Prestressed steel area	No. 3/8" strand	Weight basic member
24	25	105,000	39,500	2.22	...	1.20	15	12,500
26	27	116,000	40,900	2.20	...	1.36	17	13,450
28	29	126,000	42,900	2.25	18	1.60	20	14,400
30	31	138,000	44,200	2.30	...	1.76	22	15,350
32	33	148,000	43,800	2.62	...	2.00	25	16,300
34	35	159,000	47,600	2.75	...	2.16	27	17,250

Fig. 13-2a. Details of typical rectangular box beams. The beams shown here are the standard of American-Marietta Co., which calls them AMDEK sections. See text for AMDEX design notes.

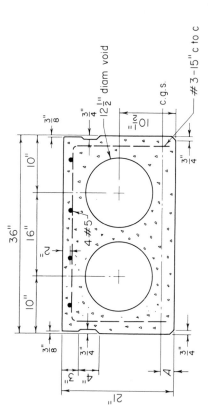

21-in. DEPTH—H20—S16—44

Clear span, ft	C. to c. bearing, ft	Max allowable superimposed moment, ft-lb	Max allowable superimposed shear, lb	A, in.	B, in.	Prestressed steel area	No. ⅜" strand	Weight basic member
36	37	170,000	43,500	2.30	...	1.76	22	22,100
38	39	186,000	49,300	2.31	18	1.92	24	23,200
40	41	201,000	51,600	2.64	...	2.16	27	24,350
42	43	216,000	54,800	3.20	...	2.48	31	25,550

FIG. 13-2b. Typical rectangular box beams (AMDEK sections). See text for AMDEK design notes.

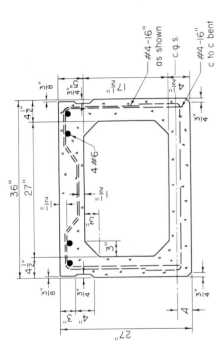

27-in. DEPTH—H20—S16—44

Clear span, ft	C. to c. bearing, ft	Max allowable superimposed moment, ft-lb	Max allowable superimposed shear, lb	A, in.	B, in.	Prestressed steel area	No. ⅜″ strand	Weight basic member
44	45	222,000	40,700	2.30	⋮	1.76	22	27,100
46	47	227,000	40,800	2.26	⋮	1.84	23	28,200
48	49	263,000	41,600	2.27	⋮	2.00	25	29,300
50	51	281,000	42,300	2.35	18	2.24	28	30,500
52	53	290,000	43,400	2.63	⋮	2.40	30	31,600
54	55	299,000	44,700	2.93	⋮	2.56	32	32,800
56	57	322,000	46,000	3.23	⋮	2.80	35	33,400

FIG. 13-3a.   Typical rectangular box beams (AMDEK sections).   See text for AMDEX design notes

239

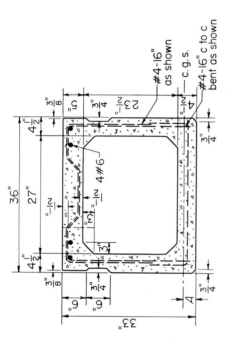

33-in. DEPTH—H20—S16—44

Clear span, ft	C. to c. bearing, ft	Max allowable superimposed moment, ft-lb	Max allowable superimposed shear, lb	A, in.	B, in.	Prestressed steel area	No. 3/8" strand	Weight basic member
58	59	340,000	27,800	2.47	...	2.32	29	39,900
60	61	354,000	28,200	2.63	...	2.48	31	41,300
62	63	371,000	29,500	3.03	18	2.64	33	42,600
64	65	387,000	30,700	3.38	...	2.88	36	43,900
66	67	403,000	31,700	3.63	...	3.04	38	45,200
68	69	418,000	33,300	3.90	...	3.28	41	46,500

FIG. 13-3b. Typical rectangular box beams (AMDEK sections). See text for AMDEK design notes.

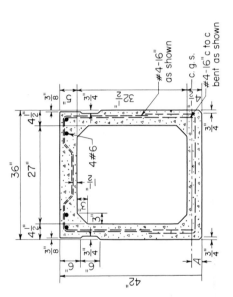

42-in. DEPTH—H20—S16—44

Clear span, ft	C. to c. bearing, ft	Max allowable superimposed moment, ft-lb	Max allowable superimposed shear, lb	A, in.	B, in.	Prestressed steel area	No. 3/8″ strand	Weight basic member
70	71½	444,000	26,200	3.12	...	2.72	34	51,300
72	73½	465,000	26,700	3.28	...	2.88	36	52,960
74	75½	476,000	28,100	3.69	18	3.04	38	54,620
76	77½	448,000	29,800	4.07	...	3.20	40	56,280
78	79½	496,000	30,800	4.32	...	3.36	42	57,940
80	81½	514,000	32,300	4.62	...	3.52	44	59,600

FIG. 13-4. Typical rectangular box beams (AMDEK sections). See text for AMDEK design notes.

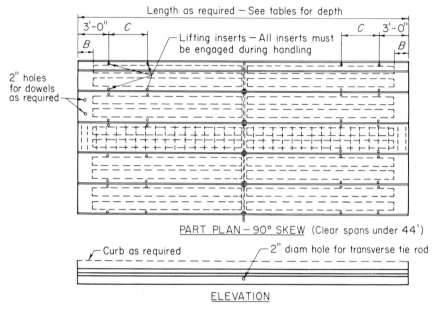

PART PLAN — 90° SKEW (Clear spans under 44')

ELEVATION

FIG. 13-5. Details of bridge assemblies using AMDEK sections by American-Marietta Co.

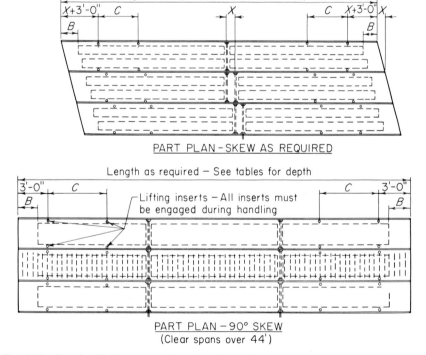

PART PLAN – SKEW AS REQUIRED

PART PLAN — 90° SKEW
(Clear spans over 44')

FIG. 13-6. Details of bridge assemblies using AMDEK sections by American-Marietta Co.

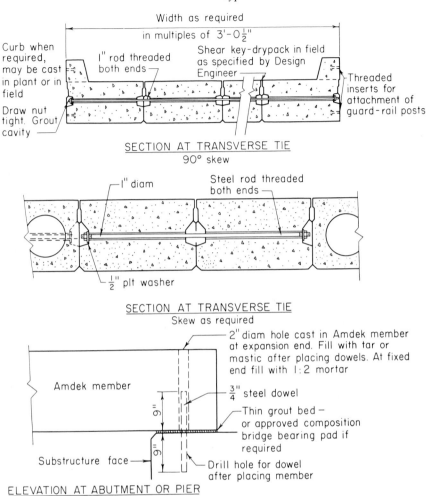

Fig 13-7. Details of bridge assemblies using **AMDEK** sections by American-Marietta Co.

Maximum tensile stress in concrete of the extreme bottom fibre on application of design load is zero (0).

Where top fibre tensile stress in concrete exceeds 240 psi tension steel is provided in the top of the member, but in no case does the top fibre tensile stress exceed 480 psi.

Where principal tensile stress in the concrete on application of design load exceeds 150 psi the principal tensile stress is carried by properly designed stirrups.

Where maximum diagonal tension in the concrete at ultimate load exceeds 400 psi proper stirrups are provided.

The ultimate moment is not less than $1 DL + 3 LL$ or $2(DL + LL)$ whichever is greater.

Design based on max. skew of 60°, for greater skews the dead load moments must
be checked to determine if additional prestressing steel is required.
NOTE: The details shown are intended only as suggestions and may be varied to
suit job conditions.

13-3. Modified T-section Bridges. For long-span bridges, 75 to 80 ft
and up, the dead weight of the poured-in-place slab becomes a big factor
in the stresses in the precast I beam for the type of bridge described in
Art. 13-1, and it is advisable to check their cost against that of other types.
Since the high stresses are due to the weight of the slab which is carried
by the I beam only, the cure is to design a member in which the entire
cross section including the slab helps to carry the entire dead weight. The
modified T section meets this requirement.[7]

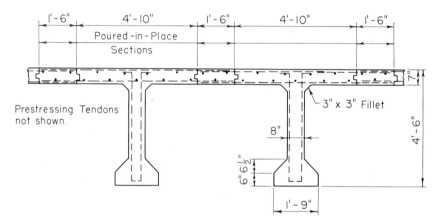

Fig. 13-8.   Typical modified T-section bridge.

Modified T sections prove most economical for the longer spans where
conditions are such that precast members are preferable to poured-in-
place members.

For simplicity in the first design analysis presented in the book in
Chap. 4 it was assumed that the modified T sections were placed flange
to flange with a shear key where they touched. In actual practice they
are usually erected with a space of about 18 in. between flanges. Reinforcing bars project from the top slabs to lap bars in the poured-in-place
slab between the sections, thus creating a deck slab that can carry both
positive and negative moment to distribute wheel loads. Figure 13-8
shows general details for a bridge of this type. Where diaphragms are
required, the diaphragm is precast with the T section for the full width

of the top slab. The 18 in. of diaphragm between the sections is poured with the 18-in. slab between the sections.

13-4. Long-span Monolithic Bridges. A simple poured-in-place bridge of rectangular girders, slab deck, and post-tensioned tendons often proves to be the most economical solution for the longer spans. The entire dead weight is supported by forms until the tendons are tensioned, after which the entire cross section functions in carrying both dead and live load. A typical structure with a 28-ft-wide roadway for a 120-ft span would have four rectangular girders each 12 in. wide by 6 ft deep spaced 8 ft center to center and capped with a 7-in.-thick concrete slab.[8]

Although the girder is post-tensioned in place for long spans, there is seldom any problem of part of the tensioning force being dissipated to the piers because, for long spans, one end of the girder will be supported on a rocker. A computation is made to determine how much the girder will shorten owing to prestress, and the rocker is pretilted so that after the tensioning is complete, the rocker will be at the desired angle.

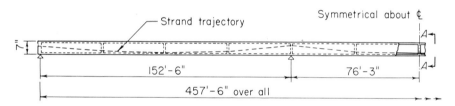

FIG. 13-9. Elevation of three-span post-tensioned hollow-box bridge. (*From Eng. News-Record, Dec. 27, 1956.*)

The poured-in-place section of rectangular girders and top slab is also efficient for two-span continuous bridges. The bridge is anchored to the center pier, and rockers are used at the end piers. Each tendon is tensioned from both ends at one time.

13-5. Post-tensioned Hollow-box Bridges. The longest prestressed concrete bridges are the hollow-box type illustrated in Figs. 13-9 to 13-11. Two styles have been used. The three-span continuous structure shown in Fig. 13-9 is one.[9] The other has a long main span with cantilever ends that are from one-sixth to one-fourth the length of the main span. All the weight of the cantilever ends is carried by the two main piers, thus creating a large negative moment over the piers which in turn reduces the positive moment in the main span.[10]

Figure 13-10 shows details of a hollow-box bridge at mid-span. This type of cross section makes maximum use of the concrete by putting the majority of it in the top and bottom flanges with a minimum amount in the webs.   The structure is supported on falsework until it has cured and the galvanized strands have been pulled through the hollow boxes into position and post-tensioned.   The galvanized strands are sometimes given

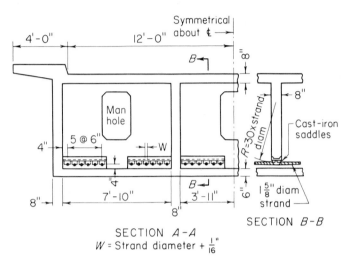

FIG. 13-10.   Details at mid-span of post-tensioned hollow-box bridge shown in Fig. 13-9. (*From Eng. News-Record, Dec. 27, 1956.*)

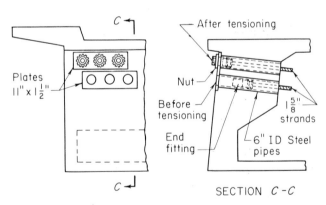

FIG. 13-11.   Details at end of post-tensioned hollow-box bridge shown in Fig. 13-9.   (*From Eng. News-Record, Dec. 27, 1956.*)

the additional protection of a coat of bitumastic paint after they have been tensioned.   Strands can be inspected at any time during the life of the structure.   If the designer desires, the details can readily be worked out so that any strand can be removed and replaced by a new one.

A pleasing architectural effect can be achieved by making these structures deep at the piers and shallow at the center of span. If this difference in depth is kept within reasonable limits, the stresses remain reasonable also.

When checking ultimate strength of a structure of this type with unbonded tendons, refer to Sec. 209.2.2.(b) of Tentative Recommendations for Prestressed Concrete.

13-6. Sections for Buildings. The most popular standard sections for buildings are pretensioned double T's and the channels and joists that can be made in double-T forms as illustrated in Fig. 6-5. Standard double-T sections vary in depth from 10 to 24 in. and in width from 4 to 6 ft. The channels and joists made in the same forms vary accordingly.

Many casting yards also have standard beam and girder sections for use in conjunction with double T's, channels, or joists.

There are so many different styles of double T's and girders throughout the country that no attempt will be made here to tabulate dimensions and section properties. Each casting yard has complete span-load tables for the members it produces. The literature distributed by most yards includes sketches showing suggested framing details for their members.

When designing a structure which incorporates standard-type members, the engineer or architect should obtain data on available standard sections from casting yards located within a competitive distance of his structure and make his drawings and specifications in accordance with them. Where more than one type of acceptable section is available, the architect's drawings can show loadings, limiting clearances, etc., leaving the exact cross section of members to the competitive bidders. Chapter 10 covers design computations for a typical double-T section.

There is practically no limit to the variety of special sections that can be fabricated to accommodate particular architectural and structural conditions. Special sections can be pretensioned when there is sufficient duplication to make it economical. If only a few are needed, post-tensioning will probably prove more economical.

Precast prestressed building members are fastened together by one of two methods. In one, steel plates, usually ⅜ or ½ in. thick, anchored by the reinforcing bars which are welded to them, are cast in each member. When the members are assembled, the steel plates come into contact with each other and are held permanently in position by field welds. In the other method, reinforcing bars are allowed to project from each member. When the members are assembled, the bars from both members project into a common space which is filled with concrete, thus tying the members together.

One of the criteria for economical design with many building materials is the use of girders to span the long way of a bay and shallow members to span the short way. This is not necessarily true with prestressed concrete. It is sometimes more economical, for instance, to use girders for the short span and double T's for the long span. With span-load tables furnished by the fabricators it is a simple matter to compare the cost of long girders and short double T's with that of short girders and long double T's.

Figure 13-12 shows details of a prestressed concrete building. A structure of this type can be erected in a minimum length of time, since

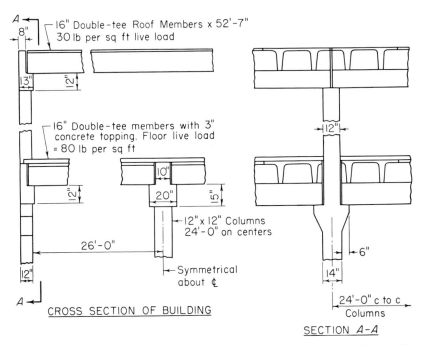

Fig. 13-12. Details of a prestressed concrete building. Welded connections of double T's to girders and girders to columns similar to Fig. 13-13. Flanges of double T's in roof to be welded as shown in Fig. 13-13.

all the members are precast and practically no forming is required.[11] The only field work required besides the erecting of the precast members is welding them together at the joints, pouring the 3-in. floor slab, and applying the roofing material. In the building illustrated the columns are precast reinforced concrete, the double T's are standard prestressed sections, and the girders are standard or special prestressed sections depending upon the facilities of the casting yard.

Figures 13-13 to 13-17 show some of the more common framing details and types of sections used in buildings.

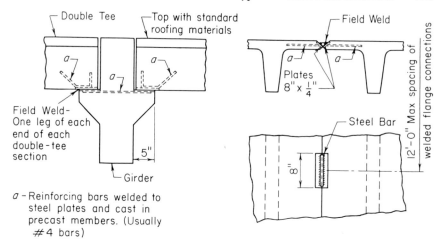

FIG. 13-13. Prestressed concrete roof details with standard double T's on one type of pre-stressed girder.

Double-tee sections with 3" poured-in-place slab for normal floor loads.

Channel sections with 3" poured-in-place slab for long spans or heavy floor loads.

FIG. 13-14.   Floor sections composed of prestressed precast sections and poured-in-place slabs.

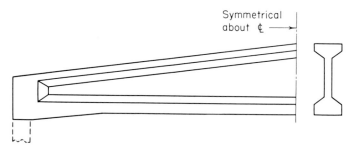

FIG. 13-15.   Tapered girder.   The bottom flange of this girder also tapers down near the end to permit use of straight tendons without causing tensile stresses in the top.

13-7. Lift Slabs. Prestressed concrete lift slabs often prove economical for buildings up to five or six stories high. The basic principle of lift-slab construction is that of casting all floor slabs and roof at ground level and then raising the finished slabs to their final elevation after they have been cured and prestressed.[12-14]

The following steps are typical in the construction of a lift-slab building:

1. Steel columns are placed on their footings and anchored. Usually

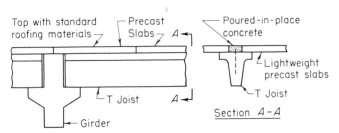

FIG. 13-16. Prestressed girder and prestressed T joists supporting light precast slabs. T joists are spaced 4 to 8 ft on centers depending on span of joist and capacity of precast slab.

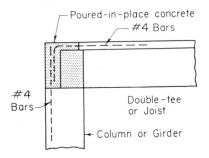

FIG. 13-17. Connection of double T or joist to girder or column using projecting reinforcing bars and poured-in-place concrete. See comments in Chap. 15 concerning unintentional use of rigid or partially rigid joints.

there are two rows of columns. The slabs will span between the two rows and cantilever beyond each row as shown in Fig. 13-18.

2. The bottom slab of the building is cast on grade in its final position.

3. When the bottom slab has set, it is covered with paper or other bond-preventing material.

4. A steel collar for the first-floor slab is placed around each column. The function of these collars is to transfer the load from the floor slab to the column when the slab has been lifted to its final position.

5. Prestressing tendons, electrical conduits, etc., are placed, and the first-floor slab is poured.

6. When the first-floor slab has set sufficiently, steps 3, 4, and 5 are carried out for the second-floor slab. This procedure is repeated for each slab until all floors have been cast.

7. Each slab is prestressed before it is lifted. The exact time at which the tendons are tensioned can be chosen to suit the contractor as long as

FIG. 13-18. Prestressed concrete lift slabs in Litchfield County Hospital, Winsted, Conn. Each of the five large slabs is 182 by 43 ft by 8½ in. The slabs were post-tensioned with Freyssinet cables and the lifting operation was carried out by New England Lift Slab Corporation, a licensee of the Youtz-Slick Lift Slab Method. The Freyssinet cables run the full length of the slab in both the 182- and 43-ft directions. They are near the bottom of the slabs in the center of the bays and near the top of the slabs in the column lines.

the concrete has reached its required strength. If a slab is prestressed while other slabs are resting on it, some of the prestress may be transferred by friction to other slabs. However, as each slab is lifted, this friction is lost and all the tension in its tendons is carried by the slab itself, giving it the proper prestress.

8. The top slab is lifted to its final elevation, and each collar is permanently welded or bolted to its column.

9. The next slab is lifted to its final elevation and permanently attached to the columns, etc., until all slabs are in place.

The lifting operation is the most precise part of the entire construction procedure. Jacks are mounted on top of each column and attached to the slab by long threaded rods. The jacks are operated simultaneously from a central control panel so that the slab is kept level as it is raised. Maintenance of the necessary level at each column requires a complicated control system and an experienced operator. The jacking equipment, controls, and operators are usually rented to the general contractor by a firm specializing in lifting slabs.

In the taller buildings the columns may be too slender to permit raising the top slab to its final position without lateral bracing. For a structure of this type with six slabs to be lifted, one erection procedure would be as follows:

1. Erect columns that extend slightly above the third-floor level and mount jacks on them.

2. Raise the top slab to the top of the columns and bolt it temporarily in place.

3. Guy the top slab to the ground.

4. Raise each of the next two slabs and bolt them temporarily in place.

5. Raise the third-floor slab and fasten it permanently to the columns.

6. Raise the second- and first-floor slabs and fasten them permanently to the columns.

7. Provide the necessary bracing between columns up to the third floor or guy the third floor to the ground.

8. Release guys from the top slab.

9. Remove the jacks, splice on the remainder of the columns, and place the jacks on top.

10. Raise the top slab to the final position, etc.

The economy of lift-slab construction comes from the virtual elimination of forms plus the labor saved by casting all the concrete at ground level. Prestressing the slabs permits wider spacing between columns and keeps the weight of slab to be lifted to a minimum.[15]

The slabs in the structure illustrated in Fig. 13-18 are solid slabs 8½ in. thick. Another common type of lift slab is the waffle design. These are thinner slabs with ribs running in both directions on the underside of the slab. Each rib has one or more tendons.

13-8. Segmental Members. Section 207.3 of Tentative Recommendations for Prestressed Concrete refers to "segmental elements" and allows no tensile stress in the concrete of these members. A segmental prestressed concrete beam is composed of several precast concrete blocks assembled in a line and placed under compression by some type of prestressing tendon to form a beam. A beam of this type is similar to other prestressed concrete beams except that, as soon as the compressive stress is offset by bending moments, a crack will appear between the precast blocks because there is nothing to carry tensile stress.

Some of the first prestressed concrete members put in service in the United States were of the segmental type.[16] The precast blocks were made on an ordinary building-block machine but were of high-strength concrete. These beams were made by placing the blocks face to face with a mortar joint about ¼ in. thick. Prestressing strands were passed through the holes in the blocks for the full length of the beam and anchored against steel bearing plates in the special end blocks.

Later developments include special dies on the block machine to make blocks of the most efficient cross section and the use of seven-wire bonded strands in some of the special-shape blocks. The group of seven-wire strands is threaded through a hole in the block, tensioned, and anchored against temporary end bearing plates with temporary fittings. The hole around the strands is filled with grout, and when the grout has reached sufficient strength, the end plates and anchors are removed for reuse.

Properly designed and fabricated segmental beams are structurally sound and prove economical for a number of applications at those locations where block manufacturers have the equipment for producing them.[17]

13-9. Slabs on Grade. Prestressed concrete is an excellent material for slabs on grade which are subjected to heavy load concentrations as in airport runways. Joints, one of the chief sources of maintenance problems in slabs, can be spaced 500 ft or more apart and specially designed.[18] Slabs less than half the thickness required in ordinary concrete are feasible.

The *Journal of the American Concrete Institute*[19] contains a comprehensive report of tests on a 7-in.-thick prestressed slab. The data in this report and the *Highway Research Board Bulletin*[20] can be used as a basis for computing the required prestress in a slab, friction between slab and subbase, etc. In common with the first prestressed concrete structures of other types, this slab was post-tensioned. Later studies indicate that pretensioned bonded strands have several advantages over post-tensioned, at least in the longitudinal direction.

One of the big problems in prestressed slabs on grade is friction. Friction between the slab and subgrade is kept to a minimum by placing a 1-in. layer of round sand on the subbase. The sand is covered with a layer of waterproof building paper, and the slab is poured on the paper. When the slab is prestressed, it shortens and therefore moves with respect to the base. The only friction resisting this motion is the shear developed within the sand layer, which is equivalent to a coefficient of about 0.50.

Where the post-tensioning method is used, friction between the tendon and its enclosure becomes quite large in the long longitudinal tendons.

Use of pretensioned strands completely eliminates this friction, since the strands are entirely in the open at the time of tensioning. Pretensioned strands can be tensioned in any length that proves economical on a given project. Where the strands stretch across an expansion joint, the slab can be formed at each side of the joint, and after the concrete has cured to the required strength, the strands can be burned off at the faces of the slab.

Worn or otherwise inadequate runways can be rehabilitated by covering them with a 1-in. layer of sand and then a relatively thin, 3- or 4-in., prestressed concrete overlay. The same principle can be applied to a new slab by casting an unreinforced base and covering it with a thin prestressed slab.[21] Pretensioned strands in the longitudinal direction can be used economically with either of these types because the bottom slab will serve to hold the tension in the strands while the top slab is being poured and cured. When the load of the strands is released into the top slab, it shortens and the bottom slab lengthens.

Use of pretensioned tendons in the transverse direction creates a problem in pouring the slab. The tendons must be placed for the full width before any concrete is poured. Since paving-equipment units are not wide enough to pour the entire width at one pass, the slab must be poured in lanes, which means that one of the rails supporting the paving unit will cross all the transverse tendons. This problem plus the fact that transverse tendons are relatively short usually makes post-tensioned tendons more efficient for transverse prestressing.

Suggested procedure for fabrication of a slab with pretensioned longitudinal strands and post-tensioned transverse tendons is as follows:

1. Prepare the subbase, cover with a sand layer and waterproof paper.

2. Place and tension longitudinal strands for the width of one lane. These can be continuous for the full length of the runway if desired and anchored to abutments at each end.

3. Place transverse tubes for transverse tendons. These tubes can be thin-wall steel or flexible metal hose. In each tube use a pipe just slightly smaller than the tube to keep it straight. The pipe should be a little longer than the lane width.

4. Place any needed reinforcing bars, expansion-joint connections, etc., and pour the lane.

5. Place and tension the longitudinal strands for the second lane.

6. Attach a small-diameter wire rope to the outside end of each of the pipes in the transverse holes. Pull the pipes into the second lane, leaving the end of the pipe in the first lane, and cover the pipe in the second lane with metal hose.

7. Repeat step 4, etc., until all lanes are poured and have cured to the required strength.

8. For each transverse tendon there is now a cast-in-metal tube with a small-diameter wire rope pulled through it. Attach a post-tensioning tendon to each rope, and pull the tendon into place in the tube.

9. Tension, anchor, and grout all the transverse tendons. (If the longitudinal prestress were applied first, each lane would not necessarily shorten the same amount as the adjacent lane and the transverse tendons would be pinched at the joint between the lanes, thus preventing proper prestressing.)

10. Release the tension in the longitudinal strands from their anchors into the slab. To prevent large motions at the ends of the slab, cut a few strands at each anchor and in each expansion joint, then a few more at each point, etc., until all are released.

Although prestressed concrete runway slabs offer many advantages including economy, especially for heavy planes, they have been slow to gain acceptance. Recent technical periodicals should be checked for articles on the newest developments.[25]

BIBLIOGRAPHY

1. Bender, M. E.: Prestressed Concrete Bridges for the Illinois Toll Highway, *Proc. World Conf. on Prestressed Concrete*, 1957.
2. Bender, M. E.: Novel Prestressing Techniques for Bridges, *Eng. News-Record*, August 19, 1954, pp. 32–38.
3. Dean, W. E.: Prestressed Concrete Difficulties Overcome in Florida Bridge Practice, *Civil Eng.*, June, 1957, pp. 60–63.
4. Ozell, A. M.: Behavior of Simple-span and Continuous Composite Prestressed Concrete Beams, Part 1, *J. Prestressed Concrete Inst.*, June, 1957, pp. 18–31.
5. Ozell, A. M., and J. F. Diniz: Composite Prestressed Concrete Beams under Repetitive Loading, *J. Prestressed Concrete Inst.*, March, 1958, pp. 19–27.
6. Long, James B.: Prestressed Precast Bridge Deck Erected in Eight Days (Total Length 380 Ft), *Civil Eng.*, March, 1957, pp. 51–53.
7. Latest Methods for Prestress Bridge, *Western Construct.*, March, 1957.
8. Linberg, Gordon C., and M. Schupack: Concrete Set Slowed down to Step up Bridge Construction, *Civil Eng.*, March, 1958, pp. 37–41.
9. Preston, H. Kent: Design of Prestressed Hollow-box Girder Bridges, *Eng. News-Record*, Dec. 27, 1956.
10. Saenz, Luis, and Ignacio Martin: Prestressed Concrete Bridge in Cuba Spans Nearly 300 Ft., *Civil Eng.*, December, 1955, pp. 48–51.
11. Sixty-six Precast Bays Go up in Eleven Days, *Eng. News-Record*, May 24, 1956, pp. 44–46.
12. Minges, James S., and Donald S. Wild: Six Stories of Prestressed Slabs Erected by Lift-slab Method, *J. Am. Concrete Inst.*, February, 1957, pp. 751–768.
13. Perry, John P. H.: Office Building of 370,000 Square Feet Erected by Lift-slab Method, *Civil Eng.*, June, 1955, pp. 43–47.
14. Brownfield, Allen H.: Growing Pains in Prestressed Concrete Buildings, *Civil Eng.*, February, 1958, pp. 46–49.
15. Rice, Edward K.: Economic Factors in Prestressed Lift-slab Construction, *J. Am. Concrete Inst.*, September, 1958, pp. 347–357.
16. Bridge Built of Blocks Strung Like Beads, *Eng. News-Record*, Jan. 18, 1951, pp. 39–42.

17. Bryan, Ross H.: New Designs Cut Prestressed Block-beam Costs, *Eng. News-Record,* Apr. 22, 1954, pp. 32–34.
18. Prestressing Promises Nearly Joint-free Design, *Civil Eng.,* August, 1958, pp. 34–37.
19. Cholnoky, Thomas: Prestressed Concrete Pavement for Airfield, *J. Am. Concrete Inst.,* July, 1956, pp. 59–84.
20. Prestressed Concrete Pavement Research, *Highway Research Board, Bull.* 179, Washington, D.C.
21. Jointless Prestressed Floor Resists Heavy Loads in Warehouse, *Eng. News-Record,* Jan. 6, 1949.
22. Van Buren, Myers: Concrete Bridge across Lake Pontchartrain Completed in Record Time, *Civil Eng.,* February, 1957, pp. 33–37.
23. Blaschke, Theodore O., and David A. Hopkins: Prestressed Deck Proves Cheapest for New Hoboken Pier, *Civil Eng.,* February, 1954, pp. 50–53.
24. Kienow, K. K.: "Design Table for the AASHO-PCI Joint Committee Standard Prestressed Bridge Beams," Engineering Experiment Station, University of Arizona, Tucson, Ariz.
25. Prestressed Pavement—A World View of Its Status, Report by Subcommittee VI, ACI Committee 325, *J. Am. Concrete Inst.,* February, 1959, pp. 829–838.
26. Lemcoe, M. M., and C. H. Mahla: Prestressed Overlay Slab for San Antonio Airport, *J. Am. Concrete Inst.,* July, 1959, pp. 25–35.

CHAPTER 14

CONTINUOUS STRUCTURES

STRUCTURES WITH CONTINUOUS TENDONS

14-1. Characteristics. For structures in which tendons are continuous over a pier and in which the tendons are curved so that they carry shear, the familiar equation (1-1) for stress in the concrete due to the prestressing force is not applicable. In a continuous member with continuous tendons the vertical loads applied to the member by the curvature of the tendons are not distributed to the supports in the same proportions as in the simple beam which is the basis for Eq. (1-1).

Mathematical procedures leading to a direct solution for the prestressing force and its eccentricity have been developed, but they are involved and seem difficult for some designers to follow. A procedure based on relatively simple mathematical formulas is suggested in the following section.

14-2. Design Procedure. Step 1. Establish a trial path for the center of gravity of the tendons. At points of maximum negative moment, over the intermediate piers, place the tendons as close to the top of the member as details permit, and at points of maximum positive moment, near the centers of the spans, place the tendons as close to the bottom of the member as details permit. At the ends of the member the tendons can be placed at any elevation the details permit and which does not create excessive stresses. For simplicity in the first computation we shall place the tendons at the center of gravity of concrete at the ends of the member.

The tendons are usually placed in a parabolic curve between the control points which have been established. If, at some point in the calculations, it is found that the path of tendons chosen is not satisfactory, a new path should be established to correct the difficulty found with the first one.

Step 2. Assume an arbitrary final tension F_A in the tendons. Any value will do; it need not be close to the actual final value.

Step 3. Compute the vertical loads applied to the member by the tendons due to F_A.

Step 4. Compute the stresses in the member due to the vertical loads from the tendons found in Step 3.

Step 5. Compute the direct compressive stress F_A/A_c in the member.

Step 6. Compute bending moments and unit stresses due to eccentricity of tendons at the ends of the member. If tendons are on the c.g.c. at the ends of the member, eccentricity is zero and there are no moments or stresses from this factor.

Step 7. Add algebraically the stresses from Steps 4, 5, and 6 to get the net stresses f_{F_A} due to F_A.

Step 8. Compute moments and stresses due to dead load.

Step 9. Compute maximum positive moments and stresses and maximum negative moments and stresses due to live load.

Step 10. Use the stresses from Steps 8 and 9 to compute maximum dead- plus live-load stresses. Choose what appears to be the point on the structure which will require the maximum F, and establish the amount of compressive stress $f^b{}_F$ required.

Step 11. Compute the required final prestress F from Eq. (14-1).

$$F = \frac{F_A f^b{}_F}{f^b{}_{FA}} \qquad\qquad (14\text{-}1)$$

Check the entire structure, combining this value with dead load only and also with dead load plus critical live loads. Consider the economy of the section. Would a smaller or differently shaped cross section be more economical? Check initial prestress plus dead load.

Step 12. Compute reactions on piers. Since the tendons carry some of the shear, the pier reactions will not be the same as for an unprestressed structure with the same elastic properties. The pier reactions due to prestress plus dead load can be computed in four steps.

a. Compute the reactions due to dead load, considering the structure as elastic.

b. Compute the pier reactions due to the upward forces of the tendons against the structure. These will be negative reactions.

c. Compute the reactions from the downward forces of the tendons over the piers.

d. Add algebraically the values computed in *a, b, and c* to get the pier reactions due to prestress plus dead load.

Since the structure is fully elastic under design live load, the formulas used for elastic structures are used in computing these reactions.

Step 13. Check ultimate strength. See Secs. 213.4 and 205.3.2 of Tentative Recommendations for Prestressed Concrete. Some authorities feel that moment redistribution should be used in the computation of ultimate strength. Others feel that there are not enough available data and point out that moment redistribution has not yet been included in reinforced concrete specifications. Section 213.4 says "It is recommended that moment redistribution not be considered at the present time."

Step 14. Compute shear. The shear is the same as for any elastic structure less the shear carried by the tendons.

Step 15. Check camber.

Step 16. Work out details of tendons, anchorages, shear steel, etc.

14-3. Numerical Example. For the purpose of this example we shall consider a bridge of two 125-ft spans with both the concrete and the

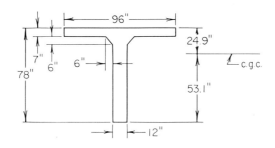

Section Properties – Taking Moments About Top

	A, sq in	y, in	Ay	Ay^2	I_0
96 x 7 =	672	3.5	2,350	8,220	2,745
12 x 71 =	852	42.5	36,200	1,538,000	358,000
6 x 6 x $\frac{2}{2}$ =	36	9	324	2,915	72
	1,560		38,874	1,549,135	360,817
				360,817	
				1,909,952	

$$Y_t = 38,874 \div 1,560 = 24.9''$$
$$Y_b = 78 - 24.9 = 53.1''$$
$$I = 1,909,952 - 1,560(24.9)^2 = 943,000$$
$$Z_t = 943,000 \div 24.9 = 37,880$$
$$Z_b = 943,000 \div 53.1 = 17,760$$
$$\text{Weight} = 1,560 \frac{150}{144} = 1,625 \text{ lb per ft}$$

FIG. 14-1. Cross section and section properties of concrete section to be used in design example.

tendons continuous over the center pier. The cross section is a poured-in-place beam and slab type with the beams 8 ft 0 in. on centers. Figure 14-1 shows one beam and the slab which functions with it. The design live load is 1,000 lb per lin ft. (A uniform live load has been used to simplify calculations. The only change for the design of an actual bridge would be computation of live-load moments and shears on the basis of truck loads or standard uniform plus concentrated loads.) Design is based on allowable stresses, etc., in Tentative Recommendations for Prestressed Concrete in Art. 8-2.

$$f'_c = 5,000 \text{ psi}$$

Follow the steps outlined in the foregoing procedure. An elevation of the structure is shown in Fig. 14-2. Slide-rule calculations are normally of sufficient accuracy for prestressed concrete design and have been used in this example.

Step 1. In order to locate the tendons as near to the concrete surfaces as possible, we should have some idea of the magnitude of F. The uniform compressive stress F/A_c in an efficient continuous bridge design is usually around 800 to 1,000 psi. For the section shown in Fig. 14-1 try an F of 1,200,000 lb. Select a group of tendons to give this force and plot typical patterns at top and bottom of the concrete cross section. The

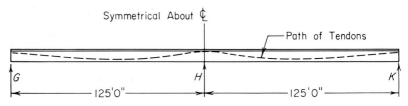

FIG. 14-2.   Elevation of two-span bridge in design example.

c.g.s. can easily be located within 8 to 10 in. of the concrete surface. We shall place the c.g.s. 10 in. from the top over the center pier, 10 in. from the bottom near the centers of span, and on the c.g.c. at the end piers.

A diagram for the path of the c.g.s. is shown in Fig. 14-3. The known dimensions on this diagram are

$$R = 125 \text{ ft } 0 \text{ in.} = 1,500 \text{ in.}$$
$$D = 10 \text{ in.}$$

Since the c.g.s. has been placed on the c.g.c. at the ends,

$$M = y_t - D = 24.9 - 10 = 14.9 \text{ in.}$$

When M is small with respect to R, as it is in this example, the difference in elevation between the lowest point on the curve and the curve at the center of span is negligible. For our first trial we shall assume these elevations are the same, which gives

$$B = E - 0.5M = 58 - 7.45 = 50.55 \text{ in.}$$

From Fig. 14-3 the lowest point on the curve occurs at

$$X = \frac{R}{2} + \frac{RM}{8B} = \frac{1{,}500}{2} + \frac{1{,}500 \times 14.9}{8 \times 50.55}$$

$$= 750 + 55 = 805 \text{ in.}$$

At this point from Fig. 14-3

$$y_B = 14.9\,\frac{805}{1{,}500} = 8.0 \text{ in.}$$

$$y = 4 \times 50.55\,\frac{805}{1{,}500}\left(1 - \frac{805}{1{,}500}\right) = 50.2 \text{ in.}$$

$$y_{B+y} = 58.2 \text{ in.}$$

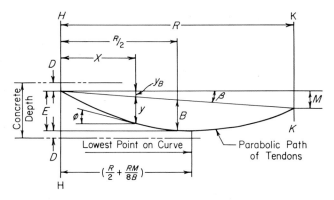

$y = 4B\frac{X}{R}(1-\frac{X}{R})$ See tabulation Fig. 11-5.

$y_B = M\frac{X}{R}$

Tan $\phi = \frac{4B}{R}(1-\frac{2X}{R}) + \frac{M}{R}$

Length of tendon along parabolic curve = L

$L = R(\text{Sec. }\beta + \frac{2.67n^2}{\text{Sec.}^3\phi})$

$n = \frac{B}{R}$

w_T = uniform upward load applied to concrete by tendons

$w_T = \frac{8BF}{R^2}$

V_H and V_K = concentrated downward loads applied at supports
            by tendons = F tan ϕ

At H, $X = 0$ and tan $\phi = \frac{4B+M}{R}$

At K, $X = R$ and tan $\phi = \frac{M-4B}{R}$

FIG. 14-3. Geometry of parabolic path of tendons where ends of parabola are at different elevations.

The distance from the bottom of the concrete to the c.g.s. at $X = 805$ in. (the lowest point on the curve) is

$$78 - (10 + 58.2) = 9.8 \text{ in.}$$

This is so close to the 10 in. originally chosen that there should be no problem in arranging a satisfactory tendon pattern to suit this dimension. (For those problems in which this value proves to be too small, a new value of B should be chosen and the calculations repeated. The new value of B would be the old value of B minus the distance the c.g.s. needs to be raised. If we needed to raise the c.g.s. to 10 in. in this example, the amount to be raised would be $10 - 9.80 = 0.20$ in. and the value of B for the second trial would be $50.55 - 0.20 = 50.35$ in. We shall continue with the values in our first trial.

Step 2. Let $F_A = 1,000,000$ lb.

Step 3. From Fig. 14-3

$$w_T = \frac{8BF_A}{R^2} = \frac{8 \times 50.55 \times 1,000,000}{1,500^2} = 179.6 \text{ lb per in.}$$

Step 4. From Fig. 14-4 the bending moment M_T due to the uniform load w_T is the coefficient in the table for uniform load full length $\times$ $w_T(2R)^2$. In this case $w_T(2R)^2 = 179.6 (2 \times 1,500)^2$. Since w_T is an upward load, the sign of the moment will be opposite to that given in the table in Fig. 14-4. Using the coefficients in the table and the section properties from Fig. 14-1 we get

		Station on girder				
	G or K	1	2	3	4	H
Moment, in.-kips	0	$-22,620$	$-29,100$	$-19,400$	$+8,080$	$+50,100$
f'_T	0	-598	-768	-512	$+213$	$+1,323$
f^b_T	0	$+1,275$	$+1,639$	$+1,092$	-455	$-2,820$

Step 5. The direct compressive stress is $1,000,000 \div 1,560 = 641$ psi.

Step 6. Since the c.g.s. is on the c.g.c. at the ends of the member, there is no bending moment due to the eccentricity of the tendons.

If the c.g.s. were above the c.g.c. at the ends, this eccentricity would create a positive moment of $F_A e$ and the moment diagram would be that shown in Fig. 14-5. The stresses due to this moment should be computed for summation in Step 7. If the c.g.s. were below the c.g.c. at the ends, the moments at G and K would be $-F_A e$ and at H would be $+0.5F_A e$.

Figure 14-6 shows the moment diagram resulting from eccentricity of tendons at the ends of a three-span continuous structure such as that shown in Fig. 13-9.

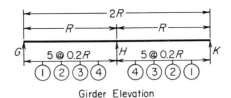

Girder Elevation

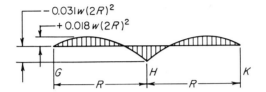

Moment Diagram – Uniform Load w Full Length

Table of Moment Coefficients

Station on girder	G or K	1	2	3	4	H
Uniform load full length	0	+0.014	+0.018	+0.012	−0.005	−0.031
Max positive moment	0	+0.017	+0.024	+0.021	+0.008	
Max negative moment	0	−0.003	−0.006	−0.009	−0.013	−0.031

Moment is coefficient from table $\times w(2R)^2$.

FIG. 14-4. Moments in a two-span continuous beam having a constant moment of inertia.

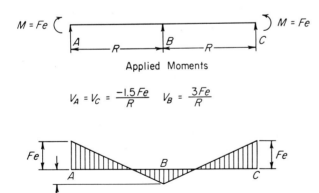

Applied Moments

$$V_A = V_C = \frac{-1.5Fe}{R} \qquad V_B = \frac{3Fe}{R}$$

Moment Diagram

This moment diagram is applicable only to a member which has a constant moment of inertia. from A to C.

FIG. 14-5. Moments in a two-span continuous beam due to eccentric application of prestressing force at ends.

Step 7. The net stresses due to F_A are the sum of those computed in Steps 4, 5, and 6, which give

	G or K	1	2	3	4	H
			Station on girder			
$f^t_{F_A}$	0	+43	−127	+129	+854	+1,964
$f^b_{F_A}$	0	+1,916	+2,280	+1,733	+186	−2,179

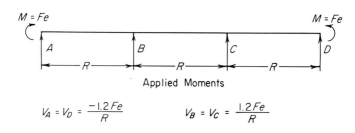

$$V_A = V_D = \frac{-1.2\,Fe}{R} \qquad V_B = V_C = \frac{1.2\,Fe}{R}$$

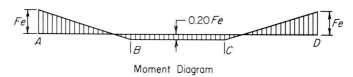

Moment Diagram

This moment diagram is applicable only to a member which has a constant moment of inertia from *A* to *D*.

Fig. 14-6. Moments in a three-span continuous beam due to eccentric application of pre-stressing force at ends.

Step 8. The dead-load moments are found by multiplying the coefficients in the table in Fig. 14-4 for uniform load full length by $w(2R)^2$. In this case $w(2R)^2 = 1,625/12\ (2 \times 1,500)^2$. The moments and stresses are

	G or K	1	2	3	4	H
			Station on girder			
Dead-load moment, in.-kips..............	0	+17,060	+21,930	+14,620	−6,090	−37,800
f^t_D...................	0	+450	+599	+386	−161	−998
f^b_D...................	0	−961	−1,236	−823	+343	+2,130

Step 9. Maximum live-load moments are found using the coefficients in the table in Fig. 14-4. For this computation $w(2R)^2 = 1,000/12 (2 \times 1,500)^2$. Maximum positive moments and stresses are

	G or K	1	2	3	4	H
			Station on girder			
Live-load moment, in.-kips.........	0	+12,760	+18,000	+15,760	+6,000	Live load
$f^t{}_L$...............	0	+337	+475	+416	+158	never causes positive moment
$f^b{}_L$...............	0	−718	−1,014	−887	−338	at this point

Maximum negative moments and stresses are

	G or K	1	2	3	4	H
			Station on girder			
Live-load moment, in.-kips.........	0	−2,250	−4,500	−6,750	−9,750	−23,250
$f^t{}_L$...............	0	−59	−119	−178	−258	−614
$f^b{}_L$...............	0	+127	+254	+380	+549	+1,310

Step 10. Adding dead-load stresses from Step 8 to stresses for maximum positive moment from Step 9 gives

	G or K	1	2	3	4	H
			Station on girder			
$f^t{}_{D+L}$	0	+787	+1,074	+802	−3	−998
$f^b{}_{D+L}$	0	−1,679	−2,250	−1,710	+5	+2,130

Adding dead-load stresses from Step 8 to stresses for maximum negative moment from Step 9 gives

	G or K	1	2	3	4	H
			Station on girder			
$f^t{}_{D+L}$	0	+391	+480	+208	−419	−1,612
$f^b{}_{D+L}$	0	−834	−982	−443	+892	+3,440

Comparison of the stresses computed in this step with the stresses produced by the prestressing force as summarized in Step 7 suggests that the governing condition is found at station 2 on the girder under dead load plus positive moment from live load. This stress is $-2,250$ psi.

Step 11. Using Eq. (14-1), find the required F.

$$F = \frac{F_A f^b{}_F}{f^b{}_{FA}}$$ (14-1)

$$F_A = 1,000,000 \qquad f^b{}_F = 2,250 \qquad f^b{}_{FA} = 2,280$$

$$F = \frac{1,000,000 \times 2,250}{2,280} = 987,000 \text{ lb}$$

Stresses due to this value of F will be

$$\frac{987,000}{1,000,000} = 98.7\% \text{ of those due to } F_A$$

Using this ratio, the stresses due to $F = 987,000$ lb are

	G or K	1	2	3	4	H
		\multicolumn{6}{c}{Station on girder}
$f^t{}_F$	0	$+42$	-125	$+127$	$+843$	$+1,938$
$f^b{}_F$	0	$+1,891$	$+2,250$	$+1,710$	$+184$	$-2,150$

One of the critical conditions is F plus dead load only. The sum of the stresses due to F and the stresses due to dead load is

	G or K	1	2	3	4	H
		\multicolumn{6}{c}{Station on girder}
$f^t{}_{F+D}$	0	$+492$	$+474$	$+513$	$+682$	$+940$
$f^b{}_{F+D}$	0	$+930$	$+1,014$	$+887$	$+527$	-20

A second critical condition is F plus dead load plus maximum positive live-load moments. The sum of the stresses under this loading is

	G or K	1	2	3	4	H
		\multicolumn{6}{c}{Station on girder}
$f^t{}_{F+D+L}$	0	$+829$	$+949$	$+929$	$+840$	$+940$
$f^b{}_{F+D+L}$	0	$+212$	0	0	$+189$	-20

A third critical condition is F plus dead load plus maximum negative live-load moments. The sum of the stresses under this loading is

	Station on girder					
	G or K	1	2	3	4	H
f^t_{F+D+L}	0	+433	+355	+335	+424	+326
f^b_{F+D+L}	0	+1,057	+1,268	+1,267	+1,076	+1,290

Under all three critical conditions the compressive stresses are well below the allowable of 2,000 psi. The only tensile stress is 20 psi in the bottom fiber at H. Since this is negligible, we can say that the member is satisfactory under the design load condition.

At this point we should consider the economy of the section being designed. The maximum compressive stress under any of the critical conditions is 1,268 psi in the bottom fiber at station 2 under F plus dead load plus maximum negative moment. This is only 63.4 per cent of the allowable 2,000 psi. What would happen if we decreased the depth and/or width of the 12-in. stem so that this stress was increased to 2,000 psi? We would save some concrete, and it appears that all the compressive stresses would remain within allowable limits. The 20-psi tensile stress at H would increase but should not be too large to be taken care of with some reinforcing bars. Although these factors seem to indicate that a redesign with a smaller cross section would save material, we shall continue with the section shown in Fig. 14-1 because previous experience with continuous structures of this type shows that the dimensions of the required section are determined by ultimate moment requirements more often than by design load requirements.

In some cases the designer may find that the tensile stress in the bottom fiber at H is too large to be disregarded. This tensile stress could be eliminated by revising the path of the tendons to place them at a lower elevation at point H. Although this procedure will eliminate the tensile stress at H, calculations based on the new path of tendons will show that a larger F is required to offset the tensile stress at stations 2 and 3.

Section 207.3.2b says that, under design loads, bridge members shall have zero flexural tension "in the precompressed tensile zone." As the tensile stress under consideration is not in this zone but in a zone which is subjected to compressive stress by any live or dead load applied to the structure, it is the author's feeling that a reasonable amount of tensile stress $(6\sqrt{f'_c})$ can be permitted. Reinforcing bars should be provided to carry the tensile stress.

Now that the final value of F has been established, we must check the fourth critical condition, which is initial prestress plus dead load. Details of the tendons will not be worked out in this example, so we shall assume that they are of 0.196-in.-diameter wire with an initial stress of 175,000 psi and a final stress of 150,000 psi. This means that F_I will be $(175,000/150,000) F = 1.166 \times 987,000 = 1,151,000$ lb. The stresses due to F_I will be $1,151,000/1,000,000$, or 1.151 times those due to F_A, which gives

		Station on girder				
	G or K	1	2	3	4	H
$f^t{}_{F_I}$	0	$+49$	-146	$+148$	$+982$	$+2,260$
$f^b{}_{F_I}$	0	$+2,205$	$+2,623$	$+1,995$	$+214$	$-2,508$

The stresses due to F_I plus dead load are

		Station on girder				
	G or K	1	2	3	4	H
$f^t{}_{F_I+D}$	0	$+499$	$+453$	$+534$	$+821$	$+1,262$
$f^b{}_{F_I+D}$	0	$+1,244$	$+1,387$	$+1,172$	$+557$	-378

All the compressive stresses are well within the allowable, and the only tensile stress is the 378 psi in the bottom fiber at H. Section 207.3.1.b.1 permits a tensile stress of $3\sqrt{f'_{ci}}$ for members without reinforcing bars. For this problem this is $3\sqrt{5,000} = 212$ psi. We shall provide reinforcing bars to carry the tension in accordance with the following computation.

The diagram in Fig. 14-7a shows the stress distribution which would exist if the tension were carried by the concrete. Under this condition the center of the compressive force is 20 in. below the top of the girder. For a trial computation we shall assume that the center of the group of reinforcing bars to be provided can be located within 4½ in. of the bottom, so that $y = 53\frac{1}{2}$ in.

The bending moment to be resisted by the reinforcing bars is the section modulus of the section for its bottom fiber times its tensile stress, or $17,760 \times 378$. Thus the tension the bars must carry is $(17,760 \times 378)/53.5 = 125,500$ lb. At 20,000 psi (Sec. 207.2) we need 6.275 sq in. of reinforcing steel. Use six #9 bars with a total area of 6 sq in. These can be placed in a satisfactory pattern as shown in Fig. 14-7b. Since the bottom fiber stress goes from -378 psi at H to $+557$ psi at station 4, the reinforcing bars will all be relatively short. Points at which each layer of bars can be stopped should be computed by plotting the curve for $f^b{}_{F_I+D}$ from H to 4.

As a check on the most economical design, computations should be made with the tendons at a lower elevation at H to determine the total force required when all tensile stress in the concrete is eliminated at H. The cost of these tendons for the full length of the structure should then be compared with the cost of the tendons and reinforcing bars as designed in this example.

Step 12. *a.* From the shear and moment diagrams for a two-span elastic structure as found in any handbook the reactions under uniform load are

$$R_G = R_K = 0.375wR \qquad \text{and} \qquad R_H = 1.25wR$$

which give, for dead load,

$$R_G = R_K = 0.375 \times 1{,}625 \times 125 = 76{,}200 \text{ lb}$$
$$R_H = 1.25 \times 1{,}625 \times 125 = 254{,}000 \text{ lb}$$

b. Using the formula from Fig. 14-3,

$$w_T = \frac{8BF}{R^2} = \frac{8\,(50.55/12)\,987{,}000}{125^2} = 2{,}130 \text{ lb per ft}$$

Applying the standard formula used in *a*,

$$R_G = R_K = 0.375 \times 2{,}130 \times 125 = -99{,}800 \text{ lb}$$
$$R_H = 1.25 \times 2{,}130 \times 125 = -333{,}000 \text{ lb}$$

c. Use formulas in Fig. 14-3 to find **concentrated** downward loads applied to piers by tendons.

At H, $$\tan \phi = \frac{4B + M}{R} = \frac{(4 \times 50.55) + 14.9}{125 \times 12} = 0.1447$$

At K, $$\tan \phi = \frac{M - 4B}{R} = \frac{14.9 - (4 \times 50.55)}{125 \times 12} = -0.1249$$

Then

$$R_H = F \tan \phi = 987{,}000 \times 0.1447 = 142{,}800 \text{ lb}$$

This is the reaction at H from the tendons between H and K. There is an equal reaction at H from the tendons between H and G. Thus the total reaction at H is $142{,}800 \times 2 = 285{,}600$ lb.

$$R_G = R_K = 987{,}000 \times 0.1249 = 123{,}300 \text{ lb}$$

This is a positive downward reaction. The negative sign for $\tan \phi$ at K simply indicates that the slope of the tendons is in the opposite direction to that for which the equation was set up.

d. Adding the values in *a, b,* and *c*, we get the following net reactions on the piers under final prestress plus dead load:

$$R_H = 254{,}000 - 333{,}000 + 285{,}600 = 206{,}600 \text{ lb}$$
$$R_G = R_K = 76{,}200 - 99{,}800 + 123{,}300 = 99{,}700 \text{ lb}$$

The sum of the reactions $R_G + R_H + R_K$ is 406,000 lb, which checks the total dead weight of 1,625 lb per ft $\times$ 125 $\times$ 2.

When a uniform live load is distributed over the portions of the span where it will cause the most shear, the maximum reactions which can be developed are

$$R_G = R_K = 0.438wR \qquad \text{and} \qquad R_H = 1.25wR$$

Using numerical values

$$R_G = R_K = 0.438 \times 1,000 \times 125 = 54,750 \text{ lb}$$
$$R_H = 1.25 \times 1,000 \times 125 = 156,250 \text{ lb}$$

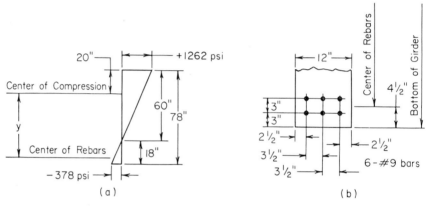

FIG. 14-7. Stress diagram at station H under initial prestress plus dead load. Reinforcing bars used to take the tension in the bottom.

Step 13. From Sec. 205.3.2 the required ultimate strength for a bridge is $1.5D + 2.5L$. As indicated in Sec. 213.4 this is not necessarily the most severe condition in a continuous structure. At some points on the structure the maximum ultimate moment may be due to $1.0D$ on part of the structure and $1.5D$ plus $2.5L$ on the rest of the structure.

The first problem, therefore, is to plot the curve of maximum ultimate moment. For greater simplicity in calculations this can be expressed as $1.0D$ for the full length of the structure and $0.5D$ plus $2.5L$ on those parts of the structure which create maximum moments.

The dead-load moments have already been computed in Step 8.

The additional load will be $(0.5 \times 1,625) + (2.5 \times 1,000) = 3,312$ lb per ft. Using $w = 3,312$ and the coefficients in the table in Fig. 14-4, compute maximum positive and maximum negative moments. For this computation $w(2R)^2$ is $(3,312/12)(2 \times 1,500)^2$. Combine each of these values with the dead-load moment to find the critical values for ultimate moment as follows (moments are given in inch-kips):

		Station on girder					
	G or K	1	2	3	4	H
A = dead-load moment	0	+17,060	+21,930	+14,620	−6,090	−37,800
B = max pos moment	0	+42,200	+59,600	+52,180	+19,870	
C = max neg moment	0	−7,450	−14,900	−22,350	−32,300	−77,000
$D = A + B$	0	+59,260*	+81,530*	+66,800*	+13,780*	−37,800
$E = A + C$	0	+9,610	+7,030	−7,730*	−38,390*	−114,800*

The possible critical ultimate moments are those marked with an asterisk (*). We must now compute the ultimate capacity of the structure at these points.

In checking ultimate moments we need values for A_s and f'_s. In Step 11 we set $F = 987,000$ lb, using 0.196-in.-diameter wire at a final stress of 150,000 psi. From this $A_s = 987,000 \div 150,000 = 6.58$ sq in. The ultimate strength of 0.196-in.-diameter wire is $f'_s = 250,000$ psi.

First check ultimate negative-moment capacity at H. Under negative moment this section would be considered as a rectangular section, since only the rectangular section is in compression. Use formula (*a*) from Sec. 209.2.1(a) of Tentative Recommendations. From Fig. 14-1 the width b of the compression area at H is 12 in. However, if we use a value of 12 in., we shall be completely ignoring the reinforcing steel shown in Fig. 14-7*b*. Since the Tentative Recommendations do not outline a design procedure including reinforcing steel in compression under ultimate conditions, the following transformed section method is suggested.

Under design load conditions the addition to the section provided by the reinforcing steel is in the ratio of the E of the steel to the E of the concrete, since both materials are working at stresses below their yield points. Under ultimate moment conditions each material will have reached its yield point. If one material reaches its yield point ahead of the other, it will continue to change length without an appreciable increase in stress while the other material is subjected to additional stress by the continuing change in length.

In this problem the concrete $f'_c = 5,000$ psi and concrete under ultimate bending conditions is assumed to yield at 85 per cent f'_c, so its yield point is $5,000 \times 85\% = 4,250$ psi. The minimum yield point of the intermediate-grade bars is 40,000 psi. Thus adding the steel bars is equivalent to adding an area of concrete equal to $(40,000/4,250 − 1) A'_s = 8.4A'_s$ in which A'_s is the area of reinforcing steel. Since the center of gravity of the bars is 4½ in. from the bottom of the girder, the center of the additional area will act at this point. We shall assume that the additional area is a uniform width 9 in. deep. The additional area is 8.4 × 6 sq in. = 50.4 sq in., and its width is 50.4 ÷ 9 = 5.6 in. Our transformed section now has a flange with a width b of 12 + 5.6 = 17.6 in. and a depth of 9 in. as shown in Fig. 14-8.

Refer to Tentative Recommendations for procedure in computing ultimate strength.

From Fig. 14-1 and Step 1, $d = 78 - 10 = 68$ in.

$$p = \frac{A_s}{bd} = \frac{6.58}{17.6 \times 68} = 0.0055$$

From Sec. 209.2.2(a)

$$f_{su} = f'_s \left(1 - 0.5 \frac{p f'_s}{f'_c}\right)$$

$$= 250,000 \left(1 - \frac{0.5 \times 0.0055 \times 250,000}{5,000}\right) = 216,000 \text{ psi}$$

From Sec. 209.2.(b)

$$\frac{1.4 d p f_{su}}{f'_c} = \frac{1.4 \times 68 \times 0.0055 \times 216,000}{5,000} = 22.6 \text{ in.}$$

Since the flange thickness of 9 in. is less than this, formula (b) will be used. For use in formula (b)

$$A_{sf} = \frac{0.85 f'_c (b - b') t}{f_{su}}$$

$$= \frac{0.85 \times 5,000 (17.6 - 12) 9}{216,000} = 0.98 \text{ sq in.}$$

$$A_{sr} = A_s - A_{sf} = 6.58 - 0.98 = 5.60 \text{ sq in.}$$

Formula (b) is

$$M_u = A_{sr} f_{su} d \left(1 - \frac{0.6 A_{sr} f_{su}}{b' d f'_c}\right) + 0.85 f'_c (b - b') t (d - 0.5t)$$

Substituting numerical values,

$$M_u = 5.60 \times 216,000 \times 68 \left(1 - \frac{0.6 \times 5.6 \times 216,000}{12 \times 68 \times 5,000}\right)$$
$$+ 0.85 \times 5,000 (17.6 - 12) 9 (68 - 4.5) = 81,250,000 \text{ in.-lb}$$

This is only 70.7 per cent of the required 114,800,000 in.-lb, which means that additional tensile steel is required.

Section 209.2.4.1 says we may use conventional steel at its yield point. We shall use intermediate-grade bars with $f'_y = 40,000$ psi. The tensile force in the tendons is $216,000 \times 6.58 = 1,421,000$ lb. Since this is 70.7 per cent of the required force, the amount still needed is

$$\left(\frac{100 - 70.7}{70.7}\right)(1,421,000) = 588,000 \text{ lb}$$

$$588,000 \div 40,000 = 14.7 \text{ sq in.}$$

Actually we shall need more than this because the additional steel will raise the neutral axis, which will shorten the lever arm of the steel. We shall try sixteen #9 bars with an area of 16 sq in. We shall assume that the center of gravity of the reinforcing steel is at the same elevation as

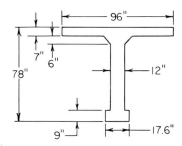

Fig. 14-8. Transformed section at station *H* resulting from reinforcing bars shown in Fig. 14-7.

the center of gravity of the tendons. Check the percentage of steel in accordance with Sec. 209.2.4.1.

$$\frac{pf_{su}}{f'_c} + \frac{p'f'_y}{f'_c} = \frac{0.0055 \times 216,000}{5,000} + \frac{0.01337 \times 40,000}{5,000}$$

$$= 0.2375 + 0.107 = 0.3445$$

Since this is greater than 0.30, the percentage of steel is too high. The best solution is to increase the width of the concrete section at *H* and for a sufficient distance each side to cover the area of critical negative moment. Try an 18-in. width as shown in Fig. 14-9. This will give a transformed section with a flange 23.6 in. wide by 9 in. deep. Now the formula in Sec. 209.2.1(b), $1.4dpf_{su}/f'_c$, must be rewritten to include the reinforcing steel. It will be $1.4d[(pf_{su}/f'_c) + (p'f'_y/f'_c)]$, and the numerical values to be used in it will be $p = 6.58/(23.6 \times 68) = 0.00413$

$$p' = 16/(23.6 \times 68) = 0.00997$$

The value of f_{su} for the new section at H is

$$f_{su} = 250,000 \left(1 - 0.5 \, \frac{0.00413 \times 250,000}{5,000}\right) = 224,000 \text{ psi}$$

Substituting in the formula,

$$1.4 \times 68 \left(\frac{0.00413 \times 224,000}{5,000} + \frac{0.00997 \times 40,000}{5,000}\right) = 25.2 \text{ in.}$$

Since this is greater than 9 in., formula (*b*) from Sec. 209.2.1(*b*) will apply, but it will be revised as follows to include the reinforcing steel.

$$M_u = (A_{sr}f_{su} + A'_s f'_y) d \left(1 - 0.6 \, \frac{A_{sr}f_{su} + A'_s f'_y}{b'd f'_c}\right)$$
$$+ 0.85 f'_c (b - b') t (d - 0.5t)$$

$$A_{sf} = \frac{0.85 \times 5,000 \, (23.6 - 18) \, 9}{224,000} = 0.96 \text{ sq in.}$$

$$A_{sr} = 6.58 - 0.96 = 5.62 \text{ sq in.}$$

Substituting numerical values in the formula,

$$M_u = (5.62 \times 224,000 + 16 \times 40,000)$$
$$68 \left[1 - \frac{0.6 \, (5.62 \times 224,000 + 16 \times 40,000)}{18 \times 68 \times 5,000}\right]$$
$$+ 0.85 \times 5,000 \, (23.6 - 18) \, 9 \, (68 - 4.5)$$
$$= 105,200,000 + 13,600,000 = 118,800,000 \text{ in.-lb}$$

which is more than the 114,800,000 in.-lb required.

In summary the cross section at H will be as shown in Fig. 14-9 with 16 sq in. of reinforcing steel in the top and 6 in the bottom. In this example the center of gravity of the reinforcing bars in the top was placed at the same elevation as the center of gravity of the tendons in order to simplify calculations. When the design is completed, the details should be checked to see that a pattern of tendons and bars can be worked out to meet this requirement. If it cannot, the best possible pattern should be worked out and the resulting ultimate strength computed.

When the centers of gravity of the bars and tendons are not the same, an equivalent one for the two groups must be computed for use in determining d. The distance to the equivalent center of gravity y_{cg} can be found by the following equation, taking moments about any desired point:

$$y_{cg} = \frac{(A_s f_{su}) y + (A'_s f'_y) y'}{A_s f_{su} + A'_s f'_y} \qquad (14\text{-}2)$$

in which y and y' represent the distances from the point about which moments are being taken to the center of gravity of the tendons and the center of gravity of the bars. Equation (14-2) applies only to calculations for ultimate moment.

The foregoing calculations for ultimate moment at H are based on the recommendation in Sec. 213.4 that "moment redistribution not be considered in design at the present time." The resultant cross section at H is sufficient to carry the full ultimate moment before extensive yielding takes place, which means that there will be no appreciable redistribution until the computed ultimate is passed.

Use of moment redistribution would probably provide a more economical structure. It would decrease the moment at H, where it is maximum and where the cross section is least efficient. It would increase the positive moments, but the section is more efficient under positive moment, and the maximum addition to the original design, if any, would probably be a small amount of reinforcing steel with no change in the concrete cross section. It is the author's feeling that use of moment redistribution in continuous prestressed concrete structures is permissible for engineers who thoroughly understand their subject.[1-4]*

Since the new section at H has a larger I than the section throughout the rest of the structure, the moment developed at H will be larger than that found in the foregoing calculations. In the design of an actual structure it would be necessary to establish the length of the heavier cross section, compute bending moments based on the nonuniform I, and check stresses. Our purpose, however, is to illustrate prestressed concrete design procedure rather than to conduct an exercise in elastic analysis. We shall assume that the new bending moments at H have been computed and were found to be

$$M_D = -38,800,000 \text{ in.-lb}$$
$$M_L = -23,830,000 \text{ in.-lb}$$
$$M_T = +50,650,000 \text{ in.-lb}$$
$$\text{Required } M_u = -118,000,000 \text{ in.-lb}$$
$$F \text{ still} = 987,000 \text{ lb}$$

Because of their considerable area the reinforcing bars were included in computing section properties in Fig. 14-9. In this computation $E_c = 1,800,000 + 500(5,000) = 4,300,000$ and $E_s = 30,000,000$. Thus

$$n = \frac{30,000,000}{4,300,000} = 7 \quad \text{and} \quad n - 1 = 6$$

---

* Superscript numbers indicate references listed in the Bibliography at the end of the chapter

Using these moments and the section properties computed in Fig. 14-9, the stresses at H under the various combinations of loading are

Direct stress from $F = 987,000 \div 2,118 = +466$ psi

$$f'_F = \frac{50,650,000}{46,500} + 466 = +1,555 \text{ psi}$$

$$f^b_F = -\frac{50,650,000}{26,920} + 466 = -1,414 \text{ psi}$$

$$f'_D = \frac{-38,800,000}{46,500} = -835 \text{ psi}$$

$$f^b_D = \frac{-38,800,000}{26,920} = +1,440 \text{ psi}$$

$$f'_{F+D} = +720$$

$$f^b_{F+D} = +26$$

$$f'_L = \frac{-23,830,000}{46,500} = -512 \text{ psi}$$

$$f^b_L = \frac{-23,830,000}{26,920} = +885 \text{ psi}$$

$$f'_{F+D+L} = +208 \text{ psi}$$

$$f^b_{F+D+L} = +911 \text{ psi}$$

We have already computed the ultimate moment capacity of the new section and found it to be 118,800,000 in.-lb, which is more than the new required value, so the new cross section is satisfactory.

It should be noted that use of moment redistribution for ultimate design not only would save the extra material used in the vicinity of H but would eliminate the design complications which go with a variable moment of inertia in a continuous structure.

Next check ultimate positive-moment capacity at stations 1, 2, 3, and 4. First we must evaluate the term $1.4pf_{su}/f'_c$ for each station to see whether to apply the formula for rectangular or flanged sections. From Fig. 14-3

$$d = D + y_B + y$$

From Tentative Recommendations

$$p = \frac{A_s}{bd}$$

$$f_{su} = f'_s \left(1 - 0.5 \frac{pf'_s}{f'_c}\right)$$

Substituting known numerical values in these formulas we get the value of f_{su} and use the appropriate formulas for ultimate moment to get

	Station on girder			
	1	2	3	4
d.....................	54.27	67.49	64.51	45.33
p.....................	0.00126	0.00102	0.00106	0.00151
f_{su}...................	242,000	243,000	243,000	240,500
$1.4dpf_{su}/f'_c$.............	4.63	4.68	4.65	4.61
M_u....................	83,200,000	105,000,000	100,000,000	68,500,000
Required M_u.............	59,260,000	81,530,000	66,800,000	13,780,000

Computations for station 4 are as follows:

$D = 10$ in.
$X = 25$ ft 0 in. $= 300$ in.
Values of M, B, etc., are given in Step 1.

$$y_B = \frac{MX}{R} = \frac{14.9 \times 300}{1,500} = 2.98 \text{ in.}$$

$$y = 4B \frac{X}{R}\left(1 - \frac{X}{R}\right)$$

$$y = 4 \times 50.55 \frac{300}{1,500}\left(1 - \frac{300}{1,500}\right) = 32.35$$

$$d = 10 + 2.98 + 32.35 = 45.33$$

$$p = \frac{A_s}{bd} = \frac{6.58}{96 \times 45.33} = 0.00151$$

$$f_{su} = 250,000\left(1 - \frac{0.5 \times 0.00151 \times 250,000}{5,000}\right) = 240,500$$

$$\frac{1.4dpf_{su}}{f'_c} = \frac{1.4 \times 45.33 \times 0.00151 \times 240,500}{5,000} = 4.61$$

Since this is less than the 7-in. flange thickness, formula (a) in Sec. 209.2.1 will apply.

$$M_u = 6.58 \times 240,500 \times 45.33 \left(1 - \frac{0.6 \times 0.00151 \times 240,500}{5,000}\right) = 68,500,000$$

Each of the positive-moment capacities is greater than the required ultimate at that point, so no revisions are necessary. It is also apparent that the increase in positive moments due to moment redistribution would have to be rather large before additional steel became necessary.

Check the ultimate negative-moment capacity at stations 3 and 4. In computing the ultimate positive-moment capacity we found d from the top to the center of gravity of the tendons. Subtracting this value of d from the depth of the member will give the value of d for the negative-moment computation. At 4, $d = 78 - 45.33 = 32.67$ in. and at 3,

$d = 78 - 64.51 = 13.49$ in.   In both cases the tendons are on the compression side of the neutral axis.   Before the load in the tendons could increase appreciably beyond F, cracks would develop in the tensile side and extend through the neutral axis to the tendons.   Such long cracks would greatly reduce the moment of inertia of the section and would result in a redistribution of moment, which is contrary to the requirement of Sec. 213.4.

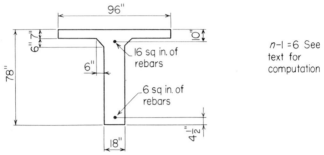

Section Properties — Taking Moments About Top

	A, sq in.	y, in	A_y	A_y^2	I_o
96 x 7 =	672	3.5"	2,350	8,220	2,745
18 x 71 =	1,278	42.5	54,300	2,308,000	537,000
$6 \times 6 \times \frac{2}{2}$ =	36	9.	324	2,915	72
Bars { 16 x 6 =	96	10.	960	9,600	
6 x 6 =	36	73.5	2,650	194,500	
	2,118		60,584	2,523,235	539,817
				539,817	
				3,063,052	

$y_t = 60,584 \div 2,118 = 28.6$
$y_b = 78 - 28.6 = 49.4$
$I = 3,063,052 - 2,118\,(28.6)^2 = 1,330,000$
$Z_t = 1,330,000 \div 28.6 = 46,500$
$Z_b = 1,330,000 \div 49.4 = 26,920$

FIG. 14-9.   Cross section and section properties at H with 18-in.-wide stem.

Development of these cracks can be kept within reasonable limits by placing a proper amount of reinforcing steel near the tensile surface of the concrete.   This gives us a condition where the centers of gravity of the bars and tendons are not at the same elevation.   In this case, however, Eq. (14-2) is not applicable.   It can be applied only when the tendons and bars are in the same general vicinity.   When the tendons are on the compression side of the neutral axis, they are usually too far from the bars for combined action. As the bending moment increases, the stress in the bars will increase but there will be practically no change in stress in the tendons. When the bars reach their yield point, they will elongate rapidly, cracks on the concrete will approach the tendons, and their tension will finally begin to increase. Here again we cannot take advantage of an increase in stress in the tendons because, before this can take place, the reinforcing bars must yield, which would result in a re-distribution of moments.

The foregoing discussion indicates that ultimate moment design at points in a structure where the tendons are on the compression side of the neutral axis and/or the tendons and reinforcing bars are too far apart to work together presents a problem entirely different from the normal condition. Reinforcing bars must be placed near the tensile surface of the concrete. These bars must be selected so that the section will carry the required ultimate moment before the bars yield. The following analysis is suggested:

1. Let T' be the total tension in reinforcing bars at their yield point.
2. The total force in the compression side of the member will be $T' + F$.
3. Since the concrete stress at ultimate moment is assumed to be $0.85f'_c$, the concrete area required to carry the total force will be $(T' + F)/0.85f'_c$.
4. The ultimate negative moment the member can carry will be ($F \times$ lever arm to center of compression force) plus ($T' \times$ lever arm to center of compression force). The simplest design procedure is to assume a value for T', determine a pattern of bars and their center of gravity, and follow the foregoing procedure to find M_u. If the result is too large or too small, the value of T' can be revised and the new M_u computed.

The required ultimate negative moment at station 4 is 38,390,000 in.-lb. Assume nine #9 bars with their center of gravity 10 in. from the top surface as shown in Fig. 14-10. Then $T' = 9 \times 40,000 = 360,000$ lb. $T' + F = 360,000 + 987,000 = 1,347,000$ lb. Required concrete area to resist this force is $1,347,000/(0.85 \times 5,000) = 317$ sq in. Since the concrete section is 12 in. wide, its depth will be $317 \div 12 = 26.4$ in. and the distance from the bottom to its center of gravity is 13.2. Using the lever arms shown on Fig. 14-10,

$$M_u = 360,000 \times 54.8 + 987,000 \times 19.47 = 38,950,000 \text{ in.-lb}$$

which is satisfactory. The designer should draw the ultimate negative-moment diagram from station 3 to H and compute the required rein-forcing at points along the diagram.

Step 14. In Step 12 we found the dead-load reactions on the piers and the reactions on the piers from the tendons. The shear in the concrete section at a pier is the reaction on the pier minus the vertical load carried by the tendon. Thus under the dead-load condition, using values computed in Step 12,

$$V_G = V_K = 99,700 - 123,300 = -23,600 \text{ lb}$$

This means that the vertical component of the tension in the tendons is greater than the reaction on the pier and the concrete section has a negative shear of 23,600 lb.

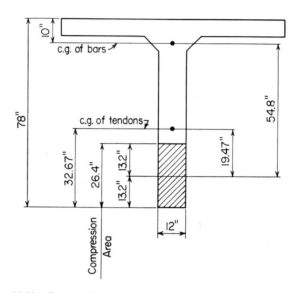

FIG. 14-10.   Cross section at station 4 under ultimate moment conditions.

The dead-load shear on either side of the pier at H is

$$V_H = \left(\frac{206,600 - 285,600}{2} \right) = -39,500 \text{ lb}$$

which is also a negative shear.

The shear in the concrete section is negative for the full span because the vertical upward load applied to the concrete by the tendons is 2,130 lb per ft and the dead load is only 1,625 lb per ft, leaving a net upward load of 505 lb per ft.

The maximum live-load shear at G and K is 54,750 lb, giving a net maximum of

$$V_G = V_K = 54,750 - 23,600 = 31,150 \text{ lb positive shear}$$

At H the maximum live-load shear is $156,250 \div 2 = 78,125$, giving a net of $V_H = 78,125 - 39,500 = 38,625$ lb positive shear.

It is apparent from these figures that design load shear is not critical. We shall not go through the calculations here, but ultimate load shear must be computed. The ultimate shear requirement should be computed in the same manner as the ultimate moment was computed in Step 13. Thus the applied loading for ultimate shear would be $D + (0.5D + 2.5L)$ with D applied the full length of the structure and ($0.5D$ plus $2.5L$) applied in those areas which produce maximum shear. We have already computed the net shear under dead load and found it to be negative. Shear due to $0.5D + 2.5L$ applied to produce maximum shear must be added to the net dead-load shear to get ultimate shear. Ultimate shear will be positive at all points. Once ultimate shear is established, the design of stirrups will follow the procedure used in Chap. 11. Note that the shear carried by the tendons has already been included in computing dead-load shear; it should not be included again.

Step 15. Camber computations are simple, since the structure is fully elastic under dead plus live loads. The camber under dead load plus initial prestress is due to the net uniform upward load of the tendons minus the dead weight of the concrete member. In Step 11 initial prestress was found to be $1.166F$. Thus the upward load from the tendons under initial prestress will be $1.166 \times 2,130 = 2,485$ lb per ft, and the net upward load including dead load will be $2,485 - 1,625 = 860$ lb per ft. The camber under dead load plus initial prestress will be that due to a uniform upward load of 860 lb per ft applied to the elastic structure. Camber growth will be the same as in previous examples. Deflection from the dead-load position under live load will be that for the elastic structure subjected to the live load.

Step 16. In addition to details around the tendon anchors, bearing plates, etc., similar to those worked out in Chap. 11 there are several details peculiar to a continuous structure.

When the prestressing load is applied, the structure will shorten. If it is firmly attached to its piers, the piers will bend as the structure shortens and part of the prestressing force will be used to bend the piers rather than to prestress the structure. One means of eliminating this problem in a two-span structure is to anchor the structure to the center pier and support it on rockers at each end pier. The amount of shortening due to elastic compression, closing of shrinkage cracks, etc., can be computed, and the rockers can be tilted so they will be at the desired angle after the prestressing operation.

From the parabolic path of tendons shown in Fig. 14-3 it appears that the tendons come to a point at H. While this assumption is usually sufficiently accurate for computations, the path of tendons over an intermediate support should be detailed as shown in Fig. 14-11. There are so many factors influencing the value of r that it is impossible to write an equation for it that will cover all conditions. The suppliers of the tendons chosen should be consulted concerning the most efficient radius. Until the specific tendons are chosen, it is suggested that the designer estimate the number of tendons that will be used and determine the ultimate strength F_u of one tendon. Then the minimum value of r should be

$$r = 0.085 \sqrt{F_u} \qquad (14\text{-}3)$$

If details permit, a larger value of r will reduce the unit pressure between the tendon and the concrete. For a round post-tensioned tendon in a

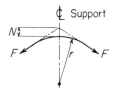

p=pressure of tendon against concrete
in pounds per linear inch where
radius of curvature of tendon is
r expressed in inches.

$$p = \frac{F}{r}$$

See text for recommended values of r

FIG. 14-11. Actual path of tendons over an intermediate pier. See text for comments on values of r, etc.

cored hole or in a metal hose, the unit pressure between tendon and concrete is not p divided by the diameter of the tendon. This would be true if the tendon were the same diameter as the hole so that they were in contact for the full 180° of the underside of the tendon. Actually the hole is larger than the tendon, and the contact surface, for a round tendon, approaches line contact. A group of parallel wires or strands in one hole will spread across the full width, and their unit pressure will approach p divided by the diameter of the hole.

Each tendon should be tensioned from both ends at one time. The tension at H will be that applied at the jack less that lost by friction between the jack and H. The tendons chosen must be large enough to give the required tension at H after friction losses. Friction is sometimes reduced for long tendons by using galvanized tendons or galvanized hose. Friction can also be reduced by filling the cavity around the tendon with water-soluble oil until the tensioning operation is finished. The oil is washed out with water before the tendon is grouted.

STRUCTURES WITH PRECAST SECTIONS

14-4. Characteristics. Precast prestressed concrete members can readily be designed and detailed for assembly into continuous and rigid frame structures. Precast prestressed members are joined to other precast prestressed members or to reinforced members. In either case, although the joint is not prestressed, full continuity can be developed.

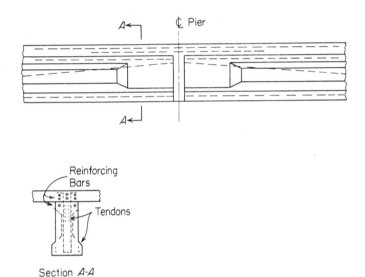

FIG. 14-12. Joint of reinforcing bars and concrete creating continuity at support between precast prestressed members.

14-5. Design Procedure. Steps in the design procedure for a structure of this type are presented herewith. They refer specifically to a multi-span bridge in which precast prestressed I beams are erected on the piers, joined over the piers with reinforcing bars, and covered with a poured-in-place slab. The bridge cross section is of the type shown in Figs. 9-1 and 9-2, and the joint as shown in Fig. 14-12. The concrete around the reinforcing bars at the piers would be poured at the same time as the deck slab, which means that the weight of the deck slab would be carried by the precast beam acting as a simple span member rather than as a continuous member. The live load would be carried by the composite section acting as a continuous elastic member. If the erection schedule and details permitted, the reinforcing bars and concrete over the piers could be placed and the concrete allowed to cure before the slab was placed. With this method the beam would act as a continuous member under the dead weight of the slab. For this method of erection or other variations from the example presented here the design procedure should be altered to suit the revised erection procedure.

Many of the computations will be similar to those shown in Chap. 9.

Step 1. Compute the stresses in the beam as a simple span member under its own dead weight.

Step 2. Compute the stresses in the beam as a simple span member under the weight of the poured-in-place slab.

Step 3. Compute the stresses in composite section composed of beam and slab acting as a continuous elastic member under live load.

Step 4. Compute the total stresses in the beam by adding stresses in Steps 1, 2, and 3.

Step 5. Compute the required prestressing force and location of the tendons to offset tensile stresses found in Step 4. Tendons should be near the top of the beam at the ends so that compressive stress in the bottom fiber will not be excessive under negative moment from live load. Tendons will extend for the length of the precast member. They will not be continuous over the supports.

Step 6. Design the connection between the beams to carry live-load negative moment over the piers. This is designed as a reinforced concrete member. Reinforcing bars to carry the tension are placed in the slab over the beam or in a cavity provided in the top of the beam. These bars must be long enough to transfer their load through the concrete to the steel in the precast beams. Provide concrete between the ends of the beams to carry the compression in the bottom of the beams and to bond the bars in the top.

Step 7. Check the structure as now designed for the critical loading conditions and for ultimate strength.

Step 8. Compute the reactions on the piers. Since the dead weight of the beam and slab is carried with the beam acting as a simple span member, the pier reactions for these loads will be computed on a simple span basis. The pier reactions due to live load will be computed as for a continuous elastic structure.

Step 9. Design the stirrups, connection between the beam and slab, and other details in the same manner as in Chap. 9.

14-6. Poured Joints. Figure 14-12 shows details of one type of joint composed of reinforcing bars and poured-in-place concrete as used to join two precast pretensioned simple span beams. Test data show that joints of this type designed to carry the full moment as reinforced concrete members produce a structure that is almost 100 per cent continuous.[2]

If the reinforcing provided at the joint is not sufficient to carry the full moment, the structure will act as fully or partially continuous, depending on the amount of reinforcing, until the reinforcing reaches its yield

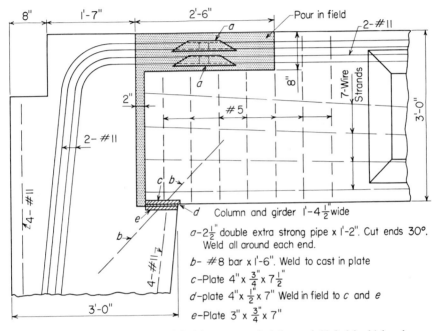

F IG. 14-13.   Rigid joint between 60-ft 0-in. span roof girder and 20-ft 0-in.-high column. Girders spaced 17 ft 0 in. center to center support pretensioned channel roof sections. Channels are 3 ft 2 in. wide by 6 in. deep. (*Details courtesy of Ross H. Bryan, Consulting Engineer, Nashville, Tenn.*)

point.   When the reinforcing yields, there will be a redistribution of moments.[3]

Poured-in-place concrete and reinforcing bars can be used to provide rigid joints between all types of precast members.   They can be used to join two members in a continuous line, to join several members at one point, or to join a horizontal member to a vertical member.

Several factors should be considered in the design and detail of a joint of this type.

1. The tendons should be located as close to the tensile side of the beam as is feasible in order to keep compressive stresses in the bottom and tensile stresses in the top within allowable limits.   These stresses should be checked near the end of the precast section.

2. Reinforcing bars and tendons should lap sufficiently to transfer all load from one to the other.

3. The degree of continuity will be proportional to the amount of reinforcing steel used in the tensile zone. If steel is designed for the full moment, continuity will be practically complete. If a smaller amount of steel is used, it will have a greater elongation, causing some rotation at the joint and thus reducing the degree of continuity.

14-7. Welded Joints. Figure 14-13 shows details of one type of joint between a horizontal and a vertical member where steel in the precast members is welded to establish a rigid connection. Joints of this type can be designed to develop full continuity.

BIBLIOGRAPHY

1. Lin, T. Y.: Strength of Continuous Prestressed Concrete Beams under Static and Repeated Loads, *J. Am. Concrete Inst.*, June, 1955, pp. 1037-1059.
2. Janney, Jack, and W. J. Eney: Full Scale Test of Bridge on Northern Illinois Toll Highway, *Proc. World Conf. on Prestressed Concrete,* 1957.
3. Ozell, A. M.: Behavior of Simple Span and Continuous Composite Prestressed Concrete Beams, Part 2, *J. Prestressed Concrete Inst.,* June, 1957, pp. 42-74.
4. Lin, T. Y.: "Design of Prestressed Concrete Structures," chap. 10, Continuous Beams, John Wiley & Sons, Inc., New York, 1955.
5. Parme, A. L., and G. H. Paris: Designing for Continuity in Prestressed Concrete Structures, *J. Am. Concrete Inst.,* September, 1951, pp. 45-64.
6. Moorman, B. B.: Continuous Prestressing, *Proc. Am. Soc. Civil Engrs. Structural Div.,* Separate No. 588.
7. Morice, P. B., and H. E. Lewis: Prestressed Continuous Beams and Frames, *Proc. Am. Soc. Civil Engrs. Journal Structural Div.,* Paper 1055.
8. Fiesenheiser, E. I.: Rapid Design of Continuous Prestressed Members, *J. Am. Concrete Inst.,* April, 1954, pp. 669-676.
9. Leonhardt, Fritz: Continuous Prestressed Concrete Beams, *J. Am. Concrete Inst.,* March, 1953, pp. 617-634.

CHAPTER 15

PRACTICAL CONSIDERATIONS AND GENERAL INFORMATION

PRACTICAL CONSIDERATIONS

The basic objective in prestressed concrete design is to produce a *safe* and *economical* structure. This can be accomplished only by having a thorough understanding of the product so that all unnecessary restrictions can be eliminated without reducing the structural stability of the members.

15-1. Specifications. As stated in Chap. 8 an engineer cannot follow any specification blindly. He can use the specification as a guide but must apply his own knowledge to check against any conditions which could influence the safety of the structure.

Tentative Recommendations for Prestressed Concrete, printed in Art. 8-2, are the best guide available for prestressed concrete design. They include a number of qualifications which should be complied with. For example, Sec. 209.2.2 gives a formula for f_{su} which can be used only if the two conditions listed are satisfied. The formula for shear steel in Sec. 210.2.2 may have to be revised if the prestress is low or if only part of the reinforcement is prestressed.

It is suggested that the reader turn back to Art. 8-2 and read carefully through Tentative Recommendations for Prestressed Concrete. As he reads, he should make notes in the margins to call his attention to qualifications and other factors which he will want to check in future designs.

15-2. Pretensioned Strands. Some of the rules established for handling seven-wire strands are based on procedures which are obviously on the side of safety because of lack of proof that other procedures give satisfactory results. It seems reasonable to depart from one or more of these rules in the interests of economy when experience shows that such a departure does not reduce the soundness of the structure.

Section 404.2.3 of Tentative Recommendations requires that "the force in the prestressing steel be transferred to the concrete smoothly and gradually." This restriction was imposed to prevent damage to the bond between the strand and the concrete at the ends of the concrete member. If a strand between two concrete members is cut while under tension, its load is applied suddenly to the concrete and the impact could conceivably damage the bond.

A number of casting yards, whose procedures were established before Tentative Recommendations became available, made a practice of severing strands by burning while they were under tension. Their experience indicates that there are no detrimental effects from this procedure as long as a proper sequence of cutting is followed and the concrete has sufficient strength. Section 404.2.3 should not be arbitrarily disregarded, but it seems reasonable for the engineer to permit cutting of strands under tension when, in his judgment, the methods and details involved will not damage the properties of the structure.

Cutting strands under tension instead of unjacking can eliminate some of the problems involved in detensioning a bed of members with deflected strands when the following procedure is used:

1. Cut several strands in the deflected group at all points between members and between end members and end anchorages.

2. Cut several strands in the straight group at all points between members and between end members and end anchorages.

3. Repeat steps 1 and 2 one or more times until the predetermined number of strands has been released. (The engineer should compute the number of strands that must be cut to create sufficient prestress so that releasing the hold-downs will not cause cracks in the top of the member. Obviously there will be no cracking problem if all the strands are cut before the hold-downs are released, but the prestressing from the straight strands tends to increase camber, which creates additional load in the hold-downs. If the hold-downs have sufficient capacity to carry the additional load, all strands can be cut before the hold-downs are released.)

4. Release hold-downs.

5. Repeat steps 1 and 2 until all strands have been cut.

From the fabricator's point of view the simplest procedure might be to repeat step 1 several times until all deflected strands had been cut, release the hold-downs, and then cut or unjack the straight strands. If more than a few strands are deflected, this procedure could cause serious cracks in the concrete. When only the deflected strands are cut, they create a large compressive force near the top of the member at each end. This force tends to shorten the top of the member and thereby creates a shear in the web, since the bottom has no tendency to shorten. In fact, the bottom is restrained from shortening by the straight strands which are still attached to the casting bed anchors.

Infrequently a single wire in a seven-wire strand will break during or after the pretensioning operation. Unless other wires are damaged too, such as by exposure of the strand to excessive heat or electric arc, it is seldom necessary to delay production by replacing the strand. In many members the designer does not need all the strands shown in the details. If his calculations call for 9.63 strands, he will, of course, show 10 strands on the drawing. When one wire breaks in a group of 10 strands, it represents one-seventh of one strand, which leaves 9%, or 9.86, strands intact. Since the operation of replacing a strand often represents a considerable expense, it should not be required unless it is necessary for the stability of the structure. At the time the design is prepared, the engineer can compute the number of permissible broken wires. Since the subject is not covered by any of the available specifications, it is suggested that the number of wire breaks be limited to one per strand, one in a group of 12 strands or less, two in a group of 13 to 24 strands, and three for 25 or more strands.

The engineer may find it desirable to use his judgment in the establishment of initial tension when elongation and jack readings do not coincide within the accuracy specified in Sec. 404.2.2 of Tentative Recommendations. In general the elongation of the seven-wire strands gives the most consistent results. One quick check which often definitely locates the source of error is to compute the E_s of the strand using its measured elongation and the corresponding load read from the jack. If E_s is greater than 29,000,000, we know that the jack reading is too high because the wire from which the strand is made has an E of 29,000,000 and the E of a seven-wire strand is necessarily less than that of the wire from which it is made. The converse is not necessarily true because improper stranding techniques can produce a strand with a low modulus.

15-3. Concrete Details. In addition to computing section properties, stresses, etc., and providing a properly located prestressing force of the necessary magnitude, the designer must give careful consideration to the details of the prestressed concrete members. Several factors which can cause trouble if overlooked are discussed herewith.

In reinforced concrete design it is standard practice to disregard certain parts of the concrete cross section if there is some question as to whether their full area will function or not. In reinforced concrete this is always on the conservative side, but in prestressed concrete it can lead to seriously underprestressed members. In Art. 8-2 see Tentative Recommendations, Sec. 209.1, and author's comment which follows it.

Prestressed concrete sections are generally thinner than reinforced concrete sections and often have both top and bottom flanges. These properties increase the need for generous fillets between webs and flanges to minimize cracks.

When the stability of a post-tensioned cross section is reviewed, the holes cored for the tendons should be considered as permanent holes even though they will later be filled with grout. Metal ducts around tendons should not be considered as adding to the strength of the section unless they are inflexible and have a wall thickness in excess of $\frac{1}{16}$ in. When grout is placed in the hole or duct, the tensioning operation has already been completed. This means that the concrete around the hole is under compression but that the grout is never prestressed. Since the unprestressed grout and the surrounding concrete are dissimilar materials, a grout-filled hole may be little better than an unfilled hole except that the grout bonds the tendon to the member. Figure 15-1 shows one detail where the holes for post-tensioned tendons cause a "plane of weakness" which invites longitudinal cracks above or below the tendons. When such a detail must be used, transverse reinforcing should be placed above and below the holes. This is seldom a serious problem in pretensioned members because all the concrete is cast and prestressed as a unit.

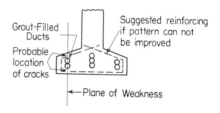

FIG. 15-1. Plane of weakness due to holes cored for tendons and reinforcing to prevent serious longitudinal cracks.

The details of the joint between two prestressed members should coincide with the design. If the member is designed as simply supported at the end, then the joint should be detailed so that it is incapable of taking moment. If the joint is detailed so that it will carry moment, both members must be checked for the moment which will be developed.

15-4. Camber. The formula for E_c in Sec. 203.2 of Tentative Recommendations in Art. 8-2 is only approximate. The amount of growth, Sec. 303.3, is dependent upon local conditions, and the value used must be based on experience under the existing conditions.

Some engineers find it difficult to realize that camber can increase with time because they are familiar with reinforced concrete which always increases in deflection under constant load. In a prestressed concrete member the growth of camber or deflection due to creep in the concrete under constant stress will be in the same direction as the short-time camber or deflection. Thus, if the member has an upward camber under prestress plus its long-time loading, the growth in camber will also be upward, resulting in a greater camber. If the member has a downward deflection under prestress plus long-time loads, the growth will also be downward.

15-5. Safety Precautions. In addition to the normal precautions required on any construction work it must be remembered that a prestressed concrete tendon under tension as high as 175,000 psi contains a tremendous amount of energy. The tendon and/or any fittings or equipment connected to it can whip across working areas with lethal results if its pent-up energy is suddenly released by some type of equipment failure.

The good safety record established by prestressed concrete producers during the first years of operation in the United States can be maintained if both old and new operators will remember the dangers involved and continue to observe the logical precautions even though they have not had any difficulties. There are several factors which merit special attention.

The wedge-type temporary grips used for holding seven-wire pretensioned strands under load should be handled in accordance with the instructions issued by their suppliers. One requirement, for example, is that they be kept clean. Dirt between a wedge and the steel case around it will retard the motion of the wedge into the case and can cause premature failure or slippage of the strand.

As discussed in Art. 6-4, excessive heat or an electric arc can destroy the high strength of a tendon. Such damage is not necessarily apparent to the naked eye and is discovered only when the tendon fails during the tensioning operation. This danger can be eliminated by proper storage and handling of tendons.

Operation and maintenance of hydraulic jacking equipment are not new problems. Proper procedures are important in prestressed concrete work because of the damage that can be done by the sudden release of load in a tendon due to an equipment failure.

If a flaw or weak spot exists in a tendon, fitting, or the equipment, it is most likely to show up during the tensioning operation. It is therefore a reasonable safety precaution to remove personnel from the area until tensioning is complete. In a post-tensioning operation the tendon is usually encased in the concrete member and cannot whip around. The chief danger is at the ends, and the normal tendency here is to fly away from the end of the member. The strands in a pretensioned bed are not confined and can whip in any direction.

The foregoing should not cause anyone to be afraid of prestressed concrete production. Properly operated plants have excellent safety records because the management is fully aware of the conditions discussed here and takes the necessary precautions.

GENERAL INFORMATION

Miscellaneous topics of interest in the study of prestressed concrete but which have not found a place in previous chapters have been collected under this heading.

15-6. Partial Prestress. The term "partially prestressed" refers to a prestressed concrete member which has flexural tension in the precompressed tensile zone under the design load condition. Partial prestress is used to reduce excessive camber and in some cases to effect an economy by reducing the amount of steel required.

The requirements for ultimate strength of a partially prestressed member are the same as for a fully prestressed member. These requirements are met in one of several ways.

Tendons are designed to meet the ultimate-strength requirement. Using these tendons the member is checked under design load conditions, and it is found that the tensile stress in the concrete exceeds that allowed by the specification. This member can be used if the properties of a partially prestressed member meet the requirements of the structure. In this case the quantity of steel needed is less than that based on standard specifications.

When a member is designed in accordance with standard specifications and found to have excessive camber, the magnitude of the prestressing force is arbitrarily reduced to a value which will give a desirable camber. Tendons are selected for this force, and the ultimate strength of the member is checked. If the ultimate strength is too low, reinforcing bars are added in the zone of high moment to bring the ultimate strength up to specification. This method gives camber control and some reduction in the total cost of steel.

An alternate method of reducing camber is to use prestressing tendons at a unit stress lower than that permitted by the specification. An ultimate-strength calculation is made to determine the number of tendons required, and these tendons are tensioned to the load which gives the desired camber. This method gives camber control and in many cases uses less steel than is required for a fully prestressed member.

Section 209.2 of Tentative Recommendations for Prestressed Concrete in Art. 8-2 can be used in computing the ultimate strength of partially prestressed members. Section 209.2.2.2 says that the method given for computing f_{su} is correct only when "the effective prestress after losses is not less than $0.5f'_s$." In the author's experience this requirement is on the conservative side and a lower effective prestress will not reduce the ultimate strength. However, if the effective prestress is less than $0.5f'_s$ and the designer wants to be conservative, he can use $f_{su} = 0.85f'_s$. A study of the load-elongation curves of all types of prestressing steels will show that the elongation from zero stress to $0.85f'_s$ is less than from $0.56f'_s$ (a normal effective stress) to f_{su}. This means that while the stress in the prestressed steel is going from $0.56f'_s$ to f_{su}, the stress in unprestressed high-strength steel will go from zero to $0.85f'_s$ or higher.

Since there is no established specification for partially prestressed members, their design can be based on the Tentative Recommendations for Prestressed Concrete with a few variations. In fact, the allowable tensile stress of $6\sqrt{f'_c}$ in Sec. 207.3.2.b.1.b is already a big step into partial prestress. It represents the highest tensile stress that can be used if the designer wishes to maintain a relatively crack-free structure. Section 207.3.3 gives this formula for the ultimate tensile strength of concrete: $f'_t = 7.5\sqrt{f'_c}$.

If tensile stresses in excess of $6\sqrt{f'_c}$ are used, it is probable that cracks will develop. In fact it is quite possible that a member designed to $6\sqrt{f'_c}$

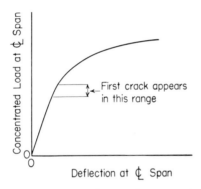

FIG. 15-2. Load-deflection curve for typical prestressed concrete beam.

will crack at points weakened by shrinkage or will be overloaded to cracking stress.

Figure 15-2 shows the load-deflection curve of a prestressed member. The shape of these curves will vary from one member to another, depending upon the shape of the cross section, span-depth ratio, percentage of steel, etc., but they all have a reasonably straight line to the first crack and then a rapidly changing slope as cracks open up and reduce the effective moment of inertia of the member.

Deflection may be a limiting factor in some designs. As an example consider a flat roof composed of double-T sections. If a loading condition brings the center of the span to an elevation lower than the ends, serious overloading can result. Rain water can fill the depressed area, causing additional load and deflection which makes a deeper depression for more rain water, etc. Structures in which deflection can create such problems should be designed to retain at least a small amount of camber under full design load.

Computation of deflection in a partially prestressed member is the same as in a fully prestressed member. The elastic formulas apply only up to the cracking load. Beyond the cracking load there are so many variables influencing deflection that no formulas are offered. Test data from similar members will offer the best indication of what to expect.

Control of excessive camber is especially important in deck-type structures such as roofs and floors where precast members are erected adjacent to each other to form a level surface. When the computed camber is large, the difference in camber between two supposedly identical members tends to be greater than the difference in camber between two members with a smaller camber. Partial prestress can often be used to bring a large camber down to a satisfactory camber. If a designer has difficulty in obtaining a satisfactory combination of camber and deflection, he should reconsider his choice of section. It is probable that the section he is using does not have sufficient moment of inertia. An increase in depth can solve the problem by giving increased stiffness without a great increase in dead weight.

Since typical prestressed concrete specifications do not include a limitation on the span-depth ratio, some designers tend to use rather shallow members, especially for long spans with light loads. The conservative designer will check the deflection on such members, and if it seems large, he will use a deeper member.

Another factor which should be considered in the design of a partially prestressed member is shear. Section 210.2.2 of Tentative Recommendations for Prestressed Concrete gives a formula for "prestressed members of usual dimensions and properties" and says "Since the formula does not involve the prestress force it may not be conservative for very low prestress or where only a portion of the reinforcement is stressed. For such cases it may be necessary to increase the factor of ½ as the member approaches the condition of conventionally reinforced concrete." The designer of a partially prestressed member must use his judgment based on the amount of prestress he has used in determining whether the factor of ½ or a higher one should be used.

15-7. Fire Resistance. Prestressed concrete has good fire-resistant properties. Section 215 of Tentative Recommendations for Prestressed Concrete gives recommended ratings for various amounts of concrete cover.

In 1958 Underwriters' Laboratories, Inc., conducted the first of a series of tests sponsored by the Prestressed Concrete Institute.[2]* This test

---

* Superscript numbers indicate references listed in the Bibliography at the end of the chapter.

showed a 2-hr rating for 2 in. of concrete cover over a seven-wire strand. Copies of reports on subsequent tests should be available from PCI as they are completed.

Although prestressed concrete carries its load under fire conditions, it may undergo deflection which is not completely recovered when the fire is over and the load removed.

15-8. Patents. There are many patents on prestressed concrete, but the majority of those which are economically feasible deal with end terminals or with tensioning methods and equipment. Purchase of the patented terminals and purchase or rental of patented equipment include rights of use.

ACI-ASCE Committee 323, which wrote Tentative Recommendations for Prestressed Concrete, has a subcommittee on patents, The subcommittee has prepared a list of patents which apply to prestressed concrete.

15-9. Research. When prestressed concrete was first introduced into the United States, its growth was almost directly proportional to the development of test data proving its dependability.

The first major prestressed concrete structure completed in the United States was the Walnut Lane Bridge in the city of Philadelphia. As a requirement for acceptance the contract called for fabrication and test to destruction of a full-scale girder. The test, in October, 1949, of the 160-ft girder demonstrated the elastic properties of prestressed concrete and confirmed the method of analysis. It also showed that the wire, which had been made in the United States, was far superior to that being used in Europe.

In the pretensioned field the question of satisfactory bond on seven-wire strands soon became the chief concern of designers and fabricators. The first pretensioned members were made with ¼-in. strand. Requirement for a larger prestressing force in the same space soon led to the use of 5/16-in. strand. When 3/8-in. strand was suggested, the question of bond was raised. How large a strand could be bonded at the extremely high unit stresses involved? The answer had to come through tests, not through theoretical analysis. Pull-out tests proved to be of little value because the strand unscrewed and thereby lost the benefit of mechanical bond due to concrete in the valleys between the wires (see Fig. 5-6). When the strands were cast in a beam and the beam was loaded to failure, satisfactory bond was developed.

Results of a series of fatigue tests were reported to the Convention of the American Concrete Institute at Denver, Colo., in February, 1954, by Professors Nordby and Tulin of the University of Colorado. In these tests it was found that 5/16- and 3/8-in. strand maintained their bond properties under fatigue loading but that 0.196-in.-diameter smooth wire, which developed full bond under static load, had a tendency to develop progressive bond failure under a large number of repeated loads. Subsequent tests to determine bond properties have been of the repeated load type.

When the 1957 revised edition of PCI Specifications for Prestressed Concrete was published, sufficient test data were available to justify the inclusion of $\frac{7}{16}$-in. strand. As additional tests are conducted, it is probable that later editions will include even larger strands. Some tests on bond of $\frac{1}{2}$-in. strand have been reported by Lehigh University and the University of Florida.

In addition to research being conducted by the Prestressed Concrete Institute and Portland Cement Association, there are long-range programs at universities cosponsored by manufacturers, producers, and government engineering groups. Although the most urgent problems have been settled, these programs continue to broaden the application and increase the design economy of prestressed concrete.

15-10. Latest Development. In closing this text the author wishes to emphasize the importance of keeping abreast of the latest developments. Basic principles, methods of design analysis, etc., should not change, but range and type of structures that are economical in prestressed concrete will continue to grow. Use of the latest edition of any specification is of particular importance.

BIBLIOGRAPHY

1. Abeles, Paul William: Static and Fatigue Tests on Partially Prestressed Concrete Constructions, *J. Am. Concrete Inst.,* December, 1954, pp. 361–376.
2. Prestressed Concrete Institute Report R-104-58 entitled "Underwriters' Laboratories, Inc. Report R-4123-1."

APPENDIX A

Table A-1. Properties of Stress-relieved Prestressed Concrete Wire*

Diameter, in.	Min ultimate strength, psi	Area of wire, sq in.	Weight per 1,000 ft, lb
0.276	236,000	0.05983	203.2
0.250	240,000	0.04909	166.7
0.196	250,000	0.03017	102.5
0.192	251,000	0.02895	98.32

* By permission from John A. Roebling's Sons Corporation.

Table A-2. Properties of Seven-wire Uncoated Stress-relieved Prestressed Concrete Strands*

Nominal diameter, in.	Weight per 1,000 ft, lb	Approx area, sq in.	Ultimate strength, lb	Tensioning load at 70% of ultimate strength, lb	Final design load for 20% stress loss, lb
¼	122	0.0356	9,000	6,300	5,040
⁵⁄₁₆	198	0.0578	14,500	10,150	8,120
⅜	274	0.0799	20,000	14,000	11,200
⁷⁄₁₆	373	0.1089	27,000	18,900	15,120
½	494	0.1438	36,000	25,200	20,160

* By permission from John A. Roebling's Sons Corporation.

Table A-3. Properties of Galvanized Prestressed Concrete Strands *

Diameter, in.	Weight per ft, lb	Area, sq in.	Minimum guaranteed ultimate strength, lb	Recommended final design load, lb
0.600	0.737	0.215	46,000	26,000
0.835	1.412	0.409	86,000	49,000
1	2.00	0.577	122,000	69,000
1⅛	2.61	0.751	156,000	90,000
1¼	3.22	0.931	192,000	112,000
1⅜	3.89	1.12	232,000	134,000
1½	4.70	1.36	276,000	163,000
1⁹⁄₁₆	5.11	1.48	300,000	177,000
1⅝	5.52	1.60	324,000	192,000
1¹¹⁄₁₆	5.98	1.73	352,000	208,000

* By permission from John A. Roebling's Sons Corporation.

Table A-4. Properties of Stressteel Bars*

Bar size, ϕ, in.†	Weight, lb per lin ft	Area, sq in.	Initial tensioning load at 80% of ultimate strength, lb	Final design load at 60% of ultimate strength, lb	Minimum guaranteed strength, lb‡
¾	1.50	.442	51,300	38,500	64,100
⅞	2.04	.601	69,700	52,300	87,100
1	2.67	.785	91,000	68,300	113,800
1⅛	3.38	.994	115,300	86,400	144,100
1¼	4.17	1.227	142,300	106,700	177,900

* By permission from Stressteel Corporation.

† ½- and ⅝-in.-diameter bars available on special request.

‡ Based on 145,000 psi.

APPENDIX B

Prestressed Concrete Institute
Specifications for Pretensioned Prestressed Concrete*
Revised Edition 1957 (Tentative)

Section 1. SCOPE

(A) These specifications cover the design and use of Pretensioned Prestressed Concrete, in any structure to be erected under the provisions of these specifications.

Section 2. DEFINITIONS

(A) The term Pretensioned Bonded Prestressed Concrete refers to concrete in which the prestressing strands or wire are tensioned prior to placing the concrete and released after the concrete has gained sufficient strength to retain the prestressing force by bond.

(B) The definitions of all other terms pertaining to prestressed concrete shall conform to the latest report of Joint ACI-ASCE Committee 323.

Section 3. MATERIALS

(A) Strand

    (1) All strands shall be of the 7 wire type having one center wire and six outside wires. The center wire shall be enough larger than the outside wires to guarantee that each of the outside wires will bear on the center wire, thus gripping it when tensioned.

    (2) All strands shall be stress-relieved as a unit after the wires have been formed into a strand.

    (3) Strand properties shall conform to the following table:

Strand Diameter	Approximate Area Square Inches	Minimum Ultimate Strength (lbs.)
$\frac{1}{4}$	.0356	9,000
$\frac{5}{16}$	.0578	14,500
$\frac{3}{8}$	.0799	20,000
$\frac{7}{16}$	.1089	27,000

Minimum 0.2% yield stress equals 0.85 of ultimate.
Minimum elongation in twenty-four (24) inches equals 4%.

---

* Reprinted by permission from Prestressed Concrete Institute.

299

(B) Wire
  (1) All wires shall be of stress-relieved type and not larger than ⅛" in diameter. Their properties shall conform to the following:

> Minimum ultimate strength equals 250,000 psi.
> Minimum 0.2% yield stress equals 0.80 of ultimate.
> Minimum elongation in ten (10) inches equals 4%.

(C) Reinforcing Steel
  (1) All deformed steel bars and/or welded steel wire fabric for concrete reinforcement shall meet the standards of the latest ASTM specifications.

(D) Concrete
  (1) Concrete shall meet the required strength as called for on the plans and shall be manufactured, transported and deposited in accordance with the latest recommended practices of American Concrete Institute.
  (2) Except poured-in-place topping, concrete shall have a minimum 28-day cylinder strength of 4000 psi.
  (3) Air entraining cement or suitable admixtures may be used to increase workability of concrete.
  (4) The size of coarse aggregate in the concrete shall meet the spacing requirements of prestressing steel and/or reinforcing steels. The size of aggregates shall "generally" be no larger than one (1) inch.

Section 4. DESIGN STRESSES

(A) Prestressing Strand and Wire
  (1) Initial stresses shall not exceed 70% of minimum ultimate strength for stress-relieved strand and/or wire.
  (2) Loss in initial prestress due to creep, shrinkage and plastic deformation shall be assumed to be 20% or greater unless substantiated by computations.
  (3) When concrete of light weight aggregate is used, data on stress losses due to creep, shrinkage and plastic deformation should be determined and these losses used instead of those listed under 4(A)(2).

(B) Concrete
  (1) Design shall be based on both the elastic and the ultimate theory. It must be ascertained that the resulting structure will perform properly under the service conditions and will possess sufficient strength to carry occasional overloads. Proper performance shall mean that camber, deflection, creep, shrinkage and cracks are within control.
  (2) Designed by the elastic theory, the maximum allowable stresses shall be limited to the following:
    (a) Maximum allowable stresses in concrete at the time of transfer or prestressing shall be as follows:
    Compression in bridge and building members . . . . $0.60\,f'_{ci}$
    Tension in extreme fiber for both bridge and building members, unless additional tension is taken by reinforcing steel . . . $0.06\,f'_{ci}$
    (Where f'_{ci} denotes compressive strength of concrete at time of prestress)

(b) Maximum allowable stresses under final dead and live load conditions shall be as follows:

Compression in bridge members . . . . $0.40 f'_c$
Compression in building members . . . . $0.45 f'_c$
Tension in bottom fiber in bridge members . . . . $0.$
Tension in bottom fiber in building members . . . . $0.05 f'_c$
Tension in top fiber . . . . $0.04 f'_c$
Unless the additional tension (not to exceed $0.08 f'_c$), is carried
    by reinforcing steel
Diagonal tension . . . . $0.04 f'_c$

These values may be exceeded provided it is shown that the structures will behave properly under service conditions and will meet the requirement of occasional overloads, except that tension in bottom fibers which exceeds $0.10 f'_c$ shall be substantiated by tests. Structures of unusual proportions and designs must be investigated for proper behavior and ultimate strength even if all the stresses are within the above specified limits.

(3) Designed by the ultimate theory the load factors for buildings shall be at least $1.4D + 2.3L + 0.0W$ or $1.4D + 1.0L + 1.8W$ whichever is greater, where W, when required, is the greater of either the wind or the earthquake load effect. Load factors for bridges shall be at least $1.6D + 2.4L$ or $1.6D + 1.0L + 2.0W$ whichever is greater.

(4) All members shall be checked for net deflections (upward or downward) with all dead loads and again with all live loads.

Section 5. DESIGN DETAILS

(A) The spacing of prestressing strands and/or wire at the ends of beams or in that length required for bonding shall be the largest of the following:
(1) The center to center distance of prestressing wires shall not be less than five times the wire diameter.
(2) The center to center distance of prestressing strands shall not be less than four times the strand diameter.
(3) In either case, the clear spacing between strands and/or wires shall not be less than one and one-half times the maximum size of coarse aggregates.
(B) The minimum distance from any concrete face to the center of a wire or strand shall be three times the wire or strand diameter, or one-half its diameter plus one inch, whichever is greater.
(C) All members to be designed for composite action shall have projecting steel from the prestressed member to the topping for bond and to transmit horizontal shear.

Section 6. CONSTRUCTION

(A) All materials, details and procedures shall be as called for on the plans or by the engineer.
(B) Prestressing strands or wires, and all reinforcing steel as called for on the plans shall be accurately placed in position before concrete is poured.

(C) Care should be exercised to keep strands or wires clean of form oil and other substances harmful to bond.

(D) Strands or wires may be tensioned and anchored all at once or one or more at a time at the discretion of the manufacturer.

(E) When two or more strands or wires are tensioned simultaneously, means, as approved by the engineer, shall be provided to obtain equal tension in each strand or wire as it is practical.

(F) For stress-relieved strand or wire, pretensioning force shall be determined by elongation based on the load elongation curve of the strand or wire.

(G) Forms are preferably of permanent type of steel or concrete. Wood forms of quality to produce smooth finished product may also be used.

(H) Concrete shall be deposited, vibrated, finished and cured in accordance with the latest recommended practices of American Concrete Institute. Steam curing may be permitted.

(I) Where the surface of a prestressed member is to receive a concrete topping, this said surface shall be finished rough, by brushing it with a steel wire brush, or equal means, so as to increase the bond between the member and its topping.

(J) At least three standard test specimens shall be prepared at the time the concrete is deposited for each production line to determine the concrete strength of the casting at different ages.

(K) Pretension in the strands or wires shall be released from the anchorage gradually and simultaneously.

(L) Unless otherwise approved by the engineer, this transfer of prestressing force shall be done when the concrete has reached a strength of 3000 psi or greater.

(M) Forms shall be so designed and aligned that they will not restrict the longitudinal movement of the casting when the prestressing force is transferred.

(N) Unless approved by the engineer, the finished products of prestressed concrete shall be lifted and/or supported at the points shown on the plans, or at the supporting points of the member when it is put into service.

(O) Bearing and anchorage of the prestressed concrete members shall be in accordance with the plans.

(P) Before shipment, all prestressed concrete members shall be inspected to make certain that materials and workmanship conform to the requirements of these specifications.

Prestressed Concrete Institute
Specifications for Post-Tensioned Prestressed Concrete*
Published February, 1958 (Tentative)

Section 1. SCOPE

(A) These specifications cover the design and use of post-tensioned prestressed concrete in any structure to be erected under the provisions of these specifications.

---

* Reprinted by permission from Prestressed Concrete Institute.

Section 2. DEFINITIONS

(A) The term Post-tensioned Prestressed Concrete refers to concrete to which a prestressing force is applied after the concrete has reached a required compressive strength. The prestressing force is transmitted from tensioned steel tendons, through end anchorages, to the concrete. The tendons may or may not subsequently be grouted to the concrete member.

(B) Forces and losses
  (1) Working Force is the final force left in the tendons after all losses have occurred.
  (2) Jacking Force is the force exerted by the ram on the tendon.
  (3) Initial Force is the force left in the tendon immediately after stressing and anchoring.
  (4) Tensioning Losses are those incurred at the time of stressing and anchoring the tendons in a member and include:
    (a) Elastic Shortening Losses
    (b) System Losses which may vary with the post-tensioning system used, and are due to tendon friction and anchorage.
  (5) Gradual Losses are the reduction from the initial force to the working force and are due to shrinkage, creep of the concrete and stress relaxation of the steel.

(C) The definitions of all other terms pertaining to prestressed concrete should conform to the latest report of the Joint ACI-ASCE Committee 323.

Section 3. MATERIALS

(A) Post-tensioning Steel Tendons
  (1) General
    (a) All post-tensioning steel tendons shall be free of deleterious oil, lubricants, loose rust and scale. Adequate precautions shall be taken to protect the tendons from excessive corrosion both before and after tensioning.
    (b) Tendons of high tensile wire or of alloy steel bars which are to be grouted after stressing shall be ungalvanized. Tendons of strand assemblies which are to be grouted after tensioning may be galvanized.
    (c) Tendons which are to remain ungrouted after stressing shall be hot galvanized. In lieu of this galvanization, other means of corrosion protection may be used, if approved by the Engineer.
    (d) Tendon supplier shall furnish stress-strain or load-elongation curves.
  (2) Parallel Wire Assemblies
    (a) Assemblies shall consist of a number of individual high tensile steel wires.
    (b) Wires shall be cold drawn and stress relieved to the following requirements:

Min. ultimate tensile strength	200,000 psi
Min. elongation at rupture in 10″	4%

Min. yield strength (0.2% offset)	80% of ult. strength
Approx. Modulus of Elasticity	29,000,000 psi
Wire diameter tolerance	±0.002″

(3) Alloy Steel Bars

(a) High tensile bars shall be proof stressed to a minimum stress of 130,000 psi. After proof stressing the bars shall conform to the following requirements:

Min. ultimate tensile strength	145,000 psi
Min. yield strength (0.2% offset)	130,000 psi
Approx. Modulus of Elasticity	27,000,000 psi
Min. elongation at rupture in 20 diameters	4%
Min. reduction of area at rupture	20%
Bar diameter tolerances	plus 0.03″
	minus 0.01″

(4) Strand Assemblies

(a) Assemblies are to be made up of 7, 19, 37 or more individual stranded high tensile wires, usually with factory attached end fittings.

(b) Wires used in making the strand shall be cold drawn and either stress relieved (for uncoated strands) or hot galvanized (for galvanized strands).

(c) The finished strand shall have a minimum ultimate tensile strength of 220,000 psi for uncoated strand, 200,000 psi for galvanized strand, based on the gross area including galvanizing. Approximate modulus of elasticity to be 24,000,000 psi.

(B) Post-tensioning Anchorages

(1) Post-tensioning tendons shall be secured at the ends by means of approved anchorages which shall develop full rated strength of the tendons.

(C) Post-tensioning Splices and Couplers

(1) Parallel wire tendons and strand assemblies are to be full length, without splices, except that manufacturing splices in individual wires of strand are permissible when made and spaced in accordance with standard strand specifications.

(2) If couplers are to be used for extending alloy steel bar tendons, they shall be capable of developing the rated strength of the tendon when one coupled bar is pulled at an angle of 2° with respect to the other.

(3) Couplers shall not be placed in the areas of maximum bending moment or in areas of moment reversal unless approved by the engineer.

(4) Couplers shall be enclosed in a housing long enough to permit the necessary elongation.

(D) Grout

(1) If grouted, the enclosure shall first be thoroughly cleaned of all foreign materials that would impair bonding. Grouting shall be done with sufficient pressure to insure the filling of all voids.

(2) The grout used for the protection and bonding of the steel tendons shall be composed of either cement and water or of cement, fine sand and water. Suitable admixtures may be used to improve the properties of the grout.

(3) The consistency of the grout shall be that of thick paint.

(E) Reinforcing Steel
    (1) All deformed steel bars and/or welded steel wire fabric for concrete rein-forcement shall meet the standards of the latest ASTM specifications.

(F) Concrete
    (1) Concrete shall meet the required strength as called for on the plans and shall be manufactured, transported and deposited in accordance with the latest recommended practices of American Concrete Institute.
    (2) Except poured-in-place topping, concrete shall have a minimum 28-day cylinder strength of 4000 psi.
    (3) Air entraining cement or suitable admixtures may be used to increase workability of concrete.
    (4) The size of coarse aggregate in the concrete shall meet the spacing require-ments of prestressing steel and/or reinforcing steels.

Section 4. DESIGN STRESSES

(A) Post-tensioning Tendons
    (1) The plans shall clearly indicate the force to be applied to the tendons, specifying whether it is an initial force or a working force and specifying its location along the length of the tendon.
    (2) The design working force in a tendon at the point of maximum moment of the member, shall not exceed 60% of the minimum guaranteed ultimate strength of the tendons.
    (3) When necessary, suitable computations or test results shall be applied to evaluate tensioning losses in order to determine the required jacking force and tendon elongation.
    (4) The jacking force before anchoring the tendon, as computed in 4(A)(3), shall not exceed 80% of the guaranteed ultimate strength of the tendon or the manufacturer's recommendation, whichever is less.
    (5) Gradual losses shall generally be assumed to be at least 15% or 20,000 psi, whichever is greater, unless substantiated by calculations.

(B) Concrete
    (1) Design shall be based on both the elastic and the ultimate theory. It must be ascertained that the resulting structure will perform properly under the service conditions and will possess sufficient strength to carry occasional overloads. Proper performance shall mean that camber, deflection, creep, shrinkage and cracks are within control.
    (2) Designed by the elastic theory, the maximum allowable stresses shall be limited to the following:
        (a) Maximum allowable stresses based on the net section of concrete at the time of prestressing shall be as follows:

Compression in bridge and building members	$0.60 f'_{ci}$
Tension in extreme fiber for both bridge and building members, (unless additional tension is taken by reinforcing steel)	$0.06 f'_{ci}$

        (Where f'_{ci} denotes compressive strength of concrete at time of prestress).

(b) Maximum allowable stresses under final dead and live load conditions shall be as follows:

Compression in bridge members	$0.40 f'_c$
Compression in building members	$0.45 f'_c$
Tension in bottom fiber in bridge members	$0.$
Tension in bottom fiber in building members	$0.05 f'_c$
Tension in top fiber	$0.04 f'_c$
Diagonal tension	$0.04 f'_c$

These values may be exceeded provided it is shown that the structures will behave properly under service conditions and will meet the requirements of occasional overloads, except that tension in bottom fibers which exceeds $0.10 f'_c$ shall be substantiated by tests. Structures of unusual proportions and designs must be investigated for proper behavior and ultimate strength even if all the stresses are within the above specified limits.

(3) Designed by the ultimate theory the load factors for buildings shall be at least $1.4D + 2.3L + 0.0W$ or $1.4D + 1.0L + 1.8W$ whichever is greater, where W, when required, is the greater of either the wind or the earth-quake load effect. Load factors for bridges shall be at least $1.6D + 2.4L$ or $1.6D + 1.0L + 2.0W$ whichever is greater. Shear, diagonal tension and flexure shall be checked for these load factors. These factors are to be modified or changed to agree with the latest accepted Specification of ACI-ASCE.

(4) All members shall be checked for net deflections (upward or downward) with all dead loads and again with all live loads.

Section 5. DESIGN DETAILS

(A) Spacing
(1) The spacing between ducts for post-tensioning tendons shall be one and one-half times the maximum aggregate size. However, if necessary, two ducts may be in contact horizontally, provided such grouping will not prevent proper placement of the concrete. Ducts may be in contact vertically if provisions are made so that the tendon will not break through into an adjacent duct when tensioned.
(2) The minimum spacing between anchorage units and edge distances shall be according to the manufacturer's recommendations provided bearing stresses and tensile stresses are within reasonable limits.
(B) The minimum clear distance between any concrete face and the post-tensioning tendon or duct shall be 1½".
(C) All members designed for composite action shall include provisions to resist horizontal shear and to resist the separation of the elements in a direction normal to their plane of contact. One or more of the following methods may be used:

Rough bonding surface
Concrete or steel shear keys
Projecting steel
Welded ties

(D) Members shall be properly reinforced to resist the net shear and diagonal tension, but in all cases webs of prestressed members shall be reinforced with stirrups. The maximum spacing of stirrups will be ¾ of the depth of the member, and the minimum steel area will be 0.08 per cent of the web area of the concrete. Adequate reinforcement shall be provided to resist the transverse tensions in the anchorage zone.

Section 6. CONSTRUCTION

(A) All materials, details and procedures shall be as called for on the plans or by the engineer.

(B) Prestressing tendons and/or ducts and all reinforcing steel as called for on the plans shall be accurately placed in position before concrete is poured. The tendons and/or ducts shall be carefully aligned and secured to minimize accidental curvature.

(C) Forms are to be of a quality to produce smooth finished concrete, and are to be properly braced.

(D) Concrete shall be deposited, vibrated, finished and cured in accordance with the latest recommended practices of the American Concrete Institute. Steam curing, or other approved method of elevating temperatures, may be used.

(E) When the surface of a prestressed member is to receive a concrete topping, the surface shall be finished with a rough broom, wood float or other satisfactory means, so as to increase the bond between the member and its topping.

(F) At least three standard test specimens shall be prepared for any concrete pour to determine the concrete strength of the casting at different ages.

(G) Before tensioning, the tendons shall be moved in their ducts, or other methods employed to assure that the tendons are not bonded.

(H) Partial stressing to facilitate handling may be commenced at a strength lower than specified, but stresses shall at all times be within the limits provided under section 4(B).

(I) Tendons are to be stressed from one end unless the tensioning losses are such that a jacking stress greater than $0.8f'_s$ would result.

(J) Tendons shall be stressed in a sequence such as to avoid excessive stresses in the concrete member.

(K) In tensioning tendons, the applied force will be measured by both, the elongation of the tendon and the hydraulic pressure applied. Reasonable agreement between these methods will be obtained.

(L) As a field condition tolerance to overcome unexpected frictions, the jacking force may be increased to 85 per cent of the guaranteed minimum strength of a tendon.

(M) Burning and welding operations in the vicinity of prestressing steel shall be carefully performed so that those portions of the prestressing steel which are stressed or are to be stressed shall not be subjected to excessive temperatures.

(N) Forms and form supports shall be designed so that they will not restrict the longitudinal shortening and the cambering of the member when the prestressing force is applied. Supports under the bearings of the member shall be adequate to support the full weight of the member in its cambered condition.

APPENDIX C

Criteria for Prestressed Concrete Bridges*
U.S. Department of Commerce
Bureau of Public Roads

PREFACE

The Criteria for prestressed concrete bridges presented in this pamphlet have been developed in the hope that they may be useful until such time as more complete specifications, covering the subject in far greater detail, may be presented to the civil engineering profession by American specification and code writing bodies.

The Bureau of Public Roads recognized in 1952 that the prestressed method of concrete construction had great possibilities in the building of better and more economical highway bridges of reinforced concrete, and that in many instances prestressed concrete might become a competitor of structural steel also.

There were no American standard codes governing the design of prestressed concrete bridges at that time. In recognition of the need for a guide to design which would provide structures acceptable for Federal-aid projects, the Bureau, in March 1952, prepared and distributed a Design Criteria for Prestressed Concrete Bridges (Post Tensioning).

Although the scope of the criteria was very limited, the issue attracted considerable attention, and many constructive comments and suggestions were received from American and European engineers engaged in prestressed concrete design and construction. On the basis of these comments and suggestions, a rough draft of a new and greatly enlarged criteria, covering design, materials, and construction, was prepared and submitted in September 1953 to a number of authorities in the field both in this country and abroad. Thoroughly revised in light of their comments, the criteria are now issued in this pamphlet, together with supporting discussion and source references.

During the writing of these criteria a joint committee, composed of delegates from the American Society of Civil Engineers and the American Concrete Institute, was set up to develop a code of practice for prestressed concrete. When such a code is published, the Bureau's criteria will be reviewed in the light of the Committee's findings.

NOTATION

A_{bs} = steel area for a balanced section (sq. in.).
A_c = the maximum area of that portion of the end of the beam which is geometrically similar and concentric to the area of the bearing plate (sq. in.).

---

* By permission from Bridge Division, Office of Engineering, Bureau of Public Roads.

A_p = bearing area of the anchorage plate (sq. in.).

A_s = steel area (sq. in.).

b = average width of the compression area (in.), assuming $k = 0.23$.

D = dead load (lb.).

d = depth of section from the compression face to the centroid of the steel (in.).

E_c = modulus of elasticity of concrete (p.s.i.).

E_s = modulus of elasticity of steel (p.s.i.).

f_{cpa} = allowable unit stress on the concrete under the bearing plates (p.s.i.).

f_{cs} = concrete stress at the centroid of the prestressing steel. Where the stress varies from end to end of the beam it shall be taken as the average value (p.s.i.).

f_{si} = initial prestress (p.s.i.).

f'_c = ultimate cylinder 28-day strength of concrete (p.s.i.).

f'_{ci} = ultimate cylinder strength of concrete at the time of prestressing (p.s.i.).

f'_s = ultimate stress in the prestressing steel (p.s.i.).

f'_{sy} = stress in prestressing steel at 0.2 per cent plastic set (p.s.i.).

I = impact load (lb.).

k = depth from extreme compressive fiber to neutral axis divided by the effective depth d.

L = live load (lb.).

m_u = ultimate moment (in.-lb.).

$p = A_s/bd$.

P_b = value of p for a balanced section $= A_{bs}/bd$.

CRITERIA FOR PRESTRESSED CONCRETE BRIDGES
DESIGN

Temporary Stresses

Temporary stresses before creep and shrinkage shall not exceed the following:
Concrete:

Compression in extreme fiber pretensioned	$0.60f'_{ci}$
post-tensioned	$0.55f'_{ci}$
Tension	$0.05f'_{ci}$
Prestressing steel: Tension	$0.80f'_s$

Stress under dead, live, or impact load

Stress after creep and shrinkage under dead, live, or impact load, or any combination of these forces, shall not exceed the following:
Concrete:

Compression in extreme fiber	$0.4f'_c$
Tension in extreme fiber	0

Where the computations show tension in the extreme fiber, unprestressed reinforcement may be used, and designed to take the total tensile stresses, provided that the computed tension in the concrete before the unprestressed steel is added does not exceed $0.08f'_c$.

Prestressing steel . . . . $0.6f'_s$ or $0.8f'_{sy}$, whichever is less.

Creep, shrinkage, and elastic deformation

Decrease in prestress in steel due to creep, shrinkage, and elastic deformation shall be assumed to be as follows:

Pretensioned concrete . . . . $6,000 + 16f_{cs} + 0.04f_{si}$

Post-tensioned concrete . . . . $3,000 + 11f_{cs} + 0.04f_{si}$

In these criteria the efficiency of the anchorage has been assumed to be 100 per cent. The designer should add to the figure given for creep and shrinkage an amount sufficient to allow for the anchorage efficiency, as determined by test. Light-weight aggregate: An amount to be determined by tests.

Decrease in prestress due to friction

Where the prestressing steel is "draped" and wherever minor irregularities occur in the alinement of the ducts, the stress in the interior of the beam will be somewhat less than that at the jack, due to friction. This loss shall be estimated and verified in the field as given in the section on construction under the heading "Post-tensioning method." A guide to the estimation of the loss will be found in the discussion.

Ultimate strength

The ultimate strength must be such as to withstand the following loads without failure:

$$D + 3(L + I) \text{ or } 2(D + L + I), \text{ whichever is greater.}$$

In figuring the ultimate strength, use f'_s and $0.8f'_c$ (see under the heading "Computing ultimate strength of beam," below).

Principal tensile stress

The principal tensile stress shall not exceed the following: Dead, live, or impact load, or any combination thereof: $0.03f'_c$ to be carried by the concrete and the excess over $0.03f'_c$ to be carried by properly designed stirrups. Ultimate loads, without stirrups: $0.08f'_c$. If this stress is exceeded, stirrups shall be designed to take the total principal tensile stresses.

In the case of both working loads and ultimate loads, the maximum shears may be taken at a point 1.5 times the depth of the beam, measured from the nearest support.

End anchorage bearing plates for prestressing steel

Bearing plates shall be designed so that the bending stresses in the plates due to dead, live, and impact load do not exceed that allowable for the type of steel used, and the unit pressure on the concrete does not exceed:

$$f_{cpa} = 0.4f'_c \sqrt[3]{\frac{A_c}{A_p}} \text{ or } f'_c, \text{ whichever is less.}$$

Computing ultimate strength of beam

Unless a more exact method is preferred, the following shall be used:

Where the prestressing elements are bonded to the concrete, the reinforcement shall be assumed "balanced" (i.e., when the steel and concrete fail simultaneously) if:

$$P_b = 0.23 \, \frac{0.8f'_c}{f'_s}$$

The ultimate moment m_u shall be determined as follows:
Where p is equal or less than p_b,

$$m_u = 0.9A_s f'_s d$$

Where p is greater than p_b,

$$m_u = 0.9 \sqrt{A_s A_{bs}} f'_s d$$

Where the prestressing elements are not bonded to the concrete, the prestressing steel shall be considered as an external force and shall not be figured as reinforcement.

Stirrups

It is recommended that stirrups be used, whether or not computations show that they are needed. The maximum stirrup spacing shall be not more than three-fourths of the depth of the beam. The sum of the cross-sectional areas of the legs of the stirrup should be not less than 0.08 per cent of the cross-sectional area of the pre-stressed beam for the maximum spacing. Metal mesh of the same cross-sectional area per foot of beam may be substituted for stirrups at the option of the engineer.

Diaphragms

Diaphragm spacing shall be shown on the plans.

Size, spacing, and cover of prestressing steel

Where tension in the prestressing steel is maintained by bond and there is no adequate end anchorage provided, 0.2 inch shall be the maximum size of wire permitted, where the wires are used singly. Where the wires are used in seven-wire strands, the maximum strand permitted shall be ⅜-inch.

The minimum spacing, both vertically and horizontally, shall be three times the diameter of the wire or strand, measured center to center. In no case, however, shall the clear spacing between wires or strands be less than 1½ times the maximum size of the coarse aggregate.

The minimum cover distance for all prestressing steel shall be 1½ inches or one diameter of bar, strand, or duct, whichever is greater.

Where adequate end anchorage is provided, the above limitations are not applicable, except that a clear spacing horizontally of 1½ times the maximum size of the coarse aggregate shall be maintained.

Composite construction

Where precast and cast-in-place concrete are designed to act integrally, as when precast beams are used to support a cast-in-place slab, the horizontal shear shall be provided for by positive means, such as keys, and the two types of concrete held firmly together by stirrups extended up into the slab.

MATERIALS

Concrete

Any portland cement and aggregate may be used which is suitable for ordinary concrete.

Prestressing reinforcement

Prestressing reinforcement shall be high-tensile wire, high-tensile wire strand or rope, or high-tensile alloy bars.

Steel to be bonded to the concrete shall not be galvanized. If the steel is to be left unbonded, it shall be protected against corrosion as described in the section on construction under the heading "Unbonded steel."

If wire or strand is used, it shall have an elongation at rupture of not less than 3 per cent in 10 inches. Bars, if used, shall have an elongation at rupture of not less than 4 per cent in a distance of 20 diameters.

Permissible variations in gage of wire

The dimensions of the wire, on any diameter, shall not vary more than plus or minus 0.003 inch from the specified nominal diameter. The difference between the maximum and minimum diameters, as measured on any given cross-section of the wire, shall not be more than 0.003 inch.

Finish of wire

The wire shall be free from injurious defects and shall have a workmanlike finish with smooth surface.

Testing

All wire, strand, or bars to be shipped to the site shall be assigned a lot number and tagged for identification purposes. Anchorage assemblies to be shipped shall be likewise identified.

All samples submitted shall be representative of the lot to be furnished and, in the case of wire or strand, shall be taken from the same master roll.

All of the materials specified for testing shall be furnished free of cost and shall be delivered in time for tests to be made well in advance of anticipated time of use.

Where the engineer intends to require nondestruction testing of one or more parts of the structure, special specifications shall be drawn giving the required details of the work.

The vendor shall furnish for testing the following samples selected from each lot. If ordered by the engineer, the selection of samples shall be made at the manufacturer's plant by the inspector.

Pretensioning method—For pretensioned strands, samples at least 7 feet long shall be furnished at each strand size. A sample shall be taken from each end of every coil.

Post-tensioning method—The following lengths shall be furnished:

For wires requiring heading, 5 feet.

For wires not requiring heading, sufficient length to make up one parallel-lay cable 5 feet long consisting of the same number of wires as the cable to be furnished.

For strand to be furnished with fittings, 5 feet between near ends of fittings.

For bars to be furnished with threaded ends and nuts, 5 feet between threads at ends.

Anchorage assemblies—Two anchorage assemblies shall be furnished, complete with distribution plates of each size or type to be used, if anchorage assemblies are not attached to reinforcement samples.

Inspection

An inspector representing the purchaser shall have free entry, at all times while the work on the contract is being performed, to all parts of the manufacturer's works which concern the manufacture of the materials ordered. The manufacturer shall afford the inspector, without charge, all reasonable facilities to satisfy him that the material is being furnished in accordance with these criteria.

Rejection

Material which shows injurious defects during or previous to its installation in the work shall be rejected

CONSTRUCTION

General

Unless otherwise ordered by the engineer, the contractor shall certify to the engineer that a technician skilled in the prestressing method used will be available to the contractor to give as much aid and instruction in the use of the prestressing equipment and installation of materials as may be necessary to obtain satisfactory results.

Hydraulic jacks shall be equipped with accurately reading calibrated pressure gages. The contractor may elect to substitute screw jacks or other types for hydraulic jacks. In that case, proving rings or other approved devices must be used in connection with the jacks. All devices, whether hydraulic jack gages or other types, shall be calibrated and, if necessary, recalibrated so as to permit the stress in the prestressing steel to be computed at all times. A certified calibration curve shall accompany each device.

Safety measures must be taken by the contractor to prevent accidents due to possible breaking of the prestressing steel or the slipping of the grips during the prestressing process.

Concrete

All concrete shall be handled and placed in accordance with article 2.4.9 of the American Association of State Highway Officials' Standard Specifications for Highway Bridges (1953).

Concrete shall not be deposited in the forms until the engineer has inspected the placing of the reinforcement, conduits, anchorages, and prestressing steel and has given his approval thereof.

The concrete shall be vibrated internally or externally, or both, as ordered by the engineer. The vibrating shall be done with care and in such a manner as to avoid displacement of reinforcing, conduits, or wires.

Steam curing of the concrete will be permitted in lieu of water curing. If the contractor elects to cure with steam or by any other special method, the method and its details shall meet with the approval of the engineer.

Transportation and storage

Precast girders should be transported in an upright position, and points of support and directions of the reactions with respect to the girder should be approximately the same during transportation and storage as when the girder is in its final position. In the event that the contractor deems it expedient to transport or store precast girders in other than this position, it shall be done at his own risk.

Care shall be taken during storage, hoisting, and handling of the precast units to prevent cracking or damage. Units damaged by improper storing or handling shall be replaced by the contractor at his expense.

Pretensioning method

The prestressing elements shall be accurately held in position and stressed by jacks. A record shall be kept of the jacking force and the elongations produced thereby. Several units may be cast in one continuous line and stressed at one time. Sufficient space shall be left between ends of units to permit access for cutting after the concrete has attained the required strength. No bond stress shall be transferred to the concrete, nor end anchorages released, until the concrete has attained a compressive stress, as shown by cylinder tests, of at least 3,500 p.s.i. The elements shall be cut or released in such an order that lateral eccentricity of prestress will be a minimum.

Post-tensioning meι.

The tensioning process shall be conducted so that the tension being applied and the elongation of the prestressing elements may be measured at all times. The friction loss in the element, i.e., the difference between the tension at the jack and the minimum tension, shall be determined by the formula:

$$F_t = 2\left(F_1 - \frac{aeE}{d}\right)$$

where

F_t = total friction loss.

F_1 = observed tension at the jack.

a = cross-sectional area of the prestressing element.

e = observed elongation of the element at the jack when the force at the jack is F_1.

E = secant modulus of elasticity of the element for the stress F_1/a as determined from the stress-strain diagram of the element.

d = distance from the jack to the point of lowest tension in the element. Where jacking is done from both ends of the member, the point of minimum tension is the center of the beam; where jacking is done from one end only, d is the length of the beam.

A record shall be kept of gage pressures and elongation at all times and submitted to the engineer for his approval.

After tensioning, and wherever practicable, prestressing steel shall be bonded to the concrete.

Bonded steel

All prestressing reinforcement to be bonded to the concrete shall be free of dirt, loose rust, grease, or other deleterious substances.

Steel installed in holes or flexible metal tubes cast in the concrete preferably shall be bonded, in which case the annular space between the perimeter of the hole or tube and the steel shall be pressure-grouted after the prestressing process has been completed.

The grout shall be made to the consistency of thick paint and shall be mixed in the proportions, by volume, of 1 part portland cement to 0.75 part (max.) of sand passing a No. 30 sieve and 0.75 part (max.) of water. Within the limit specified, the proportions of sand and water shall be varied as required by the engineer. It may be necessary to eliminate the sand from the mix and use neat cement grout.

If aluminum powder is used to expand the grout, it shall be added as follows: From 2 to 4 grams of the powder (about 1 or 2 teaspoons) shall be added for each sack of cement used in the grout. The aluminum powder shall be the unpolished variety. The exact amount of aluminum powder shall be designated by the engineer. The dosage per batch of mortar shall be carefully weighed. A number of weighings may be made in the laboratory and the doses placed in glass vials for convenient use in the mixing operation. The aluminum powder shall be blended with pumicite or other inert powder in the proportion of 1 part powder to 50 parts pumicite (or other inert powder) by weight. The blend shall be thoroughly mixed with the cement and sand before water is added to the batch, as it has a tendency to float in the water. The amount of the blend used should vary from 4½ ounces per sack of cement for concrete having a temperature of 70 F. to 7 ounces for a temperature of 40 F. After all ingredients are added, the batch shall be mixed for 3 minutes. Batches of grout shall be made small enough so that the batch may be all used up in less than 45 minutes, as the action of the aluminum becomes very weak after that period of time.

Except as herein provided, all grout ingredients shall comply with articles 4.1.1, 4.2.1, and 4.3.2 of the AASHO Standard Specifications for Highway Bridges (1953). The final pressure placed on the grout shall be 50 to 100 p.s.i.

Unbonded steel

Where the steel is to be left unbonded to the concrete, it shall be carefully protected against corrosion by galvanizing and, in addition, a coating of tar or other waterproof material shall be applied. If galvanizing is not practicable, another method of protection may be approved by the engineer provided tests have shown its suitability.

Placing and fastening steel

All steel units shall be accurately placed in the position shown in the plans, and firmly held during the placing and setting of the concrete.

Distances from the forms shall be maintained by stays, blocks, ties, hangers, or other approved supports. Blocks for holding units from contact with the forms shall be precast mortar blocks of approved shape and dimensions. Layers of units shall be separated by mortar blocks or other equally suitable devices. Wooden blocks shall not be left in the concrete.

Wires, wire groups, parallel-lay cables, and any other prestressing elements shall be straightened to insure proper positioning in the enclosures. Suitable horizontal and vertical spacers shall be provided, if required, to hold the wires in place in true position in the enclosures.

Enclosures

Enclosures for prestressed reinforcement shall be accurately placed at locations shown in the plans or approved by the engineer.

All enclosures shall be water-tight. They shall be metallic, except that the contractor, at his option, may form the enclosures by means of cores or ducts composed of rubber or other suitable material which shall be removed prior to installing the prestressing reinforcement. Enclosures shall be strong enough to maintain their shape under such forces as will come upon them. They shall be one-fourth inch larger in internal diameter than the bar, cable, strand, or group of wires which they enclose. Where pressure grouting is specified, cores or ducts shall be provided with pipes or other suitable connections for the injection of grout after the prestressing operations have been completed.

Prestressing

After the concrete has attained the required strength, the prestressing reinforcement shall be stressed by means of jacks to the desired tension and the stress transferred to the end anchorage.

Tensioning of the prestressing reinforcement shall not be commenced until tests on concrete cylinders, manufactured of the same concrete and cured under the same conditions, indicate that the concrete of the particular member to be prestressed has attained sufficient compressive strength.

APPENDIX D

Figure D-1* was developed to facilitate computation of maximum live-load bending moment at any point on a simple-beam span of a bridge. It is based on H20-S16-44 loading of the American Association of State Highway Officials.

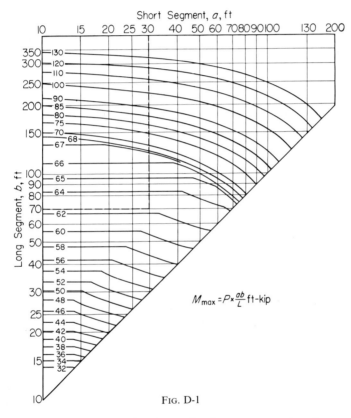

FIG. D-1

While maximum moments at the center of various spans are given in an appendix to the AASHO Standard Specification for Highway Bridges, maximum moments at other locations, though important in design, are not presented. This chart is intended to fill the gap.

* Reprinted by permission from Gerald K. Gillan, Professor of Civil Engineering, Pennsylvania State University. From *Eng. News-Record*, Oct. 7, 1954. Copyright 1954 by McGraw-Hill Publishing Company, Inc.

By means of the chart an equivalent concentrated load is obtained, from which the required bending moment can easily be computed. An equivalent concentrated load was used because it leads to small interpolation intervals and is quite accurate, even when used within the usual limitations of a small diagram.

To find the bending moment for a single-lane load at a point that is at a distance of *a* ft from one end of a span and *b* ft from the other end, enter the chart horizontally at *b* and vertically at *a*. The intersection determines the equivalent load *P* in kips, which may be read by interpolating between the heavy-line curves. The required moment is found to be the product *Pab/L*, where *L* is equivalent to the span.

For example, find the maximum moment in a 100-ft span at a point 30 ft from one end. If you enter the chart at the left side with 70 ft and at the top with 30 ft, the intersection of the two ordinates falls between the curves marked 62 and 64 and may be interpolated to be 62.3. The required moment then is $62.3 \times 30 \times 70/100 = 1{,}310$ ft-kips.

APPENDIX E

Tentative Recommendations for Prestressed Concrete:*
Report of the Joint ACI-ASCE Committee on
Prestressed Reinforced Concrete

Closure by the Committee

COMMITTEE'S CLOSURE.—

INTRODUCTION

This closure will deal with published discussions as well as unpublished comments and will include some general explanations where deemed desirable. Therefore, the best procedure is to arrange the closure in the sequence of sections in the report rather than by name of discussors.

All but one of the discussions appeared in both the Journal of the Structural Division of ASCE and the Journal of the American Concrete Institute. One discussion appeared only in the Journal of the Structural Division.

101—Objective

This report is a recommended practice, not a specification. It is presented for the guidance of professional engineers. Safety, performance, and economy will depend as much on the intelligence and integrity of engineers as on the degree to which these recommendations are followed. This is taken almost verbatim from Sec. 101. The brevity of the restatement makes the intent stand out in stronger relief. The re-emphasis seems particularly desirable because many of the comments seem to assume that the report is a code or specification.

A code is a legal document that may be incorporated, in whole or in part, in a specification that is legally binding on all parties involved. By contrast, these tentative recommendations express the viewpoints generally held by a majority of specialists in this particular field, and the advisory form of presentation was adopted as best suited to the assignment of the committee.

Attention is called to A. W. Coutris' thoughtful discussion of "Advisory Reports" as opposed to "Codes." He pleads for keeping design reports advisory rather than intransigent in form and spirit.

102—Scope

The recommendations relate mostly to beams, girders, and slabs. Tanks and pipes are specifically omitted for the reasons stated in Sec. 102.1. It has been suggested

---

* See original report, Art. 8-2.

that piling should have been included. Since stress conditions in piles differ appreciably from those in purely flexural members the same design recommendations do not apply to both types. When the report is revised, prestressed piling probably should be included in the scope.

L. D. Boswell and others suggest that a definition for "segmental elements" be added in Sec. 102.2. The committee proposes a definition as follows: A member may be cast integrally as a "single element" or comprised of a number of precast pieces, in which case it is referred to as a "segmental element."

104—Notation

Several years ago the committee prepared a report on notation which was published in the ACI Journal.* In the course of preparing the present report the original notation was modified and augmented as deemed desirable. P. W. Abeles states that "the symbols now published are greatly improved as compared with the first publication of notations." Nevertheless, he regrets that his efforts to obtain uniformity of symbols in the United States and Great Britian have been unsuccessful.

On previous occasions, Abeles proposed the adoption of an international notation for prestressed concrete. While recognizing the value of such a generally applicable notation, the committee felt it was in no position to assume the prerogative of speaking for all groups concerned with notation in the United States.

Abeles' suggestions about augmenting the definitions for k and δ in Sec. 104.4 are helpful improvements.

201.2—Mode of failure

In reference to the wording in this section, G. F. Janssonius states that "most test beams have collapsed when ultimate compressive strength of the concrete was reached." In the United States it is common to state the case just as expressed in Sec. 201.2. In almost all test beams designed to fail in flexure, ultimate *collapse* manifests itself as crushing of concrete in the compression zone; but in under-reinforced sections, ultimate strength is said to be reached when the tensile reinforcement undergoes permanent strain in its plastic region.

201.3—Design theory

T. Y. Lin apparently misinterprets the meaning and intent of this section. It simply emphasizes that both performance under service conditions and strength under ultimate conditions should be investigated.

Comparing the design approach in these recommendations with that in two other reports, Lin states that a "basic disagreement exists." It is difficult to perceive any real justification for the alleged basic disagreement.

The only specific value Lin uses "as an example of the dangerous errors contained in these allowable stresses. . ." is in reference to $3\sqrt{f'_{ci}}$ in Sec. 207.3.1(b). This is an isolated stress condition of relatively minor significance. It does not represent the general, complex conditions of "strength and behavior of beams at transfer," to which he has reference.

---

* Proposed Definitions and Notations for Prestressed Concrete, *J. Am. Concrete Inst.*, vol. 24, part 2.

204.3—Initial prestress plus dead load of member

This clause simply describes one of the significant loading stages that normally affects design. It was not intended, as Abeles infers, to explain how to compute stresses. It was thought desirable, however, to state that losses in prestress at that stage should not include long-range or sustained load effects.

Sec. 204.6—Cracking load

A brief commentary on the significance of cracking load seems desirable, especially since many unpublished comments have been received on this subject.

Recommendations related to cracking appear in Sections 204.6, 205.2, and 207.3.3. All these combined express the intent of the committee. Sec. 204.6 states that "complete freedom from cracking may or may not be necessary. . . . Type and function of the structure, and type, frequency, and magnitude of live loads should be considered." In the same vein, it is stated in Sec. 205.2 that "formation of a crack under temporary overload may not be objectionable."

Previous recommendations and criteria for cracking frequently have been quite arbitrary and inflexible. The committee feels that the profession gradually has moved away from arbitrary edicts on this subject. At one stage of the deliberations, a proposal was discussed regarding complete omission of references to cracking loads and stresses. This was rejected, however, from the viewpoint that cracking and its various effects did remain significant for many types of structures, loadings, and exposures such as in girders subject to impact, repetitive loading and exposure to harmful atmospheric vapors.

205.3—Ultimate load factors

Ultimate load capacity expresses a basic characteristic of almost all concrete structures. For prestressed concrete, the significance of ultimate load capacity is further emphasized by the fact that stresses are not linearly proportional to external forces and moments throughout the entire load range.

Considerable work had already been done by others on the subject of ultimate load factors for buildings. The principal features of this work are abstracted in the Building Code Requirements for Reinforced Concrete (ACI 318-56). Ultimate load factors for buildings in that code were incorporated in this report.

Load factors for highway bridges were studied at considerable length before the final decision was made to adopt the factors of 1.5 for dead load and 2.5 for live load. Numerous combinations of factors other than these were also tried as bases for calculations of actual bridge structures.

As a result of the bridge studies, two opposing viewpoints developed. One group felt that a single expression such as $1.5D + 2.5L$ would suffice, whereas others preferred a "dual" expression that also contained a safeguard for structures with very low ratios of live to dead load. The text in Sec. 205.3 represents a compromise in that one single expression is recommended, but with the qualification that "it may be desirable to modify or expand the load factor formulas to fit special conditions."

The recommendations related to load factors for highway bridges were formulated in cooperation with both federal and state bridge authorities.

207—Allowable steel and concrete stresses

The specific stress values in this section were chosen after thorough study of all pertinent data. During the last year before publication of the report, numerous comments were received and some modifications made in the allowable stresses. It is felt that the values published reflect the very best on which agreement could be obtained.

In reference to some of Lin's remarks about allowable stresses, it should be reaffirmed that the provisions in Sec. 207 are intended to be advisory rather than intransigent. Special circumstances may dictate a downward revision of certain values. Liberalization may be indicated in other instances where sufficient supporting data can be submitted, including analytical studies, test results, or performance records. In the latter case, the burden of proof should fall upon those who wish to deviate from the generally accepted values.

207.1—Prestressing steel

The recommendations define three allowable steel stresses:

$0.80f'_s$: for a short period of time prior to seating of anchorage.
$0.70f'_s$: immediately after seating but before losses.
$0.60f'_s$: effective steel stress after losses described in Sec. 208.

The first value was chosen because some steels have shown marked stress relaxation when stressed above $0.80f'_s$, even for relatively short periods of time. When the prestress force is transferred from the jack to the anchorage, some slip and displacement may occur in various parts of most anchorages. The loss in stresses during seating often is of appreciable magnitude. Further losses occur due to sources described in Sec. 208. The three values for allowable steel stresses are interrelated in such a way that it is impossible to discuss one without reference to the other two.

C. J. Fox indicates that he prefers $0.80f'_s$ to $0.70f'_s$ but fails to state whether this is "before" or "after" seating of anchorage. If he means $0.80f'_s$ *before* seating, then there is no disagreement.

207.3.1—Temporary stresses

G. F. Janssonius asks why the recommendations allow temporary concrete stresses of $0.60f'_{ci}$ for pretensioned members and $0.55f'_{ci}$ for post-tensioned members.

Here, production had preceded design recommendations, and the stress of $0.60f'_{ci}$ had already been widely established in the pretensioning industry. No ill effect had been reported in regard to strength and performance. Only camber proved difficult to control for certain building members.

It appeared desirable to be more conservative for post-tensioning. One reason is that the effect of holes left for post-tensioning reinforcement is frequently ignored, and designers are inclined to use gross rather than net section. Also, as cables are post-tensioned, one after the other, eccentric prestressing forces are introduced which may create temporary stress conditions not anticipated. Finally, control and inspection usually are not as good in the field as in a plant.

D. J. Oswald says his firm obtains 28-day strengths between 6,500 and 7,500 psi using Type II cement without additives.   His suggestion is that the report should have included a minimum limit for concrete strength.

Prestressed concrete can be produced with satisfactory technical results using concrete strengths varying over a large range, even if it may not be economically advantageous to use extreme values.   On this subject the committee had no access to pertinent technical information.   Local conditions differ as to types and gradations of aggregate.   Also, there may be differences in equipment and in mechanical means available for mixing, transporting and placing concrete.   It was felt that in the choice of concrete strength, it is the design engineer's problem, and the final decision is up to him.

207.3.2—Stresses at design loads

Janssonius calls attention to the values for flexural tension in Sec. 207.3.2(b): $6\sqrt{f'_c}$ for pretensioned and $3\sqrt{f'_c}$ for post-tensioned, bonded elements.   In his opinion, "so great a difference, if any, is not justified."

This is another instance in which the pretensioning industry for many years had followed a standard of production that had given satisfactory results.   Pretensioning elements usually consist of a relatively large number of strands well distributed in and bonded to the concrete.   A high degree of bond resistance ensures a good crack control.   Strictly from the viewpoint of bonding characteristics, the serviceability and behavior in regard to crack control should be better in pretensioning than in post-tensioning.

Whereas there seemed to be good reason for allowing different stresses for flexural tension, the committee had insufficient technical information on which to base the specific values in the report.   Consequently, a clause was added permitting certain variations from the values in Sec. 207.3.2(b).

207.3.3—Stress at cracking load

This clause states that when test data are not available the ultimate flexural tensile stress in psi may be assumed as:

$$f'_t = 7.5\sqrt{f'_c}$$

The particular wording was purposely chosen so as to make it plain that "test data" should be given more weight than the recommended allowable stress value, on which it was difficult to obtain agreement.

For, say $f'_c = 6,400$ psi, the value allowed for f'_t is 600 psi.   Both Abeles and Bryan propose that this could be raised to 1,000 psi under certain circumstances or in certain types of structures.   The committee does not consider the recommended stress formula restrictive in an absolute sense.   This problem may be resolved by referring to clauses in Sections 204.6 and 205.2 with a well supported argument in favor of deviation from the recommended value.

208.2.1—Friction loss in post-tensioned steel

Test results available on cable friction do not cover nearly all the variable conditions that are needed to develop a comprehensive set of accurate values for K and μ.

Values of K and μ in Sec. 208.2.1 are considered conservative for materials and construction procedures used in the United States.   It is anticipated that the values will be revised and augmented as newer research data become available. In this respect, it is advisable to note A. W. Coutris' contribution to the subject of friction and to refer to some of the sources mentioned in his discussion.

Coutris believes the values given in the table are conservative for wires, but not conservative enough for bars. One difficulty that complicates the subject of friction loss is that materials and especially workmanship may vary widely. Accuracy in placing ducts plays an important part and is difficult to control in practice and evaluate in tests.

208.2.3—Shrinkage of concrete

Several discussers suggest that more specific information be included on shrinkage. The committee felt that the effect of shrinkage in prestressed members was not such as to justify the inclusion of a comprehensive treatment.

The choice of shrinkage factor usually has no effect upon ultimate strength. At cracking load, the flexural tensile strength of concrete is equally as important as shrinkage, or more so. In camber calculations, creep rather than shrinkage tends to be the predominant factor. Also it is impossible at present to give shrinkage data that will apply to lightweight concretes in general.

208.3.2—Method 2

The assumption regarding losses in steel stresses in Sec. 208.3.2 reads:

Pretensioning	35,000 psi
Post-tensioning	25,000 psi

W. J. Jurkovich states that "the pretensioning loss of 35,000 psi appears to be on the high side. The preliminary draft of the report presented a range of losses (30,000–40,000 and 20,000–30,000) which appeared reasonable." D. J. Oswald also believes the loss of 35,000 psi is conservative and suggests reducing it to 30,000 psi. On the other hand, P. W. Abeles suggests that Method 2 either be eliminated or the loss value increased.

Actually, the ultimate strength is not significantly affected by the magnitude of steel stress loss. For camber calculations, the suggested values may be excessive. Making the distinction between "strength" and "camber" is important when applying stress losses in accordance with both methods in Sec. 208.3.

209.2—Ultimate flexural strength

The comments received on this section have been mainly discussions of the k-factors in equation (a). The symbols of k_2 and k_1k_3 were introduced originally as useful quantities in analytical studies on ultimate flexural compressive stresses in concrete. This committee incorporated the symbols in its report in order to give equation (a) a fully general form.

Research data showed that the general algebraic form of equation (a) could be simplified for the great majority of conditions by inserting 0.6 for k_2/k_1k_3. This gives slightly conservative results. The use of the ratio as a factor in the second member within the brackets in equation (a) makes illusory any high degree of refinement in the k-fractions for members and materials considered in this report.

209.2.1(b)—Ultimate flexural strength of flanged sections

A question has been asked about the definition of A_{sr}. In equation (b) the width, b', should be the average width of that particular portion of the stem which is in compression at ultimate load.

Attention is called to the fact that the value of A_{sr} in equation (b) may become negative. This happens when the web width, b', is less than 15 per cent of the total width, b. For values of b' smaller than $0.15b$ it is suggested that equation (b) be disregarded and replaced by equation (a) in Sec. 209.2.1(a).

209.2.3(b)—Flanged sections

Correction: In the first term in the equation for M_u, change b to b'.

210.2.2—Design of web reinforcement

It is stated in one unpublished discussion that "design by the conventional formula given with its factor of ½ may not be safe" because "the principal shearing stress increases far more rapidly than the increase in external load." The erroneous inference is that the equation in Sec. 210.2.2 is applicable to service loading. It is actually an ultimate strength equation as plainly shown by the notation given below the equation. The ½ is not related to a load factor.

The design recommended for web reinforcement is based on tests of limited scope, principally tests on simply supported beams with straight prestressing steel. The equation in Sec. 210.2.2 may not be applicable to continuous structures. For portions of simply supported beams where the steel is draped, the designer should consider using one of two limit values of d. Choosing d as the depth to the center of gravity of steel may be too conservative at points of the beam where steel is draped. On the other hand, using the value of d at midspan throughout the beam may not be conservative at points where steel is draped.

The required value of A_v depends on many variables including prestress force, web thickness, amount of tensile reinforcement, and shear/moment ratio. There were not sufficient data to enable the committee to evaluate all such variables in algebraic form. The expression generally applicable to reinforced concrete was adopted and the factor of one-half added to make allowance for the beneficial effect of the prestress force with the precaution added that "it may not be conservative for very low prestress or where only a portion of the reinforcement is stressed." The form of the equation is not chosen solely because it is similar to that for reinforced concrete. Actually, the formula shows good correlation with results of many tests on typical prestressed concrete members.

210.2.4—Spacing of web reinforcement

It should be noted that spacings in this section are "maximum" rather than "optimum" values. In general, maximum values are not necessarily the best to be recommended but smaller values may often be more desirable to use.

213.3—Frictional losses

G. F. Janssonius correctly states that the clause in Sec. 213.3 is not clear   It reads that "frictional losses in continuous post-tensioned steel may be more significant than in simply supported members." Whether a structure is continuous or not has no intrinsic effect on frictional losses. The trouble is that the clause is abbreviated to the point where it gives the wrong inference. It was meant to express that since continuous structures are generally longer, and the post-tensioned elements may have reverse curvature, frictional losses tend to be greater in continuous than in simply supported members.

213.4—Ultimate strength

Coutris feels that "moment redistribution should be considered in design" in order to "predict the ultimate strength of . . . continuous beams . . .," whereas Sec. 213.4 "recommends that moment redistribution not be considered in design at the present time."

Attention is called to Sec. 204.8 which reads in part: "In statically indeterminate structures, the load which causes moment in one section to reach its ultimate value may not be sufficient to cause failure of the structure because of moment redistribution. Since it is not always possible to predict that full redistribution will take place in accordance with limit design, it is suggested for the time being that moments be determined by elastic analysis."

On the subject of elastic versus limit design, the committee was cognizant of two pertinent points. Conventional reinforced concrete structures are still being designed by the elastic theory with no allowance being made for moment redistribution, and practical step-by-step procedures and design-aids are not available to be of sufficient help and guidance in limit design of continuous prestressed structures.

302.4—Strength

L. P. Marchant proposes that reference be made in Sec. 302.4 to "Recommended Practice for Evaluation of Compression Test Results of Field Concrete" (ACI 214-57) in addition to the reference now made to "Building Code Requirements for Reinforced Concrete" (ACI 318-56). The procedure outlined in the report of ACI 214 is useful for plant operation, but the committee feels the procedure has not been in use long enough to prove it is equally practical for strength evaluation of concrete mixed on the site.

304—Prestressing steel

Before any official specifications existed in the United States, prestressing steels were manufactured and used extensively in structures. Changes and improvements were made in some instances by the manufacturers wherever desirable. This is one of several instances in which production preceded specifications. Since these steels have a long and successful performance record it is surely inadvisable, as Michael Chi suggests, arbitrarily to increase requirements for ductility to a point which none of the steels can reach.

A committee appointed by the American Society for Testing Materials is preparing specifications for prestressing steel. Since ASTM possesses authority and jurisdiction, this committee has established liaison with the ASTM group but is not otherwise responsible for specifications.

It is apparently desirable to reaffirm that Sec. 304 simply describes four types of prestressing steel now in common use. This description should not be interpreted as a specification or a testimonial. If types of prestressing steel other than those described are proposed to be added or substituted, requests for specifications should be directed to ASTM.

304.2.2—Shape of stress-strain curve

The definitions of minimum yield strength in Sections 304.2.2 and 304.5.2 are inconsistent as G. F. Janssonius points out. Two basically different definitions have been in common use. One is based on "total elongation," the other on "permanent strain." When the ASTM group submitted specifications for stress relieved wire in which the definition of 1 per cent elongation was adopted, Sec. 304.2.2 was changed accordingly, but the definition of "0.2 per cent permanent strain" remained unchanged in 304.5.2.

APPENDIX F

UNCOATED SEVEN-WIRE STRESS-RELIEVED STRAND
FOR PRESTRESSED CONCRETE*†

ASTM Designation A 416-57T, issued 1957‡

These Tentative Specifications have been approved by the sponsoring committee and accepted by the Society in accordance with established procedures, for use pending adoption as standard. Suggestions for revisions should be addressed to the Society at 1916 Race St., Philadelphia 3, Pa.

SCOPE

1. These specifications cover seven-wire, uncoated, stress-relieved steel strand primarily intended for use in pretensioned, bonded, prestressed concrete construction.

BASE METAL

2. The base metal shall be carbon steel of such quality that when drawn to suitable round wire sizes and fabricated into proper strand sizes and properly stress relieved after stranding, shall have the properties and characteristics prescribed in these specifications.

WIRE

3. The wire from which the strand is to be fabricated shall have a common dry drawn finish.

STRAND

4. (a) All strand shall be of the seven-wire type having a center wire enclosed tightly by six helically placed outer wires with a uniform pitch of not less than 12 and not more than 16 times the nominal diameter of the strand.

(b) When the strand is cut without seizings, the wire shall not fly out of position.

JOINTS

5. (a) There shall be no strand joints or strand splices in any length of the completed strand unless specifically permitted by the purchaser.

---

* Under the standardization procedure of the Society, these specifications are under jurisdiction of the ASTM Committee A-1 on Steel.

† Reprinted by permission from American Society for Testing Materials.

‡ Accepted by the Administrative Committee on Standards, Sept. 13, 1957.

(b) During the process of drawing the individual wires, welding is permitted only prior to or at the size of the last heat treatment (patenting).

(c) During fabrication of the strand, butt-welded joints may be made in the individual wires, provided there is not more than one such joint in any 150-ft. section of the completed strand.

STRESS RELIEVING

6. After stranding, all strands shall be subjected to a stress-relieving continuous heat treatment to produce the prescribed mechanical properties. Temper colors, which may result from the stress-relieving operation, are considered normal for the finished appearance of the strand.

SAMPLING

7. One specimen for test shall be taken from each 20-ton production lot of finished strand. Test specimens shall be cut from the outside end of reels or either end of coils of strand. Any specimen found to contain a wire joint should be discarded and a new specimen obtained.

TENSION TEST

8. In tension testing the specimens, the ends shall be secured in the tensile machine by the use of fitted, slip-limiting grips or other suitable methods of anchorage.

Table I.   BREAKING STRENGTH REQUIREMENTS

Nominal Diameter of Strand, in.	Breaking Strength of Strand, min, lb	Nominal Steel Area of Strand, sq in.	Nominal Weight of Strands, lb per 1,000 ft
$\frac{1}{4}$	9,000	0.036	122
$\frac{5}{16}$	14,500	0.058	198
$\frac{3}{8}$	20,000	0.080	274
$\frac{7}{16}$	27,000	0.109	373
$\frac{1}{2}$	36,000	0.144	494

BREAKING STRENGTH

9. The finished stress-relieved strand shall conform to the requirements prescribed in Table I.

YIELD STRENGTH

10. (a) The minimum yield strength for all strands, measured by the 1 per cent extension under load method, shall be not less than 85 per cent of the specified minimum breaking strength.

(b) The extension under load shall be measured by an extensometer calibrated with the smallest division not larger than 0.0001 in. per in. of gage length.

(c) The initial load indicated in Table II shall be applied to the specimen, at which time the extensometer is attached and adjusted to a reading of 0.001 in. per

in. of gage length. The load shall then be increased until the extensometer indicates an extension of 1 per cent. The load for this extension shall be recorded and
shall meet the requirements prescribed in Table II.

Table II.   YIELD STRENGTH REQUIREMENTS

Nominal Diameter of Strand, in.	Initial Load, lb	Minimum Load at 1 per cent Extension, lb
¼	900	7,650
5⁄16	1,450	12,300
3⁄8	2,000	17,000
7⁄16	2,700	23,000
½	3,600	30,600

ELONGATION

11. (a) The elongation of the strand shall be not less than 3.5 per cent and shall
be measured in a gage length of not less than 24 in. The elongation shall be
determined by an extensometer which is placed on the test specimen after an initial
load has been applied. The initial load is equivalent to 10 per cent of the required
minimum breaking strength.

(b) Specimens that break outside of the extensometer or in the jaws and yet
meet the minimum specified values, are considered as meeting the elongation requirements of these specifications.

(c) If the minimum elongation requirement is met prior to initial rupture, it is
not necessary to determine the final elongation value.

SIZE OF STRAND

12. The size of the finished strand shall be expressed as the nominal diameter of
the strand in fractions of an inch.

PERMISSIBLE VARIATIONS IN SIZE

13. (a) All strands shall conform to a size tolerance of ±1⁄64 in. from the nominal
diameter measured across the crowns of the wires.

(b) The diameter of the center wire of any strand must be larger than the
diameter of any outer wire in accordance with Table III.

Table III.   DIAMETER RELATION BETWEEN CENTER AND OUTER WIRES

Nominal Diameter of Strand, in.	Minimum Difference Between Center Wire Diameter and Diameter of Any Outer Wire, in.
¼	0.001
5⁄16	0.0015
3⁄8	0.002
7⁄16	0.0025
½	0.003

WORKMANSHIP AND FINISH

14. (a) The finished strand shall be uniform in diameter and shall be free from imperfections not consistent with good commercial stranding practice.

(b) The strand shall not be oiled or greased. Slight rusting, provided it is not sufficient to cause pits visible to the naked eye, shall not be cause for rejection.

PACKING AND MARKING

15. The strand shall be furnished on reels or in compact coils having a minimum core diameter of 24 in., unless otherwise specified by the purchaser. Lengths on reels (Note) or lengths in coils shall be as agreed upon at the time of purchase. The strand shall be well protected against mechanical injury in shipping as agreed upon at the time of placing an order. Each reel or coil shall have a strong tag securely fastened to it showing the length, size, ASTM Designation A 416, and the name or mark of the manufacturer.

Note.—Standard practice is to furnish on reels having the approximate length as follows:

Nominal Diameter of Strand, in.	Approximate Lineal Feet per Reel
¼	25,000
⁵⁄₁₆	15,000
⅜	15,000 or 10,000
⁷⁄₁₆	12,000 or 10,000 or 8,000
½	9,000 or 6,000

INSPECTION

16. The manufacturer shall afford the inspector representing the purchaser all reasonable facilities, without charge, to satisfy him that the material is being furnished in accordance with these specifications. All tests and inspection shall be made on the finished strand at the place of manufacture prior to shipment and shall be so conducted as not to interfere unnecessarily with the operation of the works.

REJECTION

17. In case there is a reasonable doubt in the first trial as to the failure of the strand to meet any requirement of these specifications, two additional tests shall be made on samples of strand from the same coil or reel, and if failure occurs in either of these tests, the strand shall be rejected.

UNCOATED STRESS-RELIEVED WIRE FOR PRESTRESSED CONCRETE*†

ASTM Designation A 421-58T, issued 1958‡

These Tentative Specifications have been approved by the sponsoring committee and accepted by the Society in accordance with established procedures, for use pending adoption as standard. Suggestions for revisions should be addressed to the Society at 1916 Race St., Philadelphia 3, Pa.

SCOPE

1. These specifications cover two types of uncoated stress-relieved round high-carbon steel wire commonly used in prestressed linear concrete construction, as follows:

Type BA wire is used for applications in which cold-end deformation is used for anchoring purposes (Button Anchorage).

Type WA wire is used for applications in which the ends are anchored by wedges, and no cold-end deformation of the wire is involved (Wedge Anchorage).

PROCESS

2. (a) The steel shall be made by the open hearth or electric furnace process.

(b) The wire shall be cold drawn to size and suitably stress relieved after cold drawing by a continuous strand heat treatment to produce the prescribed mechanical properties.

(c) There shall be no welds or joints in the finished wire. Any welds or joints made during manufacture to promote continuity of operations shall be removed.

DISCARD

3. A sufficient discard shall be made from each ingot to insure freedom from injurious piping and undue segregation.

CHEMICAL COMPOSITION

4. (a) The ladle analysis of the steel shall conform to the following ranges:

Carbon, per cent . . . . 0.72 to 0.93
Manganese, per cent . . . . 0.40 to 1.10
Phosphorus, max, per cent 0.040
Sulfur, max, per cent 0.050
Silicon, per cent . . . . 0.10 to 0.35

(b) Variations in manufacturing processes and equipment among wire manufacturers necessitate the individual selection of an appropriate chemical composition, within the above ranges, at the discretion of the manufacturer.

(c) When requested, an analysis of each heat of steel showing the percentages of the elements specified in paragraph (a) shall be furnished by the manufacturer.

---

* Under the standardization procedure of the Society, these specifications are under the jurisdiction of the ASTM Committee A-1 on Steel.

† Reprinted by permission from American Society for Testing Materials.

‡ Accepted by the Society at the Annual Meeting, June, 1958.

CHECK ANALYSIS TOLERANCES

5. An analysis may be made by the purchaser from finished wire representing each heat of steel. Samples for analysis shall be obtained by milling the wire in such a manner as to obtain a sample representative of the entire cross-section. Prior to milling, the surface shall be cleaned to remove all foreign matter. All such individual determinations shall not vary from the limits shown in Section 4(a) by more than the amounts prescribed in Table I.

Table I. PERMISSIBLE VARIATION FOR CHECK ANALYSIS

Element	Permissible Variation Over Maximum Limit or Under Minimum Limit, per cent
Carbon	0.04
Manganese	0.06
Phosphorus	0.008
Sulfur	0.008
Silicon	0.02

TENSILE STRENGTH

6. The tensile strength of type BA wire and type WA wire shall conform to the requirements prescribed in Table II.

Table II. TENSILE STRENGTH REQUIREMENTS

Nominal Diameter, in.	Tensile Strength, min, psi	
	Type BA	Type WA
0.192	a	250,000
0.196	a	250,000
0.250	240,000	240,000
0.276	a	235,000

a These sizes are not commonly furnished in type BA wire.

YIELD STRENGTH

7. (a) The minimum yield strength for all wire, measured by the 1.0 per cent extension under load method, shall not be less than 80 per cent of the specified minimum breaking strength.

(b) The extension under load shall be measured by an extensometer calibrated with the smallest division not larger than 0.0001 in. per in. of gage length.

(c) The initial load corresponding to the initial stress prescribed in Table III shall be applied to the specimen, at which time the extensometer is attached and adjusted to a reading of 0.001 in. per in. of gage length. The load shall then be increased until the extensometer indicates an extension of 1 per cent. The load for this extension shall be recorded. The stress corresponding to this load shall meet the requirements for stress at 1 per cent extension prescribed in Table III.

Table III.   YIELD STRENGTH REQUIREMENTS

Nominal Diameter, in.	Initial Stress, psi	Minimum Stress at 1 per cent Extension, psi	
		Type BA	Type WA
0.192	29,000	a	200,000
0.196	29,000	a	200,000
0.250	29,000	192,000	192,000
0.276	29,000	a	188,000

a These sizes are not commonly furnished in type BA wire.

ELONGATION

8. The total elongation under load of all wire shall not be less than 4.0 per cent when measured in a gage length of 10 in.   The elongation shall be determined by an extensometer which is placed on the test specimen after a load corresponding to the initial stress prescribed in Table III is applied.

PERMISSIBLE VARIATIONS IN DIMENSIONS

9. (a) The diameter of the wire shall not vary from the nominal diameter specified by more than ±0.002 in.

(b) The wire shall not be out-of-round by more than 0.002 in.

CAST

10. A wire sample of sufficient length, when laid free on a substantially flat surface, shall form an arc of a circle not less than 12 ft in diameter.

BUTTON ANCHORAGE

11. Type BA wire shall be of suitable quality to permit cold forming of buttons for anchorage.   Splitting shall not be considered a cause for rejection if the button anchorage is capable of developing full strength of the wire.

NUMBER OF TESTS

12. Unless otherwise agreed upon between the manufacturer and the purchaser, one test specimen shall be taken from each 10 coils or less in a lot* and tested to determine compliance with Sections 6, 7, 8, 9 and 10.

WORKMANSHIP AND FINISH

13. (a) The wire shall be free from kinks.

(b) The wire shall be furnished in firmly tied coils, having a minimum inside diameter of 48 in.   Each coil shall be of one continuous length.

(c) The wire shall not be oiled or greased.   Slight rusting, provided it is not sufficient to cause pits visible to the naked eye, shall not be cause for rejection.

---

*The term "lot" means all the coils of wire of the same nominal wire size contained in an individual shipping release or shipping order.

(d) Temper colors which may result from the stress-relieving operation are considered normal as regards the finished appearance of the wire.

MARKING

14. The size of the wire, ASTM specification number, heat number, and name or mark of the manufacturer shall be marked on a tag securely attached to each bundle of wire.

INSPECTION

15. The manufacturer shall afford the inspector representing the purchaser all reasonable facilities, without charge, to satisfy him that the material is being furnished in accordance with these specifications. All tests (except check analysis) and inspection shall be made at the place of manufacture prior to shipment and shall be so conducted as not to interfere unnecessarily with the operation of the works.

REJECTION

16. Unless otherwise specified, any rejection based on tests made in accordance with these specifications shall be reported to the manufacturer within a reasonable length of time.

INDEX

337